80386
Technical Reference

Edmund Strauss

A Brady Book
New York, New York   10023

Also by Edmund Strauss
Inside the 80286

 BRADY

Simon & Schuster, Inc.
Gulf + Western Building
One Gulf + Western Plaza
New York, New York   10023

DISTRIBUTED BY PRENTICE HALL TRADE

Manufactured in the United States of America

1 2 3 4 5 6 7 8 9 10

Library of Congress Cataloging in Publication Data

Strauss, Edmund.
    80386 technical reference.

    "A Brady book."
    Includes index.
    1. Intel 80386 (Microprocessor) I. Title.
QA76.8.I2684S77   1987   004.16   87-10962
ISBN 0-13-246893-X

CONTENTS

Part 2 16-bit Programming: 80386 REAL Mode

Part 3 Full 32-bit Programming: Simple PROTECTED Mode

Part 5   PROTECTED Mode in More Depth

DEDICATION

To my wonderful and dedicated parents,
Edmund and Paulina,
as a sign of appreciation for all their efforts
throughout many years.

ACKNOWLEDGEMENTS

I am deeply indebted to Robert E. Childs for his contributions in
carefully reviewing the content and form of this entire book.
And I am grateful to Monika Feldmeier for providing the support and
enthusiasm that made this book much easier to create.
Thank you very dearly, Monika, once again!

TRADEMARKS

LIMITS OF LIABILITY AND DISCLAIMER OF WARRANTY

FOREWORD

The Personal Computer became a household word and a fact of life in business during the early 1980s. The introduction of the 80386 micorprocessor by Intel, and the Personal System /2, Model 80 by IBM, brings the power of a traditional mainframe computer to the desk of every office worker.

The available software base is even more significant than the computer hardware. The 80386 enters business establishments with a huge software base directly developed to serve the end-user of information. These users focus on the work result; they have no interest in becoming computer experts. The result is a major increase in office workers' productivity.

This text is unique in addressing the 80386 hardware and assembly language interfaces, while including the underlying concepts and suggestions for use by programmers. The author's unique experience in helping numerous designers complete 80286 and 80386-based machines shows through in the text. Ed Strauss has seen the full range of system issues and devised many practical solutions during his work for Intel.

I highly recommend this book to those seeking a very readable and practical introduction into the fundamentals of the 80386.

Robert E. Childs
80286 Architect
ROLM / an IBM Company

PART 1

INTRODUCING THE INTEL 80386
32-BIT MICROPROCESSOR

This section provides an introduction to the positive effects brought about by the power of the 80386. It describes the new 80386 features in comparison with those of the previous Intel microprocessors and in terms of their benefits to users of the new 80386 computers. Then it begins delving into the 80386 as a highly capable computing machine.

As it becomes more technical, this section lays the groundwork for a clear understanding of the 80386 by covering such basic topics as its datatypes and 32-bit memory-addressing abilities. Finally, this part of the book covers each category of the 80386 instruction set and provides detailed instruction-summary tables.

CHAPTER 1

THE 80386 MICROPROCESSOR

The Intel 80386 is perhaps the most versatile and exciting microprocessor yet developed. Certainly its performance has long been desired by computer users and computer designers alike. The appeal of the 80386 is worldwide, yet particular strengths are more important for some persons than for others. To some, the versatility of the 80386 is the key, allowing any 80386 computer to operate both as a new 32-bit processor and as a compatible 16-bit machine. To others, the 80386's computing speed is paramount, since it brings powerhouse performance to nearly every computer application. For most of us, its versatility and performance are *both* of interest, since our existing software will run faster than ever before, yet the new 32-bit software promises even more speed and added features. In this tutorial and reference book, as we come to understand the 80386, we shall learn about both its versatile architecture and its power.

Why the 80386 Is Important

The 32-bit architecture of the 80386 is important to users of the IBM Personal Computer or Personal Computer/AT built around the 8086 or 80286 microprocessors, although they have only a 16-bit architecture. The 16-bit architecture of those important chips is contained entirely within the 32-bit 80386, as a subset of its full abilities. For that reason, the 32-bit 80386 can mimic a 16-bit 8086 or 80286, making the 80386 microprocessor entirely upward-compatible with the vast pool of software written for its popular predecessors. That is, the 80386 runs the thousands of programs written for the IBM Personal Computer and for all other computers based on the 8086 and 80286.

The 80386 is the most significant microprocessor affecting the business and technical world, both because of its heritage in the 8086 family and because of the fantastic potential of its new features. These two attributes, strong heritage and future potential, together on one chip, are a bond between the present and future of much software development. Prominent technical journals, financial journals, and even general newspapers confirm that the 80386 has garnered the attention of designers and decision-makers in all areas of computer-related products.

Already, the PC software base of applications and operating systems is moving forward to take advantage of the new features offered by the 80386. This is a very promising sign that the 80386 will have continued positive impact on all of us.

Aside from its generally uplifting effect on all users of personal computers—and more from a programmer's viewpoint—the 80386 is an interesting and formidable computer. Technically, the 80386 programming architecture is quite good and efficient. Its hardware implementation is sleek and powerful, and its level of on-chip integration is wonderfully economical. Yet the sophisticated 80386 is so affordable that 80386 PCs now placed casually in offices and factories pack the computation power of 4 MIPS (Million Instructions Per Second)[1] and are programmed to perform tasks formerly reserved for dedicated workstations and minicomputers. Indeed, the 80386 is advancing our computing world a generation.

How the 80386 Operates

The 80386 is fully designed to perform 32-bit operations, yet it can also function as a fast 16-bit 8086 and 80286. To understand the 80386 easily, we need a basic knowledge of the three ways, or modes, in which it can operate. These **operating modes**, named REAL, PROTECTED, and VIRTUAL 8086 modes, give the 80386 a great deal of compatibility and flexibility. The main distinctions are the method of addressing memory and the amount of memory that can be addressed.

Figure 1.1 shows these modes and their development over time. The figure begins with the 16-bit 8086/8088, which support only REAL mode, a mode that addresses one megabyte of memory. The 16-bit 80286 added an advanced 16-bit PROTECTED mode and sixteen times as much memory addressability. Now, the 80386 adds 32-bit operation in the PROTECTED mode to address at least four gigabytes of memory. The 80386 also provides a subordinate VIRTUAL 8086 mode, the compatibility link for existing 8086 software.

The 32-bit 80386 always begins operation in the 8086-compatible mode of operation, the REAL mode. Although this is perhaps surprising at first, you can see that such a feature allows existing software, unchanged, to immediately use the speed of the 80386. The REAL mode is so-named because 8086-compatible software deals with *real*, (i.e., physical) addresses. In REAL mode, the 80386 simply operates as an extremely fast 8086. After startup, the 80386 may then be instructed to operate in its PROTECTED mode. The 80386 PROTECTED mode provides 32-bit data and addressing and full-fledged VIRTUAL memory with paging support. This mode is the target for new software development.

Table 1.1 summarizes 16-bit operation and 32-bit operation using these modes. Full 32-bit operation is hardware-provided in PROTECTED mode (16-bit operation can also occur in this mode, as the 16-bit 80286 processor can operate in PROTECTED

---

[1]This is sixteen to twenty times the power of the original PC.

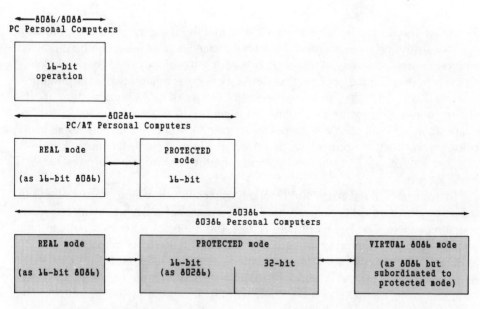

Figure 1.1   8086/8088, 80286, and 80386 Operating Mode Development.

mode). In PROTECTED mode, during either 32-bit or 16-bit operation, the 80386 can enable its paging unit for full support of VIRTUAL memory, freeing the typical programmer from the limitations of physical addressing. The 80386 protection hardware is simultaneously activated, hence the name PROTECTED mode. This on-chip protection hardware enforces several sensible policies that ensure greater system

Table 1.1   16-bit and 32-bit Operating Modes

16-bit Operation ↓	32-bit Operation ↓	Comments
REAL mode		8086-compatible mode
executing 16-bit code segment in PROTECTED mode		80286-compatible PROTECTED mode
VIRTUAL 8086 mode		8086 environment created within PROTECTED mode
	executing 32-bit code segment in PROTECTED mode	full 32-bit addressing and performance

reliability. The protection features make sure that the integrity of an operating system can always be protected from user interference and that users can be protected from other users. The overall reliability of a PROTECTED-mode system depends solely on the robustness of the operating system, not upon the reliability of user programs.

The 80386 PROTECTED mode is preferred because of its 32-bit operation, its virtual memory support, and its security. A simple PROTECTED-mode system is easy to establish, as we shall see by examples in Chapter 11, Appendix D, and Appendix E. However, PROTECTED-mode allows as extensive a level of sophistication as desired. We shall explore several options for increasing the sophistication of a PROTECTED-mode system.

In this regard, the VIRTUAL 8086 mode is especially interesting, since it allows us to run any existing 8086 software under the control of a 32-bit PROTECTED-mode operating system. The key word here is *any*. The 8086 software involved can be a standalone application program, or it can be an entire 8086 operating system, such as PC-DOS. When 8086 software is executed in VIRTUAL 8086 mode, it "believes" it is operating on a physical 8086 (or 8088). In fact, however, the master 80386 operating system in PROTECTED mode retains control of all the system resources. The VIRTUAL 8086 mode is an elegant new feature that does wonders for software compatibility across processor generations. It deserves the full coverage we shall give it, including the full listing in Appendix G of a program that actually *runs PC-DOS in VIRTUAL 8086 mode*. You can run the monitor program on any 80386 personal computer.

Processor Architecture Overview

Moving from the 80386 operating modes to the next level of detail, we reveal the 80386 architecture. The 80386 introduces a new, 32-bit architecture to Intel's line of microprocessors. Processor architecture describes the 80386 characteristics seen by a programmer using one of the operating modes discussed above. The architecture basics concern the programmable registers in the processor, the datatypes it directly recognizes, and its methods of addressing operands in memory. In addition to these fundamentals, the 80386 embodies special, interesting architectural features, such as breakpoint registers for debugging and identifiers for chip and revision level that allow software to recognize on which chip it is running. We will begin by covering the 80386 fundamentals, such as its registers.

Several 80386 user registers are utilized by typical user programs. The most frequently used are the 32-bit general registers, the instruction pointer, and the flag register. Eight 32-bit general registers hold the general data and address values currently in use. Notice that the general registers, shown in Figure 1.2, can hold not only 32-bit but also 16- or 8-bit values. A 32-bit instruction pointer references (i.e., points to) the instruction currently being executed. The 32-bit flag register contains

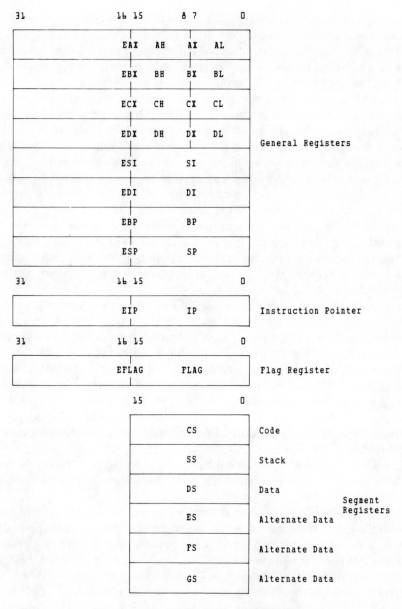

Figure 1.2   User Registers of the 80386.

several fields, 1- and 2-bits wide each, that indicate important status from recently-executed instructions.

The 80386 also has segment registers that can be used, at the programmer's discretion, to activate various segments of code or data (out of approximately 16,000 possible segments) for the programmer's use. A segment is merely a contiguous linear block of the programmer's address space; any 32-bit segment can be tremendously large, up to 4 billion BYTES in fact. One large segment declared initially is likely to be adequate for all the system needs, which is why frequent use of the segment registers is discretionary. If we choose to create several segments, the segment registers allow us to extend the programmer's address space far, far beyond the 4-billion byte limit of other 32-bit processors, up to an amazing 64 terabytes (64 thousand billion bytes) of program-addressable memory, in fact. Later on, we will explore ways of using the segment registers for simple (and not-so-simple) systems.

Besides the user registers just introduced, several **system registers** exist for system program use. These are not frequently used by the typical programmer, since they control system-wide parameters, such as the placement of paging tables and task tables, the operating mode, and coprocessor settings. System registers are shown in Chapter 2.

A processor's work typically consists of operating upon various input data to generate output *results*. With the 80386, many datatypes, such as signed and unsigned integers, bits, and strings, are directly hardware-supported for efficient operation. Except for the bit datatype, datatypes are sized in bytes. A byte is eight bits. Eight-bit signed or unsigned integers therefore are BYTES. WORDS and DWORDS are also recognized. WORDS are 16-bit signed or unsigned integers. DWORDS (double words) are 32-bit signed or unsigned integers. All these values, BYTES, WORDS (two bytes), and DWORDS (four bytes), are easily transferred between processor and memory, since the memory is byte-addressable, meaning that any particular byte or bytes can be retrieved at will.

In each of these datatypes, which are depicted in Figure 1.3, bit 0 is the *least-significant bit* (LSB), and the highest-numbered bit is therefore the *most-significant bit* (MSB).

When these datatypes are placed into a register of the 80386, bit 0 of the register holds the LSB of the datatype, as we would expect. When a datatype is stored in memory, it resides at a memory address, the number used to refer to a BYTE of data in memory. When a multibyte datatype, such as a WORD or DWORD, is stored, its address, by convention, is always that of its least-significant BYTE. When a larger datatype is stored in memory, the lowest-numbered byte address holds the least-significant byte of data, and so on, as illustrated by Figure 1.4. This convention for storage of multibyte datatypes, where the lowest-numbered address holds the least-significant byte, is called scientific ordering. This ordering is consistent with carry propagation, for example, from the least significant byte to the most significant byte.

On the 80386, data or code addressing is accomplished by using any of the processor's addressing modes to produce an effective address, the memory address

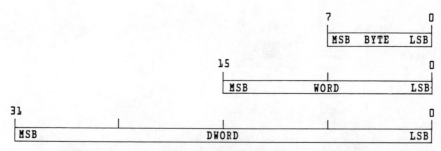

Figure 1.3   BYTE, WORD, and DWORD **Datatypes of the 80386.**

where the desired data or code is stored. The 80386 addressing architecture is highly orthogonal, meaning that any addressing mode is available to any memory-reference instruction. The programming efficiency of 80386 programs is improved over the 8086 and 80286 by the several new addressing modes provided. An effective address can be calculated from as many as four separate address components: a displacement, a base value, an index value scaled by 1, 2, 4 or 8, and a segment base. Figure 1.5 illustrates these components. When performing an effective-address calculation, the 80386 adds all requested components to form a sum, which is the effective address of the operand.

80386 addressing modes are given names, such as direct addressing (using only the displacement component), scaled index addressing (using the index component and scale factor), base plus displacement (using base and displacement components), and so forth. Including the segment base address, which is always present, any combination of the four addressing components, with or without scaling, can be utilized by the 80386 addressing modes.

Design of the 80386 Chip

The 80386, as a 32-bit machine, has the ability to process and move data 32 bits at a time. Its internal registers and datapaths have a width of 32 bits. Effective addresses are also 32-bit quantities, providing large linear address spaces 4 billion bytes (2^{32} bytes) in size.

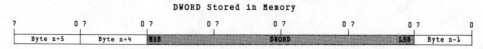

Figure 1.4   Example Memory Storage of Large Datatype.

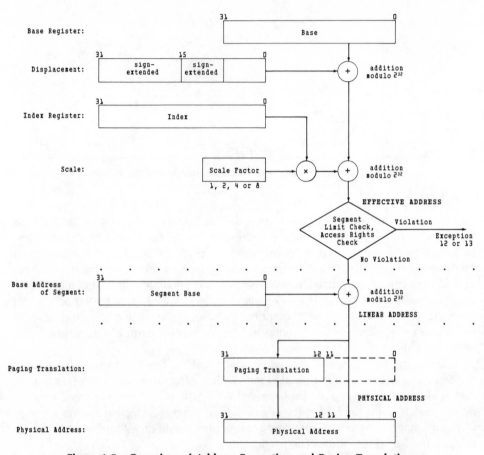

Figure 1.5   Overview of Address Formation and Paging Translation.

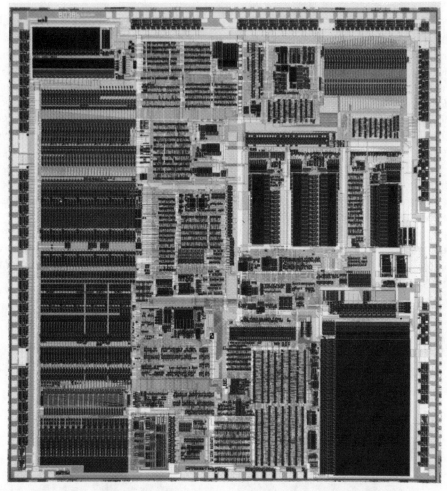

Figure 1.6   The 80386 Microprocessor Circuitry.
(Photograph Courtesy of Intel Corporation)

The microprocessor consists of 275,000 transistors etched onto a single chip of silicon and fabricated with a CMOS (complementary metal oxide semiconductor) process for low power consumption. The chip is bonded into a 132-pin package. The major units of the chip are the *instruction prefetcher*, the *instruction decoder*, the *execution unit*, and the *paging unit*. An advantage of having multiple units on chip is *parallelism*, the increased performance obtained when various units operate simultaneously, rather than one after the other. While one instruction is being executed, other instructions are being prefetched and decoded, and address calculations and paging translations are also in progress on the chip.

These units operate according to the steady cadence of a clock input signal, which paces the processor through its microinstructions. Clock rates for the 80386 now routinely run as high as 20 MHz (and will be higher in the very near future). Thus the 80386 experiences 20 million microcycles each second (4.4 MIPS). Because of its fast clock rate and an efficient design that executes an instruction every 4.5 microcycles, on average, over 4.4 million instructions are executed each second. This high instruction rate is the reason an 80386 makes fast work of large computing jobs and provides essentially instantaneous response during interactive sessions.

The high degree of on-chip integration includes a new paging unit with a self-contained cache for address-translation values. The paging unit performs memory management and provides the virtual memory capability, allowing programs to use much more memory than is actually, i.e., physically, implemented in the system with memory chips. The paging unit includes a cache to retain thirty-two recently translated values; this greatly speeds the overall translation process. This integrated paging unit eliminates the size, cost, and performance penalties of providing memory-management logic outside the chip.

Figure 1.7 The 80386 Microprocessor Chip in 132-pin Package.
(Photograph Courtesy of Intel Corporation)

A high degree of testability is built onto the 80386 chip, including a self-test the user can activate at powerup. The self-test exercises the registers as well as regular structures in the control logic. After self-test completion, the test signatures can be read in the general registers to verify the self-test results. Finally, special system registers are provided, so all memory in the paging-unit cache can be fully exercised for assurance of its functionality.

Figure 1.6 shows the circuitry of the 80386. Figure 1.7 shows the assembled chip, with the circuitry embedded in the center; note the leads from the sides of the circuitry to the 132 pins that connect it to its environment.

CHAPTER 2

DATA, REGISTER SETS
AND ADDRESSING

This chapter contains a description of the datatypes, register sets, and addressing modes of the 80836.

Data Sizes and Types

The 80386 operates on various sizes of data operands, such as bits, bytes, words, and double words. As mentioned in Chapter 1, a BYTE is 8 bits, a WORD is 16 bits, and a double word or DWORD is 32 bits.

The datatypes supported by the 80386 are bits; signed or unsigned integer data of 8, 16, or 32 bits; packed or unpacked binary coded decimal data; and strings of integer data, in which each element is 8, 16, or 32 bits. Complete address pointers, consisting of selector and offset, are also recognized. These datatypes are illustrated in Figure 2.1.

The signed and unsigned integer datatypes have the ranges shown in Figure 2.2.

Operand-Size Field and Operand-Size Prefix

The operand size for each instruction is encoded into the instruction either implicitly by the instruction opcode itself or explicitly by a field within the instruction and an optional operand-size prefix placed before the instruction.

When the operand size is explicitly encoded, operand size is determined by the *w-field* of the instruction, the operating mode of the processor, and an operand-size prefix byte that may precede the instruction.

The w-field is a single-bit field that selects either a BYTE operand size or a "larger operand" size. The w-field, shown in Figure 2.3, is contained in all instructions that explicitly encode an operand-size modifier. If w = 0, a BYTE operand size is selected. If w = 1, the larger operand is indicated, which could be either a WORD or DWORD, depending usually on the operating mode. The larger operand size is normally a 16-bit WORD if operating in any of the 16-bit modes (REAL or VIRTUAL 8086 mode) or if executing a 16-bit code segment in PROTECTED mode. However, the

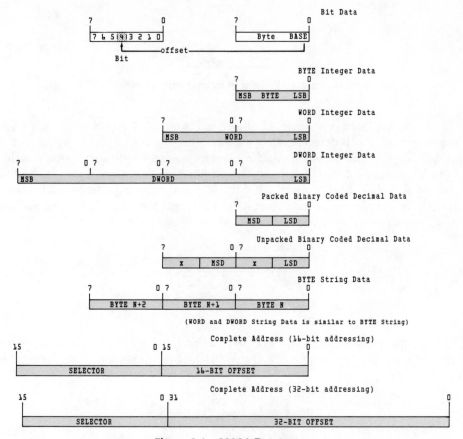

Figure 2.1 80386 Datatypes.

Size (bits)	Signed/ Unsigned	Range Hexadecimal	Decimal
8 8	Signed Unsigned	7F to 00 to 80 FF to 00	127 to 0 to -128 255 to 0
16 16	Signed Unsigned	7FFF to 0000 to 8000 FFFF to 0000	32,767 to 0 to -32,768 65,535 to 0
32 32	Signed Unsigned	7FFFFFFF to 00000000 to 80000000 FFFFFFFF to 00000000	2,147,483,647 to 0 to -2,147,483,648 4,294,967,295 to 0

Figure 2.2 Integer Data Formats of the 80386.

larger operand size is normally a 32-bit DWORD if executing a 32-bit code segment in PROTECTED mode.

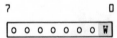

Figure 2.3   W-field in Instruction Opcode.

The operand-size prefix byte, illustrated in Figure 2.4, also helps determine the larger operand size. It does not affect the BYTE size. The operand-size prefix byte, if present, **toggles** the sense of the larger operand normally indicated by the w-field. If the larger operand would normally be WORD, then DWORD is indicated by the operand-size prefix byte. Conversely, if DWORD would normally be indicated, then WORD is indicated. The operand-size prefix affects only the instruction it precedes; it must precede every instruction where its effect is desired.

Figure 2.4   Operand-Size Prefix.

Note that the w-field and the operand-size prefix allow any operand size to be selected from any operating mode. Table 2.1 lists the conditions for selecting an operand size.

Table 2.1   Selecting Operand Size.

W-field	Operating Mode	Operand Size Prefix	Operand Size Selected
0	any mode	don't care	BYTE
1	any 16-bit mode: REAL mode VIRTUAL 8086 mode, or PROTECTED mode executing 16-bit code segment	not present	WORD
1	any 16-bit mode: REAL mode VIRTUAL 8086 mode, or PROTECTED mode executing 16-bit code segment	present	DWORD
1	PROTECTED mode executing 32-bit code segment	not present	DWORD
1	PROTECTED mode executing 32-bit code segment	present	WORD

The 80386 Registers

The 80386 has thirty-one programmable registers in the following categories:

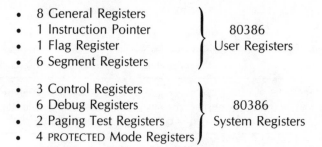

- 8 General Registers
- 1 Instruction Pointer
- 1 Flag Register
- 6 Segment Registers

80386
User Registers

- 3 Control Registers
- 6 Debug Registers
- 2 Paging Test Registers
- 4 PROTECTED Mode Registers

80386
System Registers

The typical programmer (user) directly uses the general registers, the instruction pointer, the flag register, and possibly the segment registers. The control, debug, paging test, and PROTECTED mode registers are all system registers used by the operating system to affect global aspects of the system. However, debugger utilities may also use the debug registers for their breakpointing features.

General Registers, Instruction Pointer, and Flag Register

The general registers, instruction pointer, and flag register are 32-bit registers, of which the lower 16 bits are used in the 16-bit operating modes. They all belong to the user register set, summarized in Table 2.2. The 32-bit versions of these registers are given as extended counterparts to the 16-bit registers. For example, the 32-bit instruction pointer is named EIP (Extended Instruction Pointer), while the lower 16 bits of EIP are called simply IP (Instruction Pointer). The 32-bit registers, including their 16-bit and 8-bit subsets, are shown in Figure 2.5.

Eight 32-bit general registers are available to hold data and address values. DWORD, WORD, BYTE and BIT operands may be held in these registers, as further explained in chapter 2.

The instruction pointer, EIP, is 32 bits wide, with the lower half being accessed as IP in the 16-bit modes. The instruction pointer references the next instruction to be executed within the current code segment. Operations on EIP are DWORD operations, and operations on IP are WORD operations.

The flag register, EFLAG (Extended Flag), is 32 bits wide, with the lower half accessed as FLAG in the 16-bit modes. EFLAG and FLAG contain several condition-code bits as well as several control bits, as detailed in Table 2.3. Not all 32 bits of EFLAG are defined; undefined bits read as zeros (except for bit 1, which reads as one) and are ignored when written. Operations on EFLAG are DWORD operations; operations on FLAG are WORD operations. (Exception: Instructions LAHF and SAHF load and store the lowest BYTE of FLAG.) An unabridged description of EFLAG and all its fields is found in Appendix A.

Table 2.2   80386 User Registers and Functions.

80386 System Register	Number and Name(s)	Function
General Registers	8: EAX, EBX, ECX, EDX, ESI, EDI, EBP, ESP	Used to hold general addresses or data.
Instruction Pointer	1: EIP	EIP points at the next instruction to be executed.
Flag Register	1: EFLAG	EFLAG contains 8 status fields from recent instructions and 5 control fields that enable interrupts or control other characteristics.
Segment Registers	6: CS, SS, DS, ES, FS, GS	CS identifies the current segment for code. SS identifies the current segment for stack accesses such as POP and PUSH. DS identifies the current segment for most data operations. ES, FS, and GS define alternate data segments for data operations.

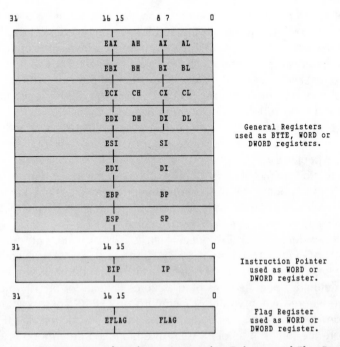

Figure 2.5   80386 General Registers, Instruction Pointer, and Flag Register.

Table 2.3   EFLAG and FLAG Contents.

EFLAG																					
					FLAG																
31	30	19	18	17	16	15	14	13 12 11 10	9	8	7	6	5	4	3	2	1	0			
0	0	0	0	VM	RF	0	NT	IOPL	OF	DF	IF	TF	SF	ZF	0	AF	0	PF	1	CF	

	Status Fields	Present in FLAG	Present in EFLAG and FLAG (i.e., new with 80386)
SF	(Sign)	Yes	
PF	(Parity)	Yes	
OF	(Overflow)	Yes	
ZF	(Zero)	Yes	
CF	(Carry)	Yes	
AF	(Auxiliary Carry)	Yes	
IOPL	(I/O Privilege Level)	Yes	
NT	(Nested Task)	Yes	
	Control Fields		
TF	(Trap Flag)	Yes	
IF	(Interrupt Enable)	Yes	
DF	(Direction Flag)	Yes	
RF	(Resume Flag)		Yes
VM	(Virtual 8086 Mode)		Yes

The Segment Registers

As mentioned, a segment is a contiguous linear block of the programmer's address space. A 32-bit segment may be up to 4 billion bytes (4 gigabytes); a 16-bit segment may be as large as 64 thousand bytes (64 kilobytes). An 80386 system may consist of many thousands of segments, if desired. Six 16-bit segment registers therefore serve to identify the currently accessible memory segments. A segment for code must be identified in the CS register; a stack segment must be identified in the SS register; and a data segment must be identified in the DS register. Other data segments can be identified in the ES, FS, and GS registers, if desired.

Operations involving the segment registers are WORD operations, and a WORD written to a segment register is called a **selector**. The selector identifies, or selects, one segment from all possible segments. For instance, a selector value written to the

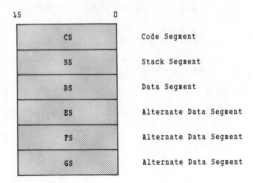

Figure 2.6   Segment Registers.

CS register selects a particular segment as the current segment, the one containing code to be fetched. Code is fetched from that segment until the code segment is reassigned by the writing of a new selector to CS. New selector values may be written to any segment register whenever the programmer desires.

Although selectors always serve to identify the current segment, selector *formats* differ slightly between REAL mode and PROTECTED mode. Selector formats are shown on page 24.

System Registers

The 80386 registers used primarily by operating system programmers are classified as system registers. These registers, for control, debug, paging test, and PROTECTED mode, provide all the functions needed to set up the 80386 system-wide features. Their functions are summarized in Table 2.4 and are fully explained in Chapters 8–17 dealing with those functions in depth. Figures 2.7 and 2.8 illustrate these registers, most of which are thirty-two bits wide.

Operations with the 32-bit control, debug and paging test registers are DWORD operations. The lower 16 bits of Control Register 0 (CR0) can also be accessed as a 16-bit Machine Status Word (MSW) for WORD operations. Operations with 32-bit PROTECTED-mode registers IDTR and GDTR are DWORD operations, while the 16-bit LDTR and TR are accessed with WORD operations.

The system registers have several noteworthy features. For instance, the evolution of these registers through the generations of Intel microprocesors is quite interesting: The 8086 has no system registers, and the 80286 has only MSW (the low half of CR0) and the PROTECTED-mode registers. Many 80386 system registers are therefore new, having been added to support the debug and paging features. Six debug registers support a new on-chip debugging facility. CR2, CR3 and the paging test registers support paging.

Other interesting points regarding the system registers:

- The debug registers are the same registers utilized by ICE-386, a powerful in-circuit emulator from Intel.
- The paging test registers allow verifying the entire paging translation cache with an assembly language program.
- In virtual memory systems, the page table base register (CR2) is the only register holding a physical address.
- In PROTECTED mode, system registers can be written from level 0 only, the most privileged level.

Table 2.4   80386 System Registers and Functions.

80386 System Register	Number and Name(s)	Function
Control Registers	3: CR0, CR2, CR3	CR0 enables PROTECTED mode, paging and controls coprocessor settings. CR2 indicates latest VIRTUAL address that caused a page fault. CR3 tells the 80386 where to find page tables for VIRTUAL address translation.
Debug Registers	6: DR0, DR1, DR2, DR3, DR6, DR7	DR0–DR3 define four independent breakpoints: 0, 1, 2, and 3. Breakpoints can be used by debugger utilities. DR6 indicates the most recent breakpoints that occurred. DR7 controls the conditions needed for each breakpoint to occur.
Paging Test Registers	2: TR6, TR7	TR6 defines the virtual address used to test the paging unit. TR7 defines the physical address used to test the paging unit.
PROTECTED-Mode Registers	4: IDTR, GDTR LDTR, TR	IDTR defines the base of the table that vectors interrupt. GDTR defines the base of the table containing global descriptors. LDTR defines the base of the table containing local (i.e. task-specific) descriptors. TR defines the base of the segment containing state information for the current task.

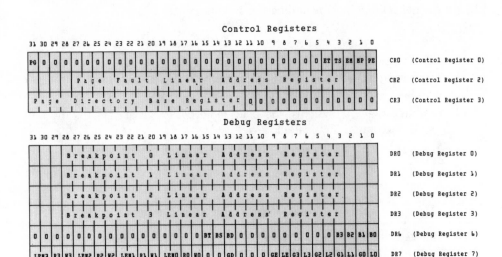

Figure 2.7 System Registers Part I: Control and Debug Registers.

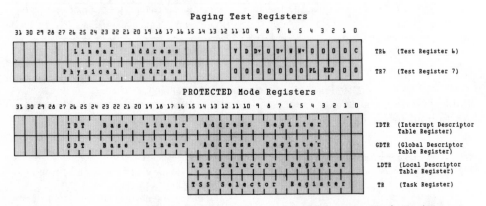

Figure 2.8 System Registers Part II: Paging Test, and PROTECTED-Mode Registers.

Data Organization
Data Organization in General Registers

BYTE, WORD, or DWORD data can be placed in the eight general registers. Each of the general registers is 32 bits wide physically yet can also be used as a 16-bit register set (8086-compatible). The 32-bit-register superset entirely contains the 16-bit registers. These general registers are illustrated in Figures 2.9 and 2.10, where, for clarity, the registers are shown as a 16-bit set and then as a 32-bit set. Notice also the 8-bit registers, AH, AL, BH, BL, CH, CL, DH, and DL, which always are available for BYTE operands.

The general registers are normally used as a 16-bit register set when operating in REAL or VIRTUAL 8086 mode or when executing a 16-bit code segment in PRO-TECTED mode. However, the general registers are normally used as a 32-bit register set when executing a 32-bit code segment in PROTECTED mode.

The operand-size prefix affects the general register set size exactly as it does the operand size, toggling the size of the register set from 16-bit to 32-bit, or vice versa. The sizes of operands and registers are therefore *always* identical. DWORD operands are placed in 32-bit registers, WORD operands are placed in 16-bit registers, and BYTE operands are always placed in 8-bit registers. The size of the register set can be changed at any time by using the operand-size prefix. Selecting the size of the register set does not clear any data being stored in the registers: this allows use of the lower half of a DWORD operand as a WORD operand, and so forth.

Register *pairing* is used for just a few specialized operations. The SHLD (Double Shift Left) and SHRD (Double Shift Right) instructions allow general register pairing for shifting of 64-bit operands for bit shifting, block transfer, insert, and delete. The double precision multiply and divide instructions use register pairing of EDX and EAX to hold 64-bit numeric operands.

Figure 2.9   General Registers Used as 16-bit Set.

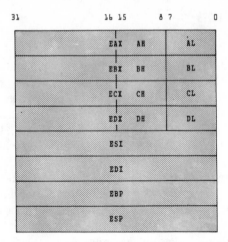

Figure 2.10   General Registers Used as a 32-bit Set.

Data Organization in Segment Registers

All operations to the segment registers are WORD operations. An operand placed in a segment register is called a *selector*, a 16-bit value that identifies a particular segment. The selector format in REAL mode or VIRTUAL 8086 mode is simply a 16-bit index identifying the segment. PROTECTED-mode selectors have a slightly modified format, since three low-order selector bits serve special purposes. The PROTECTED-mode selector includes a 2-bit privilege field (RPL) to support the four-level protection model of PROTECTED mode. It also includes a Table Indicator bit (TI) to reference the correct **descriptor table** in PROTECTED mode. More information on PROTECTED mode selectors is found in Chapter 7.

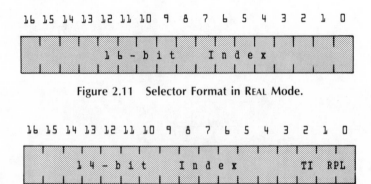

Figure 2.11   Selector Format in REAL Mode.

Figure 2.12   Selector Format in PROTECTED Mode.

Data Organization in System Registers

System registers are read or written with DWORD operations. However, data within system registers is often organized into various small fields. Data in each field is independent from data in other fields, excepting the few cases in which several fields act together in a coordinated manner. For example, four fields in Control Register 0 (CR0) together control the 80387 numeric coprocessor chip. Certain fields of the paging test registers also act as complementary pairs.

Undefined fields within system registers, shown with zeroes in Figures 2.7 and 2.8, contain no information. To avoid software incompatibilities with future processors, the programmer must not depend upon the state of undefined fields when testing defined fields. It is recommended therefore that the programmer use the Boolean instructions, such as AND, to mask undefined fields before testing the register. Such masks, corresponding exactly to the position of undefined bits, are listed in Table 2.5 for convenience.

Table 2.5   Values to Mask Undefined Bits in System Registers and EFLAG.

Register	Mask Value		Comments
	Binary	Hexadecimal	
CR0	10000000 00000000 00000000 00011111	8000 001F	
CR2	not needed	not needed	all bits defined
CR3	11111111 11111111 11110000 00000000	FFFF F000	
DR0–DR3	not needed	not needed	all bits defined
DR6	00000000 00000000 11100000 00001111	0000 E00F	
DR7	11111111 11111111 00100011 11111111	FFFF 23FF	
TR6	11111111 11111111 11111111 11100001	FFFF FFE1	
TR7	11111111 11111111 11110000 00011100	FFFF F01C	
IDTR	not needed	not needed	all bits defined
GDTR	not needed	not needed	all bits defined
LDTR	not needed	not needed	all bits defined
TR	not needed	not needed	all bits defined
EFLAG	0000000 00000011 01111111 11010101	0003 7FD5	

1: Bit is defined.
0: Bit is undefined.

Data Organization in Memory

Memory is byte-addressable. Data in memory is organized so that lower addresses hold lower-order bytes of any operand. When an operand larger than one byte is placed in memory, its address, N, corresponds to the *lowest* byte occupied and therefore to the least-significant byte of the operand. The 80386 does not require operands to be aligned on WORD addresses or DWORD addresses. For best performance, WORDS should be aligned on WORD boundaries (addresses evenly divisible by two), and DWORDS on DWORD boundaries (addresses evenly divisible by four). *The most efficient transfer occurs when data is aligned on the same byte boundary as its operand size.* Instructions do not need to be aligned either, but the most efficient operation occurs when the destinations of control transfer instructions are at DWORD boundaries, because this maximizes the chance of immediately fetching the entire next instruction.

The datatypes supported in memory by the 80386 are bits; integer data of 8, 16 or 32 bits; packed or unpacked binary coded decimal data; strings of integer data, each element 8, 16 or 32 bits; and complete address pointers, consisting of selector and offset. These operands are organized in memory as shown in Figure 2.13.

Memory Addressing

Memory references can be made for data or instructions. Instructions making data references contain information specifying the method of data access. The method used to access memory is the addressing mode, and the memory location addressed is the effective address. Addressing modes can also specify an 80386 register as the location of an operand.

Instructions may specify an operand in one of three ways:

Implicitly   The particular instruction always requires the same addressing mode for memory or register operands. For example, the PUSH instruction always uses the stack pointer for addressing.

Explicitly by register name   The instruction uses a code to refer a particular register in the 80386, for example, an instruction such as ADD AX,DX.

By addressing mode   The instruction uses a code to specify an addressing mode to calculate the effective address in memory.

The first two methods are essentially self-explanatory. This section describes the third method: the addressing modes. Addressing modes cause the 80386 to calculate an effective address, choosing one location from all possible locations in the memory space. Addressing modes are quite important. Most instructions include the specification of an addressing mode.

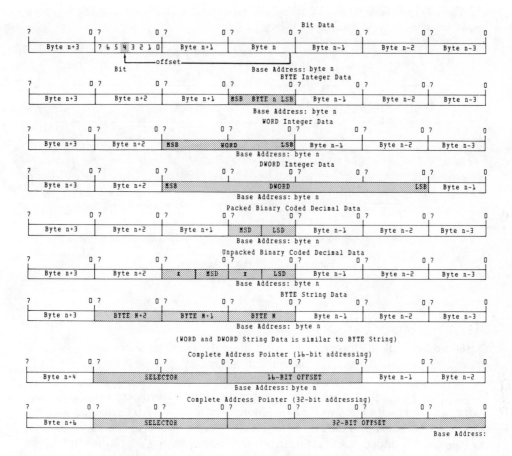

Figure 2.13   80386 Datatype Organization in Memory.

Memory Address Spaces

The 80386 supports several views of the notion of memory space. The VIRTUAL address space is that space available to the programmer; the *physical* address space is the space actually implemented with memory chips. The 80386 supports a 32-bit physical address space of 4 gigabytes (2^{32}, or 4,294,967,296 bytes) and an even larger, 46-bit virtual address space, which is nearly 16,400 times the physical space.

A virtual address contains a segment selector value and an offset value, as shown by Figure 2.14. The selector contains a 13-bit index, which, when concatenated with the table indicator bit and a 32-bit offset, provides a complete 46-bit virtual address, and therefore a virtual address space of 2^{46} bytes (64 terabytes).

The physical address is a 32-bit value, as illustrated in Figure 2.15, providing a linear physical address space of 2^{32} bytes.

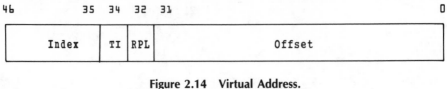

Figure 2.14   Virtual Address.

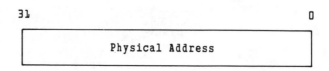

Figure 2.15   Physical Address.

Address Calculation

80386 address calculation proceeds from the virtual address space to the physical address space, through several intermediate values.

When paging is enabled, address calculation is the three-step process shown in Figure 2.16. First, up to three address components: *base, displacement,* and *scaled index,* are summed (any carry out is ignored) to form a 32-bit *effective address,* which is an offset within the current segment. Second, the base address of the current segment is added (carry out is again ignored) to form a 32-bit *linear address.* Third, when paging is enabled, the paging unit translates the linear address into a 32-bit *physical address.* During translation, the paging unit replaces the upper twenty bits with a physical page number. The lower twelve bits, the page offset, are unchanged by paging, since each memory page is 4096 bytes (2^{12} bytes).

When paging is not enabled, the linear address itself is used as the physical address. As shown in Figure 2.17, address calculation is reduced to a two-step process when paging is not enabled: effective address and then physical address are calculated.

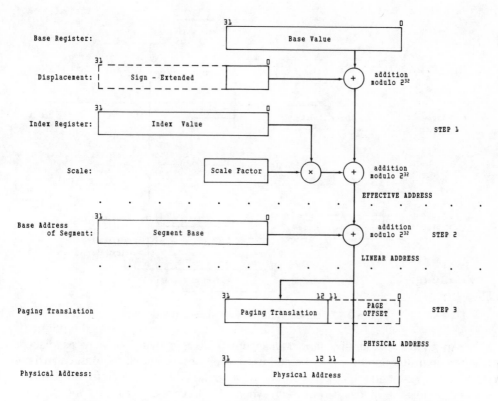

Figure 2.16   32-bit Address Calculation (with Paging Enabled).

Address Modes

The 80386 addressing modes allow full choice of which components are used in an address calculation. Of the available components (base, displacement, and scaled index), any subset or all components may be used in the effective address calculation. The components used are determined by the addressing mode chosen.

The 80386 supports 32-bit and 16-bit operation, as listed in Table 1.1, and therefore two sets of addressing modes are provided. The 32-bit addressing modes, that is, the default modes used during 32-bit operation, generically illustrated by Figures 2.16 and 2.17, all calculate a 32-bit effective address. The 16-bit addressing modes, the default modes for 16-bit operation, result in a 16-bit effective address. The 16-bit addressing modes are completely 8086-compatible; the 32-bit addressing modes are a superset offering greater flexibility and optional scaling of the index component.

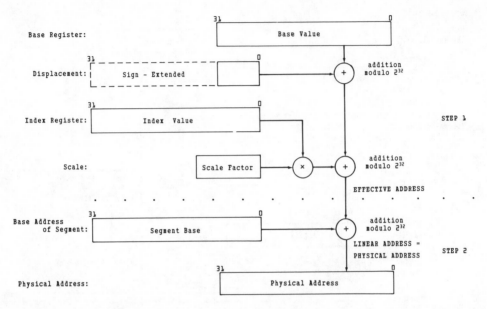

Figure 2.17   32-bit Address Calculation (No Paging).

An address-size-prefix, shown in Figure 2.18, is a byte that may be placed before an instruction to toggle the address mode from its default set to the alternate set. When 32-bit address modes are the default, the address-size prefix invokes the 16-bit addressing modes. Conversely, when 16-bit address modes are the default, the address-size prefix invokes the 32-bit addressing modes. The address-size prefix affects only the instruction it precedes. All 16-bit addressing modes are listed in Chapter 4; the 32-bit modes are listed in Chapter 7.

```
 7                  0
┌─────────────────────┐
│ 0 1 1 0 0 1 1 1 │
└─────────────────────┘
```

Address Size Prefix Byte: 67 hexadecimal

Figure 2.18   Address-Size Prefix.

Segment Register Selection

The six segment registers of the 80386 indicate which segments are currently available to an executing instruction. However, instructions that reference memory usually do not explicitly indicate the referenced segment. Usually, a segment register is chosen *implicitly*, according to the rules given in Table 2.6. As the table shows, ways use the segment indicated by the SS register; and, in general, data references use the segment indicated by the DS register. Such an arrangement is both orderly and efficient.

Table 2.6 Segment Register Selection Rules.

Type of Memory Reference	Implied (Default) Segment Use	Segment Override Prefixes Possible
Code Fetch	CS	none
Source of POP, POPA Instructions	SS	none
Destination of PUSH, PUSHA Instructions	SS	none
Other Data References, with Effective Address Using Base Register of:		
[EAX]	DS	CS, SS, ES, FS, GS
[EBX]	DS	CS, SS, ES, FS, GS
[ECX]	DS	CS, SS, ES, FS, GS
[EDX]	DS	CS, SS, ES, FS, GS
[ESI]	DS	CS, SS, ES, FS, GS
[EDI]*	DS	CS, SS, ES, FS, GS
[EBP]	SS	CS, DS, ES, FS, GS
[ESP]	SS	CS, DS, ES, FS, GS

*Data references for the destination of the string instructions STOS, REP STOS, MOVS, and REP MOVS use EDI as the base register and ES as the segment, with no segment override possible.

The implicit choice can be overridden by the use of segment-override prefix bytes. A segment-override prefix, if placed before an instruction, allows use of any segment register, overriding the implicit rules of Table 2.6. The segment-override prefixes are listed in Chapter 3. Below, in assembly language, are examples of segment-override prefix usage:

```
TEST   CS:[EBP+9]     ;operand is in CS, the code segment
MOV    EBX,ES:[EDI]   ;operand is in ES, an alternate data segment
```

CHAPTER 3

INSTRUCTION SET SUMMARY

This chapter introduces all 80386 instructions, which form a superset of the 8086 and 80286 instruction sets. These instructions, combined with the 80386 addressing modes, provide a great deal of flexibility. They are used in conjunction with the 80386 addressing modes, presented in Chapters 4 and 7.

The same set of instructions is available whether the 80386 is operating in a 32-bit or a 16-bit mode. The major operating difference between 32-bit and 16-bit modes is merely the default operand size and default address size used by instructions. The default size for operands and addressing is, naturally, the same as the operating mode: 32 bits for 32-bit modes and 16 bits for 16-bit modes. Beyond that distinction, a given instruction behaves identically in any 80386 operating mode.

The instructions perform the following categories of operations:

Data Movement   String Processing
Integer Arithmetic   Binary Coded Decimal Arithmetic
Boolean (Logical)   Program Control
Rotate, Shift, and Double Shift   System Control
Bit Manipulation   Coprocessor Data Synchronization

Instruction Summary

Throughout this instruction summary, several registers are identified by name. In addition, the following notation is used:

        genreg = any general register: EAX, EBX, ECX, EDX, ESI, EDI, EBP, ESP
                 (AX, BX, CX, DX, SI, DI, BP, SP for 16-bit operations)
        segreg = any segment register: CS, SS, DS, ES, FS, GS
             d = displacement; d8 is an 8-bit displacement
          <ea> = effective address
       <label> = assembly program label
      #<data> = immediate data; a literal integer
         stack = the top of stack, pointed to by SS:ESP
       full ptr = complete virtual address (segment selector : offset)
             C = carry bit in EFLAG register; EFLAG bit 0
             S = sign bit in EFLAG register; EFLAG bit 7

Z = zero bit in EFLAG register; EFLAG bit 6
⌐ = logical invert
∧ = logical AND
∨ = logical OR
⊕ = logical Exclusive OR

Data Movement Instructions

Data movement instructions allow BYTE, WORD, and DWORD operands to be transferred from memory to register, from register to memory, and from register to register. The MOV and XCHG instructions are used when the general registers are involved for either data values or address values. PUSH, PUSHA, POP, and POPA instructions allow stack operations, implicitly using register ESP as the stack pointer whose value is decremented *before* each PUSH and incremented *after* each POP. IN and OUT instructions perform I/O to peripherals addressed in the I/O space.

Besides the instructions just mentioned, the LCS, LSS, LDS, LES, LFS, and LGS instructions are also useful for address manipulation. They allow loading a complete virtual address's selector and offset components into a segment register and general register respectively.

Furthermore, LEA (Load Effective Address) in combination with the base + index × scale addressing mode, is probably one of the most versatile 80386 instructions. Don't overlook its potential; it can be used to perform all the functions below. If a constant is additionally specified, a constant can be added to the result, all in one 2-clock instruction.

Example	Instruction Syntax	Useful Function
LEA	EAX,[EBX]	;move value
LEA	EAX,[EAX + EBX]	;add in place
LEA	EAX,[EBX + ECX]	;add and move result
LEA	EAX,[EAX × 4]	;multiply in place ($\times 2$, $\times 4$, $\times 8$)
LEA	EAX,[EBX × 4]	;multiply and move result ($\times 2$, $\times 4$, $\times 8$)
LEA	EAX,[EAX + EAX × 4]	;multiply and add in place($\times 3$, $\times 5$, $\times 9$)
LEA	EAX,[EAX + EBX × 4]	;multiply another value and add
LEA	EAX,[EBX + ECX × 4]	;multiply, add, and move result

Conversion to a larger operand size is accomplished with the instructions MOVZX, MOVSX, CBW, CWDE, CWD, and CDQ. XLAT provides character translation based on a translation table and is well suited for translating character strings from, say, ASCII to EBCDIC.

The EFLAG register can be pushed and popped from the stack using PUSHF and POPF instructions. Instructions CMC, CLC, STC, CLD, and STD alter the carry and direction flag bits directly.

Table 3.1   Data Movement Instructions.

Instruction	Name	Operand Syntax	Operand Size	Operation
		General for Data and Address		
MOV	Move Data	<ea>,<ea> <ea>,#<data>	8, 16, 32 8, 16, 32	destination ← source destination ← immediate data
XCHG	Exchange Data	<ea>,<ea>	8, 16, 32	destination ← source
PUSH	Push Data onto Stack	<ea> #<data>	16, 32 8, 16, 32	stack ← <ea> stack ← #<data>
POP	Pop Data from Stack	<ea>	16, 32	<ea> ← stack
PUSHA	Push General Reg. onto Stack		16, 32	stack ← all genreg
POPA	Pop General Reg. from Stack		16, 32	all genreg ← stack
IN	Input Data from I/O Port	#<byte n> [DX]	8, 16, 32 8, 16, 32	EAX ← (I/O address n) [0–255] EAX ← (I/O address DX) [0–64K]
OUT	Output Data to I/O Port	#<byte n> (DX)	8, 16, 32 8, 16, 32	(I/O address n) [0–255] ← EAX (I/O address DX) [0–64K] ← EAX
		Additional for Address		
LEA	Load Effective Address	genreg,<ea>	16, 32	genreg ← effective address
LDS	Load Full Ptr. to DS:genreg	genreg,<ea>	32, 48	DS:genreg ← full ptr
LES	Load Full Ptr. to ES:genreg	genreg,<ea>	32, 48	ES:genreg ← full ptr
LFS	Load Full Ptr. to FS:genreg	genreg,<ea>	32, 48	FS:genreg ← full ptr
LGS	Load Full Ptr. to GS:genreg	genreg,<ea>	32, 48	GS:genreg ← full ptr
LSS	Load Full Ptr. to SS:genreg	genreg,<ea>	32, 48	SS:genreg ← full ptr
		Conversion		
MOVZX	Move Data Zero-extended	genreg,<ea>	8, 16, 32	genreg ← ZeroExtend(ea)
MOVSX	Move Data Sign-extended	genreg,<ea>	8, 16, 32	genreg ← SignExtend(ea)
CBW	Convert BYTE to WORD		8	AX ← SignExtend(AL)
CWDE	Convert WORD to DWORD Extended		16	EAX ← SignExtend(AX)
CWD	Convert WORD to DWORD		16	DX:AX ← SignExtend(AX)
CDQ	Convert DWORD to QUADWORD		32	EDX:EAX ← SignExtend(EAX)
XLAT	Translate BYTE Using Translation Table	AL	8	AL ← (EBX + ZeroExtend(AL))

Table 3.1 Data Movement Instructions *(Continued)*.

Instruction	Name	Operand Syntax	Operand Size	Operation	
		EFLAG Movement and Control			
PUSHFD	Push EFLAG onto Stack		16, 32	stack ← EFLAG	
POPFD	Pop EFLAG from Stack		16, 32	EFLAG ← stack	
LAHF	Load EFLAG[7..0] to AH Reg.		8	AH ← EFLAG[7..0]	
SAHF	Store AH Reg. to EFLAG[7..0]		8	EFLAG[7..0] ← AH	
CMC	Complement Carry Flag Bit		1	EFLAG[0] ← - EFLAG[0]	;carry
CLC	Clear Carry Flag Bit		1	EFLAG[0] ← 0	;carry
CLD	Clear Direction Flag Bit		1	EFLAG[10] ← 0	;direction
STC	Set Carry Flag Bit		1	EFLAG[0] ← 1	;carry
STD	Set Direction Flag Bit		1	EFLAG[10] ← 1	;direction

Integer Arithmetic Instructions

Integer arithmetic instructions perform high-speed, four-function arithmetic on operands of all sizes. Signed and unsigned arithmetic is supported, and immediate data operands are allowed on all operations but divide. All multiply instructions use an early-out algorithm to reduce the execution time in proportion to the leading zeros in <ea>. The CMP instruction is a signed comparison of two operands that is reflected in the EFLAG register; CMP leaves the operands unchanged. (See Table 3.2.)

Boolean (Logical) Instructions

Boolean instructions AND, OR, XOR, NOT, and TEST are available for all sizes of operands. Immediate data may be used for all instructions. The TEST instruction is a bit-wise ANDing of an operand with zero that is reflected in the EFLAG register; the operand remains unchanged. (See Table 3.3.)

Rotate, Shift, and, Double Shift Instructions

The 80386 rotate, shift, and double shift operations in either direction are available on all sizes of operands. Shift counts of any number (modulo 32) execute as quickly as single-bit operations, because an on-chip barrel shifter is utilized. Multibit shifts are permitted even on memory operands. Rotates can be performed through the carry flag (RLC and RRC) or bypassing carry (ROL and ROR). Shifts can be

Table 3.2   Integer Arithmetic Instructions.

Instruction	Name	Operand Syntax	Operand Size	Operation	
ADD	Integer Addition	<ea>,<ea>	8, 16, 32	destination ← destination + source	
		<ea>,#<data>	8, 16, 32	destination ← destination + immediate data	
ADC	Interer Addition with Carry Flag	<ea>,<ea>	8, 16, 32	destination ← destination + source + C	
		<ea>,#<data>	8, 16, 32	destination ← destination + immediate data + C	
SUB	Integer Subtraction	<ea>,<ea>	8, 16, 32	destination ← destination − source	
		<ea>,#<data>	8, 16, 32	destination ← destination − immediate data	
SBB	Integer Subtraction with Borrow (Carry Flag)	<ea>,<ea>	8, 16, 32	destination ← destination − source + C	
		<ea>,#<data>	8, 16, 32	destination ← destination − immediate data − C	
INC	Increment by 1	<ea>	8, 16, 32	destination ← destination + 1	
DEC	Decrement by 1	<ea>	8, 16, 32	destination ← destination − 1	
CMP	Integer Comparison	<ea>,<ea>	8, 16, 32	destination ← source	[affects EFLAG]
		<ea>,#<data>	8, 16, 32	destination ← immediate data	[affects EFLAG]
NEG	Integer Negate	<ea>	8, 16, 32	destination ← 0 − destination	
MUL	Unsigned Multiplication	<ea>	8, 16, 32	EDX:EAX ← EAX × <ea>	[unsigned dbl prec]
IMUL	Signed Multiplication	genreg,<ea>	8, 16, 32	genreg ← genreg × <ea>	[signed sgl prec]
		genreg,<ea>,#<data>	8, 16, 32	genreg ← <ea> × immed	[signed dbl prec]
		<ea>	8, 16, 32	EDX:EAX ← EAX × <ea>	[signed dbl prec]
DIV	Unsigned Division	<ea>	8, 16, 32	EAX:EDX ← EDX:EAX / <ea>	[unsigned dbl prec]
IDIV	Signed Division	<ea>	8, 16, 32	EAX:EDX ← EDX:EAX / <ea>	[signed dbl prec]

arithmetic (SAL and SAR), conveniently multiplying or dividing the value by powers of two, or they can be logical (SHL and SHR), with zeros being shifted in from either end. The double shift instructions (SHLD and SHRD), new on the 80386, allow two 32-bit operands to be used in the same shift operation. Extremely fast bit-field operations (such as insert and block transfer) can be built upon these instructions, to process bit fields of arbitrary width. (See Table 3.4.)

Table 3.3 Boolean (Logical) Instructions.

Instruction	Name	Operand Syntax	Operand Size	Operation
AND	Boolean AND	<ea>,<ea> <ea>,#<data>	8, 16, 32 8, 16, 32	destination ← destination ∧ source destination ← destination ∧ immediate data
OR	Boolean OR	<ea>,<ea> <ea>,#<data>	8, 16, 32 8, 16, 32	destination ← destination ∨ source destination ← destination ∨ immediate data
XOR	Boolean XOR	<ea>,<ea> <ea>,#<data>	8, 16, 32 8, 16, 32	destination ← destination ⊕ source destination ← destination ⊕ immediate data
NOT	Boolean NOT	<ea>	8, 16, 32	destination ← ∽ destination
TEST	Boolean Test for 0	<ea>	8, 16, 32	destination ∧ 0FFFFFFFFh {affects EFLAG}

Table 3.4 Rotate, Shift, and Double Shift Instructions.

Instruction	Name	Operand Syntax	Operand Size	Operation
ROL	Rotate Left	<ea>,#<data> <ea>,CL	8, 16, 32 8, 16, 32	
ROR	Rotate Right	<ea>,#<data> <ea>,CL	8, 16, 32 8, 16, 32	
RCL	Rotate Left Through Carry Flag	<ea>,#<data> <ea>,CL	8, 16, 32 8, 16, 32	
RCR	Rotate Right Through Carry Flag	<ea>,#<data> <ea>,CL	8, 16, 32 8, 16, 32	
SHL	Logical Shift Left	<ea>,#<data> <ea>,CL	8, 16, 32 8, 16, 32	
SHR	Logical Shift Right	<ea>,#<data> <ea>,CL	8, 16, 32 8, 16, 32	
SAL	Arithmetic Shift Left (Multiply by 2)	<ea>,#<data> <ea>,CL	8, 16, 32 8, 16, 32	
SAR	Arithmetic Shift Right (Divide by 2)	<ea>,#<data> <ea>,CL	8, 16, 32 8, 16, 32	
SHLD	Double Shift Left	<ea>,<ea>,#<data> <ea>,<ea>,CL	8, 16, 32 8, 16, 32	r/m operand reg operand
SHRD	Double Shift Right	<ea>,<ea>,#<data> <ea>,<ea>,CL	8, 16, 32 8, 16, 32	reg operand r/m operand

Bit Manipulation Instructions

Direct bit manipulation can be accomplished with the bit instructions BT, BTS, BTR, and BTC. The index of the selected bit can be given by an immediate constant in the instruction or by a value in a general register. The bit scan instructions, BSF and BSR, find the position of the first set bit, beginning from the least-significant and the most-significant end of the operand, respectively.

Table 3.5   Bit Manipulation Instructions.

Instruction	Name	Operand Syntax	Operand Size	Operation
BT	Bit Test	\<ea\>,#\<data\> \<ea\>,genreg	16, 32 16, 32	C ← (\<bit number\> of destination)
BTS	Bit Test and Set	\<ea\>,#\<data\> \<ea\>,genreg	16, 32 16, 32	C ← (\<bit number\> of destination); bit of destination ← 1
BTR	Bit Test and Reset	\<ea\>,#\<data\> \<ea\>,genreg	16, 32 16, 32	C ← (\<bit number\> of destination); bit of destination ← 0
BTC	Bit Test and Complement	\<ea\>,#\<data\> \<ea\>,genreg	16, 32 16, 32	C ← (\<bit number\> of destination) bit of destination ← ∽ (bit of destination)
BSF	Bit Scan Forward (LSB to MSB)	genreg,\<ea\>	16, 32	from least significant bit, scan for set bit genreg ← offset
BSR	Bit Scan Reverse (MSB to LSB)	genreg,\<ea\>	16, 32	from most significant bit, scan for set bit genreg ← offset

String Processing Instructions

The 80386 directly operates on strings of BYTE, WORD, or DWORD operands. The string can be processed in either direction, according to the setting of the direction flag bit in EFLAG. Strings can be moved, compared, and scanned to find a particular value, and strings can be transferred to and from the I/O space.

When a **repeat prefix** is placed before a string instruction, multiple iterations of the basic function are performed. Repeated string instructions all operate at or nearly at maximum bus bandwidth, for extremely fast processing. The repeat prefix may be unconditional (checks only for ECX to expire) or conditional (checks for a flag condition or ECX expiration).

Registers ESI and EDI are used by these instructions to reference the string operands. The registers must contain the desired address values before executing a string instruction, and they are automatically postincremented or postdecremented by the size (in bytes) of the operand. When a repeat prefix is present, register ECX is used as an iteration counter, allowing the instruction to repeat until EXC becomes zero.

Table 3.6 String Instructions.

Instruction	Name	Operand Syntax	Operand Size	Operation
MOVS	Move String Data		8, 16, 32	(ES:EDI) ← (ESI); ESI ← incremented or decremented ESI; EDI ← incremented or decremented EDI;
REP MOVS	Repeated Move String Data		8, 16, 32	while ECX <> 0 do: (ES:EDI) ← (ESI); ESI ← incremented or decremented ESI; EDI ← incremented or decremented EDI; ECX ← ECX - 1 {repeated instruction}
CMPS	Compare String Data		8, 16, 32	(ESI) − (ES:EDI); {set flags} ESI ← incremented or decremented ESI; EDI ← incremented or decremented EDI;
REPE CMPS (finds first nonmatching portion of strings)	Repeated Compare String Data if Comparison Doesn't Match		8, 16, 32	while ECX <> 0 and condition FALSE do: (ESI) − (ES:EDI); {set flags} ESI ← incremented or decremented ESI; EDI ← incremented or decremented EDI; ECX ← ECX - 1 {repeated instruction}
REPNE CMPS (finds first matching portion of strings)	Repeated Compare String Data if Comparison Matches		8, 16, 32	while ECX <> 0 and condition FALSE do: (ESI) − (ES:EDI); {set flags} ESI ← incremented or decremented ESI; EDI ← incremented or decremented EDI; ECX ← ECX − 1 {repeated instruction}
SCAS	Scan String Data		8, 16, 32	(ESI) − AL/AX/EAX; {set flags} ESI ← incremented or decremented ESI; EDI ← incremented or decremented EDI;
REPE SCAS (finds first nonmatch with AL|AX|EAX)	Repeated Scan String Data if Data Matches AL|AX|EAX		8, 16, 32	while ECX <> 0 and condition FALSE do: (ESI) − AL/AX/EAX; {set flags} ESI ← incremented or decremented ESI; EDI ← incremented or decremented EDI; ECX ← ECX − 1 {repeated instruction}
REPNE SCAS (finds first match with AL|AX|EAX)	Repeated Scan String Data if Data Doesn't Match AL|AX|EAX		8, 16, 32	while ECX <> 0 and condition FALSE do: (ESI) − AL/AX/EAX; {set flags} ESI ← incremented or decremented ESI; EDI ← incremented or decremented EDI; ECX ← ECX − 1 {repeated instruction}
LODS	Load String Data into AL|AX|EAX		8, 16, 32	AL/AX/EAX ← (ESI); ESI ← incremented or decremented ESI; EDI ← incremented or decremented EDI;
REP LODS	Repeated Load String Data into AL|AX|EAX is not meaningful.It does not exist as an instruction.			
STOS	Store AL|AX|EAX to String		8, 16, 32	(EDI) ← AL/AX/EAX; ESI ← incremented or decremented ESI; EDI ← incremented or decremented EDI;

Table 3.6   String Instructions *(Continued).*

Instruction	Name	Operand Syntax	Operand Size	Operation
REP STOS	Repeated Store AL|AX|EAX to Data String (fills memory area)		8, 16, 32	while ECX <> 0 do: (EDI) ← AL/AX/EAX; ESI ← incremented or decremented ESI; EDI ← incremented or decremented EDI; ECX ← ECX − 1 {repeated instruction}
INS	Input Data from Port to String		8, 16, 32	(EDI) ← port given in DX; EDI ← incremented or decremented EDI;
REP INS	Repeated Input Data from Port to String		8, 16, 32	while ECX <> 0 do: (EDI) ← port given in DX; EDI ← incremented or decremented EDI; ECX ← ECX − 1 {repeated instruction}
OUTS	Output String Data to Port		8, 16, 32	port given in DX ← (ESI); ESI ← incremented or decremented ESI;
REP OUTS	Repeated Output String Data to Port		8, 16, 32	while ECX <> 0 do: port given in DX ← (ESI); ESI ← incremented or decremented ESI; ECX ← ECX − 1 {repeated instruction}

Binary Coded Decimal Arithmetic Instructions

Several instructions convert binary operands for unpacked and packed BCD arithmetic. For unpacked addition, subtraction, and multiplication, the AAA, AAS, and AAM instructions should be used *following* the add, subtract, or multiply operation respectively. For unpacked division, the AAD instruction should be used immediately *prior to* the division operation. Appendix B, Instruction Set Details, describes the detailed workings of these BCD instructions.

For packed BCD addition and subtraction, the operation should be followed by the DAA or DAS instruction, respectively. Appendix B again provides full details. Notice that the operand sizes of these instructions are geared toward 16-bit operations, so for 32-bit BCD operations on the 80386, similar conversions should be accomplished using general-purpose instructions.

Table 3.7   Binary Coded Decimal Arithmetic Instructions.

Instruction	Name	Operand Syntax	Operand Size	Operation
AAA	ASCII Adjust After Addition		16	AL adjustment, if necessary; AH increment, if necessary.
AAS	ASCII Adjust After Subtraction		16	AL adjustment, if necessary; AH decrement, if necessary.
AAM	ASCII Adjust After Multiplication		16	AH ← AL / 10; AL ← AL MOD 10.

Table 3.7 Binary Coded Decimal Arithmetic Instructions *(Continued)*.

Instruction	Name	Operand Syntax	Operand Size	Operation
AAD	ASCII Adjust Before Division		16	AL ← (AH * 10) + AL; AH ← 0;
DAA	BCD Decimal Adjust After Addition		8	if AF = 1 then adjust lower nibble of AL reg; if CF = 1 then adjust upper nibble of AL reg
DAS	BCD Decimal Adjust After Subtraction		8	if AF = 1 then adjust lower nibble of AL reg; if CF = 1 then adjust upper nibble of AL reg

Program Control Instructions

Conditional and unconditional jump instructions allow program transfer when desired. The Set Byte Conditionally instructions, Scc, allow efficient return of Boolean status information by subroutines. Subroutines and interrupt routines may be invoked by the CALL and INT n instructions, respectively. The ENTER and LEAVE instructions conveniently create and remove stack frames and support the concept of lexical nesting as it applies to procedure nesting in high-level programming languages, such as C.

Table 3.8 Program Control Instructions.

Instruction	Name	Operand Syntax	Operand Size	Operation
			Conditional	
Jcc	Conditional Jump within Segment	<label>	8, 16, 32	if condition true, then EIP ← EIP + d
Scc	Set Byte Conditionally	<ea>	8, 16, 32	if condition true, then <ea> ← 1 else <ea> ← 0
JECXZ	Jump on Condition of ECX Zero	<label>	8	if ECX = 0, then EIP ← EIP + d
LOOP	Jump and Decrement ECX	<label>	8	if ECX <> 0, then EIP ← EIP + d
LOOPE	Jump on Condition Equal and Decrement ECX	<label>	8	ECX ← ECX − 1; if ECX < > 0 and Z = 1, then EIP ← EIP + d
LOOPNE	Jump on Condition Not Equal and Decrement ECX	<label>	8	ECX ← ECX − 1; if ECX <> 0 and Z = 0, then EIP ← EIP + d
			Unconditional	
JMP	Unconditional Jump	<label> <label>	8, 16, 32 48	EIP ← EIP + d EIP ← full ptr [31..0]; { offset part } CS ← full ptr [47..32] { selector part }
		(<ea>) (<ea>)	8, 16, 32 48	EIP ← (<ea>) EIP ← (<ea[31..0]>); { offset part of ptr } CS ← (<ea[47..32]>) { selector part of ptr }

Table 3.8 Program Control Instructions *(Continued).*

Instruction	Name	Operand Syntax	Operand Size	Operation
CALL	Call Subroutine (or Task)	\<label\>	16, 32	SP ← SP - 4; (SP) ← EIP; EIP ← EIP + d
		\<label\>	48	SP ← SP - 4; (SP) ← CS;
				SP ← SP - 4; (SP) ← EIP;
				EIP ← full ptr [31..0]; {offset part}
				CS ← full ptr [47..32] {selector part}
		(\<ea\>)	16,32	SP ← SP - 4; (SP) ← EIP;
				EIP ← (\<ea\>)
		(\<ea\>)	48	SP ← SP - 4; (SP) ← CS;
				SP ← SP - 4; (SP) ← EIP;
				EIP ← (\<ea[31..0]\>); {offset part of ptr}
				CS ← (\<ea[47..32]\>) {selector part of ptr}
INT n	Interrupt Instruction	\<label\>	8	SP ← SP − 4; (SP) ← CS;
				SP ← SP − 4; (SP) ← EIP;
				EIP ← full ptr [31..0]; {intr offset part}
				CS ← full ptr [47..32] {intr selector part}
ENTER	Make Stack Frame for Procedure Parameters	#\<data1\>, #\<data2\>	8, 16	construct stack frame with \<data1\> bytes of dynamic storage allocated and \<data2\> frame pointers copied from previous stack frame
LEAVE	High Level Procedure Exit			release stack space used by a procedure for its local variables (undoes actions of previous ENTER instruction)
			Returns	
RET	Subroutine Return			IP ← (SP); SP ← SP + 4 {within segment}
				IP ← (SP); SP ← SP + 4;
				CS ← (SP); SP ← SP + 4 {intersegment}
		#\<data\>	16	IP ← (SP) + immed data;
				SP ← SP + 4 {within segment}
				IP ← (SP) + immed data; SP ← SP + 4;
				CS ← (SP); SP ← SP + 4 {intersegment}
IRET	Interrupt Return (or Task Return)			IP ← (SP); SP ← SP + 4;
				CS ← (SP); SP ← SP + 4;
				EFLAG ← (SP); SP ← SP + 4

System Control Instructions

A group of machine instructions, typically used by the system programmer, control system-wide attributes. Several instructions allow loading and storing of the control, debug, and test registers. Others check protection attributes and report validity using the zero flag (ZF) bit.

Table 3.9 Machine Control Instructions.

Instruction	Name	Operand Syntax	Operand Size	Operation
		System Register Load/Store		
MOV	Move Data to System Register	CRn, <ea> DRn, <ea> TRn, <ea>	32 32 32	CRn ← <ea> DRn ← <ea> TRn ← <ea>
MOV	Move Data from System Register	<ea>, CRn <ea>, DRn <ea>, TRn	32 32 32	<ea> ← CRn <ea> ← DRn <ea> ← TRn
LMSW	Load Machine Status Word	<ea>	16	CR0[15..0] ← <ea>
SMSW	Store Machine Status Word	<ea>	16	<ea> ← CR0[15..0]
LIDT	Load Interrupt Descriptor Table Register	<ea>	48	IDT ← <ea>
LGDT	Load Global Descriptor Table Register	<ea>	48	GDT ← <ea>
LLDT*	Load Local Descriptor Table Register	<ea>	16	LDT ← <ea>
LTR*	Load Task Register	<ea>	16	TR ← <ea>
SIDT	Store Interrupt Descriptor Table Register	<ea>	48	<ea> ← IDT
SGDT	Store Global Descriptor Table Register	<ea>	48	<ea> ← GDT
SLDT*	Store Local Descriptor Table Register	<ea>	16	<ea> ← LDT
STR*	Store Task Register	<ea>	16	<ea> ← TR
		Protection Attribute Checking		
LAR*	Load Access Rights	genreg, <ea>	16, 32	genreg ← access rights; if valid, Z ← 1, else Z ← 0
LSL*	Load Segment Limit	genreg, <ea>	16, 32	genreg ← segment limit if valid, Z ← 1, else Z ← 0
VERR*	Verify Segment for Reading	<ea>	16	if readable, Z ← 1, else Z ← 0
VERW*	Verify Segment for Writing	<ea>	16	if writeable, Z ← 1, else Z ← 0
ARPL*	Adjust RPL Field of Selector	<ea>, genreg	16	adjust RPL of EA to not less than RPL of genreg
		Machine Control		
HALT	Halt until Interrupt			stop until interrupt is received

*Instruction available only in PROTECTED mode.

Coprocessor Data Synchronization Instruction

The WAIT instruction allows data synchronization with the 80287 or 80387 numeric coprocessor. When data is being transferred between the coprocessor and memory, the WAIT instruction causes the 80386 to wait for completion of the transfer before proceeding with its next instruction. This data synchronization guaranteed by WAIT is needed only when the 80386 and its numeric coprocessor are both operating on the *same* operand in memory.

Table 3.10 Coprocessor Synchronization Instruction.

Instruction	Name	Operand Syntax	Operand Size	Operation
WAIT	Wait Until Coprocessor Not Busy			wait until BUSY input signal is inactive

Instruction Prefixes

Various prefix bytes are can be placed before an 80386 instruction. Each prefix byte, if present, alters some behavior of the instruction immediately following. The five types of prefixes are listed below:

Operand Size	changes operand size from current default size
Address Size	changes address size from current default size
Segment Override	changes choice of segment from default choice
Bus LOCK	activates bus LOCK# signal (default is "not active")
Repeat	repeats the string instructions for the number of iterations shown in register ECX.

Each prefix, illustrated in Figure 3.1, has a unique purpose. Operand size and address size are affected by the operand-size prefix and address-size prefix, as explained in Chapter 2. The segment-override prefix alters the default choice for segment usage, as listed in Table 2.6. To allow choosing any current segment instead of the default, a segment-override prefix is provided for each segment register: CS, SS, DS, ES, FS, and GS as shown in Figure 3.1. The bus-LOCK prefix can activate an output 80386 signal to tell other processors (if any) that the bus is LOCKed and should not be interrupted. Finally, the repeat prefix allows multiple iterations of the string instructions, as described earlier.

It may be necessary for several prefixes to precede a single instruction. For example, a segment-override prefix and an operand-size prefix may be used in combination on the same instruction. The ordering of prefixes of different types does not matter. However, if several prefixes of the *same type* (for example, several segment-override prefixes) precede a single instruction, only the *last* such prefix has effect.

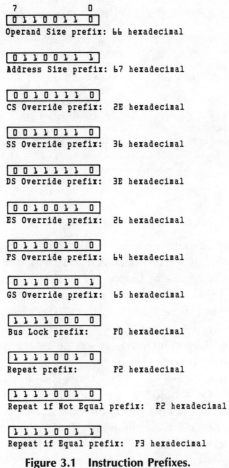

Figure 3.1   Instruction Prefixes.

Instructions of sixteen bytes or more (achievable only by excess prefixing) are illegal.

The LOCK prefix can precede only certain instructions, particularly those that exchange register data with memory and some of those that operate on a memory *destination* operand. Specifically, the LOCKable instruction forms are:

```
XCHG    <mem EA>,genreg         ;Exchange memory with
                                ; register (the 80286
                                ; and 80386 autoLOCK
                                ; this instruction).
```

```
XCHG       genreg,<mem EA>             ;Exchange register with
                                       ; memory (the 80286
                                       ; and 80386 autoLOCK
                                       ; this instruction).
ADD        <mem EA>,genreg             ;Add to memory operand
ADC        <mem EA>,genreg             ;Add using Carry flag
SUB        <mem EA>,genreg             ;Subtract from memory operand
SBB        <mem EA>,genreg             ;Subtract using Carry flag
                                       ; (borrow)
NEG        <mem EA>                    ;Negate memory operand
OR         <mem EA>,genreg             ;OR to memory operand
AND        <mem EA>,genreg             ;AND to memory operand
XOR        <mem EA>,genreg             ;XOR to memory operand
NOT        <mem EA>                    ;NOT memory operand
BTC        <mem EA>                    ;Complement memory bit
                                       ; operand
BTR        <mem EA>                    ;Reset memory bit operand
BTS        <mem EA>                    ;Set memory bit operand
```

If the LOCK prefix is placed before an instruction other than one of those above, an illegal instruction is detected. (See Chapters 6 and 16 for further information regarding violations.) Because of paging support on the 80386, the 80386 is much more restrictive about the LOCK prefix than is the 8086 or 80286. It must be restricted because in a paged environment, such as the 80386 provides there is no way to assure, for example, the successful LOCKing of a repeated string instruction. The operating system may have to intervene to service a page fault, thus interrupting a supposedly LOCKed instruction.

There is a beneficial aspect of this LOCK prefix restriction, however, since it is now more controlled. On the 80386, the LOCK prefix is available at all privilege levels, whereas on the 80286 it is available only at levels of high privilege. This means, of course, that 80386 application programs can use the LOCK prefix as desired. A typical usage would be a LOCKed ADD or SUB instruction to memory, useful for implementing counting semaphore variables.

Instruction Format

Instruction formats should be as compact and efficient as possible; with the 80386, the shortest instructions are one byte. Opcode information and addressing information can be added in byte increments. All instructions are at least one byte and can be as many as fifteen bytes in length, including prefix bytes. The general 80386 instruction, Figure 3.2, is structured into prefix bytes (optional), opcode bytes (up to two bytes), address mode bytes (up to two bytes), displacement bytes (up to four bytes), and immediate data bytes (up to four bytes).

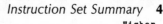

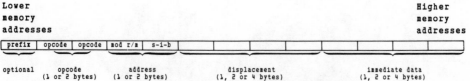

Figure 3.2   80386 General Instruction Format.

   If an instruction contains undefined opcode bytes, the 80386 signals the condition as an invalid opcode exception (exception 6). If an instruction is longer than fifteen bytes, by use of redundant prefixes, the condition is signalled as a general protection exception (exception 13). See Chapters 6 and 16 for more coverage of processor exceptions.

PART 2

16-BIT PROGRAMMING:
80386 REAL Mode

Thanks to the 16-bit REAL mode provided on the 80386, one can run existing 8086/8088 software on the 80386, faster than ever before possible. The compatibility of REAL mode has obvious attraction to many 8086/8088 users, although it represents only the tip of the iceberg of 80386 capabilities.

The purpose of this section is to make a fully accurate description of 80386 REAL mode: to consider all the nuances of running 8086/8088 software on the 80386 REAL mode, including consideration of all new 80386 features that filter down to REAL-mode operation. To carefully examine the 80386 REAL mode, this section considers the additional instructions, the additional instruction prefixes, the additional registers, and even the additional exceptions detected by the 80386.

CHAPTER 4

MEMORY ADDRESSING
IN THE 16-BIT MODES

This chapter explains memory addressing in the 8086/8088-compatible REAL mode and the 8086/8088-compatible VIRTUAL 8086 mode. Since both modes are 8086/8088-compatible, the addressing modes available for 16-bit programming are identical in both modes. The only addressing difference between REAL and VIRTUAL 8086 modes is the availability of paging in VIRTUAL 8086 mode. However, the paging feature is usually controlled by the 32-bit master program and is transparent to 16-bit software.

This chapter focusses on the *16-bit addressing modes*. In the 16-bit addressing modes, an *effective address* is calculated as the sum of up to three 16-bit address *components*: base, displacement, and index. Therefore the effective address is also a 16-bit value. The general process of 16-bit addressing is shown in Figure 4.1, and 16-bit addressing, including paging, is shown in Figure 4.2.

The effective address is considered an offset from the base of the current memory segment. Therefore, as the second step of any 16-bit addressing mode, a segment base is added to the effective address. The segment base address is the selector value multiplied by sixteen or, as Figures 4.1 and 4.2 point out, the selector value shifted four places to the left. Thus, the segment base address also becomes effectively a 20-bit value, and the linear address also becomes a 20-bit value.

The 16-bit operating modes provide a linear address space of 2^{20} bytes, in other words, one megabyte of memory. This is a direct result of the 16-bit addressing modes, which, because the segment base address has been shifted left by 4 bits, generate a 20-bit linear address.

Various combinations of 16-bit addressing components are possible, using subsets of the available components. The simpler modes use just one component, while the more complex modes use more.

Most addressing modes are *register indirect-addressing modes*. They apply to data addressing and program addressing. The 80386 provides *memory indirect-addressing modes* as well; however, they apply only to program addressing. All 16-bit addressing modes are described and illustrated in the following pages. Notice that these illustrations carefully indicate the modulus of additions performed, to show whether an addition carry is retained or lost.

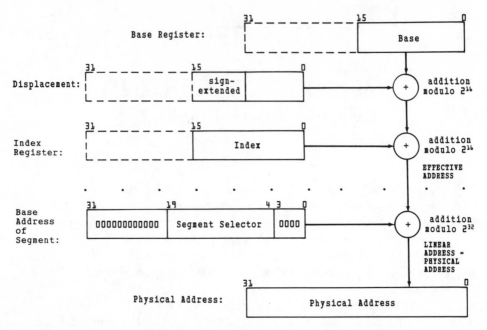

Figure 4.1   16-bit Address Calculation (In REAL mode, No Paging).

Introduction to Paging

In the VIRTUAL 8086 mode, the 80386 offers built-in support for virtual memory through paging. Paging does not affect the addressing modes, which calculate an effective address. Paging, if enabled, is a translation process performed on the linear address, before accessing memory. Sixteen-bit addressing, including paging, is illustrated by Figure 4.2 and applies to the VIRTUAL 8086 mode. During REAL mode, paging cannot be enabled.

Page translation is performed upon a 32-bit linear address, an extended form of the 20-bit linear address. As Figure 4.2 shows, page translation causes the upper 20 bits of effective address to be replaced with another 20-bit value. Replacement occurs as a function of the original 20-bit value, using a memory-resident page table. This section introduces paging, since it is related to the overall process of address translation. This is merely an introduction to paging, which is further described in Chapter 9. The remainder of this chapter covers 16-bit address formation.

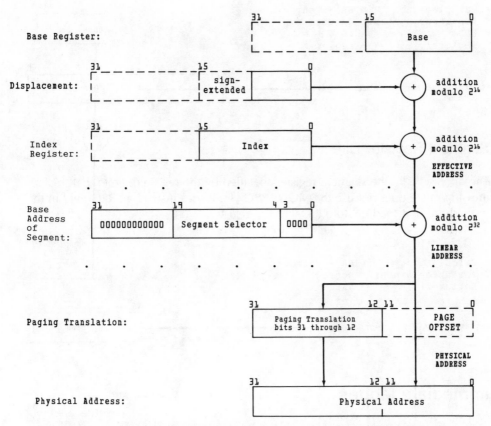

Figure 4.2   16-bit Address Calculation (In VIRTUAL 8086 Mode with Paging Enabled).

Register Direct Modes

Register direct modes specify that the operand is located in one of the eight general-purpose registers, one of the six segment registers, or one of the system registers.

General Register Direct

The operand is in the general register specified by the R/M field. The register size used may be 8, 16, or 32 bits, depending upon the data operand size for the instruction.

```
Calculation:        EA = genreg
Assembler Syntax:   genreg
MOD:                00
Register:           reg, r/m
```

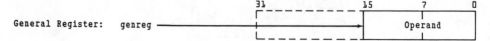

Segment Register Direct

The operand is in the segment register specified by the reg field. Note that this addressing mode does not use the MOD R/M byte. It uses instead a SREG field in the instructions that load or store the segment registers.

```
Calculation:        EA = segreg
Assembler Syntax:   segreg
Register:           SREG
```

Immediate Modes

Immediate addressing specifies that the operand is contained in the instruction itself. Immediate addressing mode can specify only a source operand, never a destination operand. The immediate operand may be a BYTE or WORD. The immediate addressing mode is not specified by the MOD R/M byte; rather, certain opcodes implicitly specify use of immediate addressing for the source operand. The same instruction can therefore include the MOD R/M byte to specify its destination operand.

```
Calculation:        EA = #<data>
Assembler Syntax:   data
Opcode:             Certain opcodes implicitly specify that
                    the instruction uses immediate data.
```

Register Indirect Modes

These addressing modes specify that the operand is in a memory segment and that the contents of one or more registers are used to calculate the effective address of the operand within the segment. The segment base address is then added, to form the 20-bit linear address of the operand.

Base Register Indirect

Register SI, DI, BX, or BP can serve as the base register containing the address of the memory operand.

```
Calculation:        EA = (genreg)
Assembler Syntax:   (genreg)
R/M:                100, 101, 110, 111
Base Register:      SI, DI, BX, BP
```

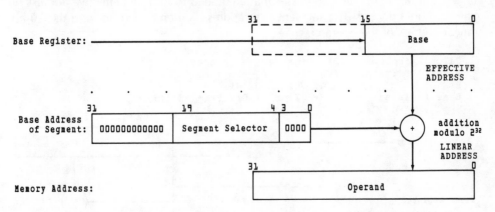

Base Register Indirect with Displacement

Register SI, DI, BX, or BP can serve as the base register containing an address that is added to a sign-extended displacement. The sum forms the effective address of the memory operand. The segment base address is then added, to form the 20-bit linear address of the operand.

```
Calculation:        EA = (genreg)
Assembler Syntax:   (genreg)
R/M:                100, 101, 110, 111
Base Register:      SI, DI, BX, BP
```

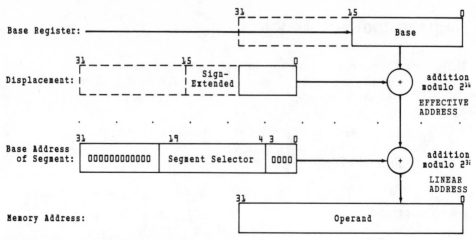

Base and Index Register Indirect

Register pairs BX + SI, BX + DI, BP + SI, and BP + DI can each serve as base and index registers containing addresses that are added to form the effective address of the memory operand. The segment base address is then added, to form the 20-bit linear address of the operand.

```
Calculation:       EA = (genreg) + (genreg)
Assembler Syntax:  (genreg) + (genreg)
R/M:               000, 001, 010, 011
Base Register:     BX + SI, BX + DI, BP + SI, BP + DI
```

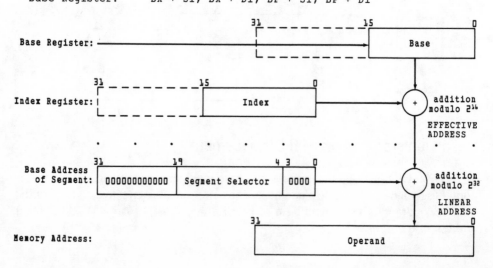

Base and Index Register Indirect with Displacement

Register pairs BX + SI, BX + DI, BP + SI, and BP + DI can each serve as base and index registers containing addresses that are added to a sign-extended displacement. The sum forms the effective address of the memory operand. The segment base address is then added, to form the 20-bit linear address of the operand.

```
Calculation:        EA = (genreg) + (genreg) + Signextend(displacement)
Assembler Syntax:   (genreg) + (genreg) + constant
R/M:                000, 001, 010, 011
Base Register:      BX + SI, BX + DI, BP + SI, BP + DI
```

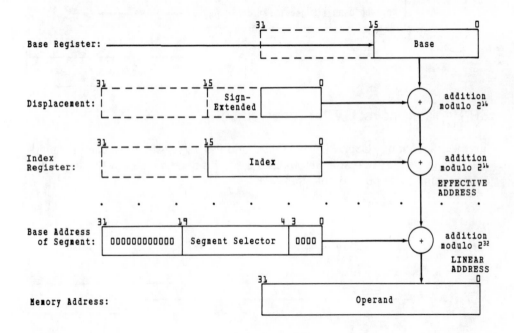

Displacement

The effective address is specified as an absolute 16-bit offset from the base of the segment. The displacement value is given in the instruction itself.

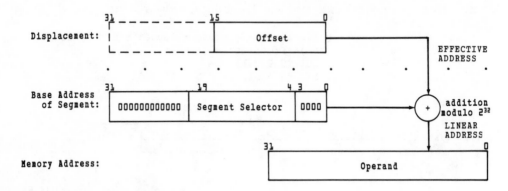

SP Register Indirect with Predecrement

For the instructions PUSH, PUSHA, CALL, and INT n, register SP contains the address of the memory operand. Before SP is used, it is decremented by the size of the data operand to be pushed onto the stack.

```
Calculation:        SP = SP - operand size;
                    EA = SP
Assembler Syntax:   Implicit with PUSH, PUSHA, CALL, or INT n opcodes
Base Register:      SP
```

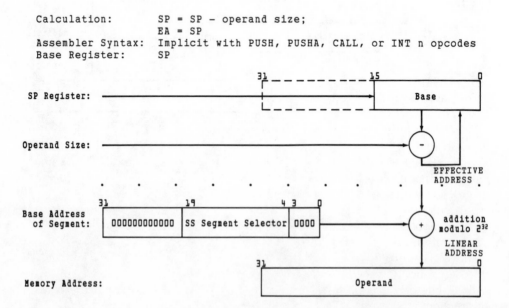

SP Register Indirect with Postincrement

For the instructions POP, POPA, RET, and IRET, register SP contains the address of the memory operand. After the SP register is used, it is incremented by the size of the data operand just popped from the stack.

```
    Calculation:          EA = SP;
                          SP = SP + operand size
    Assembler Syntax:     Implicit with POP, POPA, RET, or IRET opcodes
    Base Register:        SP
```

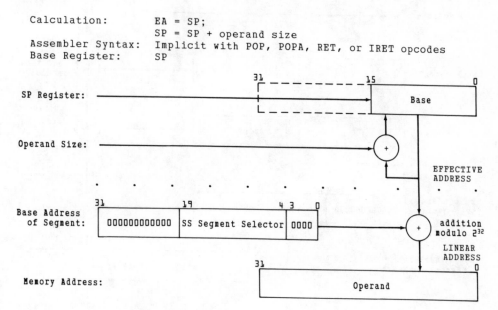

Memory Indirect Modes

The memory indirect forms of the JMP and CALL instructions use memory indirect addressing. The memory indirect-addressing mode offers all the flexibility of the register indirect modes listed in the previous section.

Memory indirect addressing functions as follows for a memory indirect JMP or CALL *within* the code segment: The address components are summed to generate a 16-bit offset, and the segment base address is then added to form a 20-bit linear address. That memory location holds the 16-bit effective address of the destination instruction within the current code segment.

Memory indirect addressing functions as follows for a memory indirect JMP or CALL to *another* code segment: The address components are summed to generate a 16-bit offset, and the segment base address is then added to form a 20-bit linear address. That memory location holds a full address (the 16-bit effective address of the destination instruction and a 16-bit selector for the destination code segment). All 32 bits of the full address are loaded and are used to fetch the destination instruction.

```
Calculation:         EA = [(genreg) + (genreg) + Signextend(displacement)]
Assembler Syntax:    ptr (genreg) + (genreg) + constant
R/M:                 000, 001, 010, 011, 100, 101, 110, 111
Base Register:       BX + SI, BX + DI, BP + SI, BP + DI, SI, DI, BX, BP
```

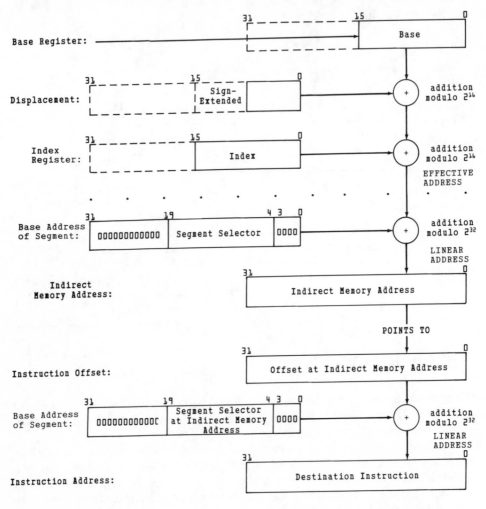

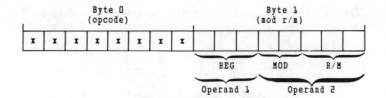

Figure 4.3 Two-operand Instruction with MOD R/M Byte.

Encoding of 16-bit Address Modes

Most instructions specify the location of an operand by the MOD R/M byte in the instruction. For most instructions, the MOD R/M byte completely specifies the addressing mode to be used for source and destination. Either the source operand or the destination operand is a general register. The second operand may also be either a general register or a memory location. If the second operand is a memory location, the addressing mode is specified. To specify both operands, the MOD R/M byte contains three fields.

The MOD R/M byte follows the opcode byte(s) of 80386 instructions, as depicted in Figure 4.3. The MOD R/M byte is subdivided into the three fields shown in the figure. A 3-bit REG field specifies the register operand. A 2-bit MOD field specifies whether the other operand is also a register operand; if so, the 3-bit R/M field specifies the other register operand. If, on the other hand, the MOD field indicates a memory operand, then the MOD field and R/M field together indicate the addressing mode to be used.

Table 4.1 defines the MOD R/M fields, including all the 16-bit memory-addressing modes. Note that only registers DX, SI, DI, and BP are used in the 16-bit addressing modes. (SP is implicitly used for memory addressing by the PUSH, POP, PUSHA, POPA, CALL, and INT n instructions.) When only a base register is specified in the addressing mode, the base can be DX, SI, DI, or BP. When a base and index register are specified, the register pairs can be BX + SI, BX + DI, BP + SI, or BP + DI. The displacement can be specified as a 16-bit value or an 8-bit value (sign-extended to 16 bits).

Various combinations of addressing components are possible when the MOD R/M byte is used, as listed in Table 4.1.

Table 4.1 Definition of MOD R/M Fields for 16-bit Addressing.

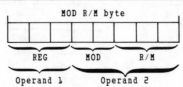

REG	Operand 1 =	MOD	R/M	Operand 2 =
000	register EAX/AX/AL	00	000	memory DS:[BX+SI]
001	register ECX/CX/CL	00	001	memory DS:[BX+DI]
010	register EDX/DX/DL	00	010	memory SS:[BP+SI]
011	register EBX/BX/BL	00	011	memory SS:[BP+DI]
100	register ESP/SP/AH	00	100	memory DS:[SI]
101	register EBP/BP/CH	00	101	memory DS:[DI]
110	register ESI/SI/DH	00	110	memory DS:d16
111	register EDI/DI/BH	00	111	memory DS:[BX]
		01	000	memory DS:[BX+SI+d8]
		01	001	memory DS:[BX+DI+d8]
		01	010	memory SS:[BP+SI+d8]
		01	011	memory SS:[BP+DI+d8]
		01	100	memory DS:[SI+d8]
		01	101	memory DS:[DI+d8]
		01	110	memory DS:[BX+d8]
		01	111	memory DS:[BP+d8]
		01	000	memory DS:[BX+SI+d16]
		01	001	memory DS:[BX+DI+d16[
		01	010	memory SS:[BP+SI+d16]
		01	011	memory SS:[BP+DI+d16]
		01	100	memory DS:[SI+d16]
		01	101	memory DS:[DI+d16]
		01	110	memory DS:[BX+d16]
		01	111	memory DS:[BP+d16]
		10	000	register EAX/AX/AL
		10	001	register EDX/DX/DL
		10	010	register ECX/CX/CL
		10	011	register EBX/BX/BL
		10	100	register ESP/SP/AH
		10	101	register EBP/BP/CH
		10	110	register ESI/SI/DH
		10	111	register EDI/DI/BH

CHAPTER 5

16-BIT INSTRUCTION DETAILS

This chapter discusses the 80386 instructions as used by a programmer in REAL mode.

In the 16-bit REAL mode, instructions are designed to function as they do on an 8086. Operand sizes of 8-bits and 16-bits are available, and 16-bit addressing modes are used as described in Chapter 4. All this supports the 8086-compatibility theme of the 16-bit operating modes.

However, some new 80386 features also filter down to these modes. Thus, strictly speaking, the REAL mode of the 80386 is a more capable environment than the 8086 or the REAL mode of the 80286, as follows. The 80386 debug registers are available to the 16-bit operating modes, and 16-bit debugger utilities may utilize them for superior debugging capabilities. Two new segment registers, FS and GS, can be used to increase programming efficiency. Bit manipulation and double-shift operations are available, as are the paging test registers and control registers, although these are needed only when preparing to enter the PROTECTED mode.

Instruction Availability

Compared to an 8086, the 80386 has thirty-two new instructions in the 16-bit REAL mode. Compared to 80286 REAL mode, twelve new instructions are available. New, full-displacement forms of the Jcc (Jump conditional) instruction and a fully general form of the IMUL (Integer Signed Multiply) instruction are available in 80386 REAL mode. Table 5.1 lists these REAL-mode additions and compares them to the instruction repertoire of an 8086.

Table 5.1 is especially interesting when writing programs for various 86 generations. It lists the instructions and instruction forms one can use to optimize programs running in the 80286 and 80386 REAL modes.

Table 5.1 REAL Mode Instructions Not on Actual 8086.

80286 REAL Mode Additions	80386 REAL Mode Additions	Description
		INSTRUCTIONS FOR GENERAL UTILITY
BOUND	BOUND	Perform array-bounds check
ENTER	ENTER	Create stack frame
IMUL #<data>	IMUL #<data>	Immediate signed multiply
INS	INS	String-input instruction
LEAVE	LEAVE	Eliminate stack frame
OUTS	OUTS	String-output instruction
POPA	POPA	Pop all general registers
PUSHA	PUSHA	Push all general registers
PUSH #<data>	PUSH #<data>	Push immediate data value
REP INS	REP INS	Repeated string input
REP OUTS	REP OUTS	Repeated string output
shift/rotate by count	shift/rotate by count	Shift/rotate by immediate count
	BT	Bit test
	BTC	Bit test and complement
	BTR	Bit test and reset
	BTS	Bit test and set
	IMUL generalized	Signed multiply general register
	MOV CRn	Move to/from control registers
	MOV DRn	Move to/from debug registers
	MOV TRn	Move to/from paging test registers
	Jcc full displ	Jump conditional—full displacement
	Scc	Set byte conditionally
	SHLD	Double shift left
	SHRD	Double shift right
		PROTECTED MODE INSTRUCTIONS
CLTS	CLTS	Clear task-switched flag
LIDT*	LIDT*	Load IDTR register
SIDT	SIDT	Store IDTR register
LGDT*	LGDT*	Load GDTR register
SGDT	SGDT	Store GDTR register
LMSW*	LMSW*	Load machine status word
SMSW	SMSW	Store machine status word

* These PROTECTED mode instructions are valid in REAL mode specifically to allow initialization for PROTECTED mode.

Not all 80386 instructions (listed in Table 3.1 through Table 3.10) are available in 80386 REAL mode, however. The nine PROTECTED-mode instructions that cannot be executed in REAL mode are listed in Table 5.2.

Table 5.2   80386 Instructions NOT Available During REAL Mode.

Instruction Mnemonic	Description
LTR	Load task register
STR	Store task register
LLDT	Load local descriptor table register
SLDT	Store local descriptor table register
ARPL	Adjust requested privilege level
LSL	Load segment limit
LAR	Load access rights
VERR	Verify access rights for read
VERW	Verify access rights for write

The first four of these instructions are not available because registers TR and LDTR are not accessible or needed in REAL mode, and the last five of these instructions are not available because the concepts of privilege level, adjustable segment limit (limit is always 64K bytes in REAL mode), and access rights do not exist in REAL mode.

Prefix Availability

All 80386 prefixes, listed in Figure 3.1, are available in REAL mode. The operand-size prefix and the address-size prefix, in particular, can add new twists to REAL-mode programming, since they do allow 32-bit data operands and 32-bit address modes. These prefixes can be useful in REAL-mode programming for 32-bit operations.

The operand-size prefix allows 32-bit data operands to be manipulated easily. For instance, using the operand-size prefix in REAL mode allows the 80386 to perform arithmetic on 32-bit operands and to process strings 32 bits at a time.

The address-size prefix is available in REAL mode, allowing access to the 32-bit addressing modes covered in Chapter 7. For example, this could be used to provide scaled index addressing. Using the address-size prefix properly in REAL mode requires great care, to avoid generating large effective addresses. An effective address larger than 65,535 in REAL mode exceeds the segment limit, which is fixed at 65,535 ($= 2^{16} - 1$) in that mode. Therefore, to use the address-size prefix successfully in REAL mode, the registers used for addressing should be cleared in bits 31–16, and the sum of the address components should not be greater than 65,535 (because 32-bit addressing modes add the components modulo 2^{32}, not 2^{16}).

To summarize, the operand-size prefix and address-size prefix can extend the capabilities of REAL-mode programs, if used carefully. For entirely new 32-bit programming, however, PROTECTED mode should be considered, since the segment limit and linear address space are much larger than in REAL mode.

REAL Mode Segment Size Limit

In REAL mode, the maximum segment size of a segment, in bytes, is 64K or 65,536 decimal. The segment limit is therefore 0FFFFh (i.e., 64K − 1, or 65,535 decimal), the maximum byte offset permitted. This limit is set automatically for all segments when in REAL mode and therefore requires all effective addresses generated in REAL mode to be 64K − 1 or less. In the case of multibyte operands, the limit therefore requires the *entire* operand to be at offsets 64K − 1 or less. In REAL mode, attempting access to operands that lie entirely or partially beyond the 64K − 1 segment limit will cause a violation. To avoid violations in REAL mode, do not allow operands to lie beyond the 64K − 1 limit, and be very careful with any use of the address-size prefix, since 32-bit address calculations can easily generate an offset larger than the 64K − 1 limit allowed in REAL mode. Segment limit violations are further described in Chapter 6.

CHAPTER 6

INTERRUPTS AND EXCEPTIONS
IN Real MODE

This chapter describes the 80386 response when interrupts and exceptions are encountered in the REAL mode of operation. As would be expected of the REAL mode, the 80386 response is much the same as that of an 8086. Before going more deeply into the processor response, however, let us describe the events themselves.

Interrupts and exceptions are similar types of events. Both suspend the present operation of the 80386, redirecting its execution to the service routine for the interrupt or exception event. They cause redirection of the 80386 from its current instruction flow to a service routine for the event. The distinction between the two is their differing points of origin: Interrupts originate from important *external events* signaled to the 80386 on dedictated pins; exceptions originate from *internal* conditions or problems the 80386 detects.

Recognition of Interrupts or Exceptions

From the programmer's point of view, interrupts and exceptions are recognized at *instruction boundaries*, that is to say, they are recognized after one instruction has completed execution and before the next instruction has begun. This simplifies the programmer's life, especially when dealing with exceptions, since the programmer is spared the nuances of 80386 internal temporary registers or pipeline stages. The 80386 performs all required maintenance and housecleaning automatically, and it deals with the interrupt or exception cleanly at an instruction boundary.

Interrupts

Interrupts provide a hardware mechanism allowing the 80386 to deal with the outside environment, which usually involves a variety of external events happening at unpredictable intervals. The occurrence of such events can be signaled to the 80386 on either of two pins: INTR (maskable INTeRrupt pin) or NMI (NonMaskable Interrupt pin). These two input pins of the 80386 are dedicated for interrupt signalling.

67

The INTR pin indicates an active interrupt when driven to a HIGH level. It is a software-maskable signal, enabled when the EFLAG IF bit is set to 1 and disabled when the EFLAG IF bit is cleared to 0.

The NMI signal indicates an active interrupt when driven by a rising edge, and therefore does not require that the level remain HIGH for a sustained period. NMI is not software-maskable; it is always enabled. NMI is typically reserved for the most critical interrupts, typically only interrupts that signal fatal conditions, such as power failure or noncorrectable memory failure.

Interrupt Hardware

Within 80386 systems, many peripherals, such as disks, timers, printers, and other outside devices, may activate interrupts. Such common interrupts are typically directed to the 80386 INTR pin. Since there is only a single INTR pin, interrupts from many devices are ORed via logic to form a single INTR signal shared by many devices. To achieve quick interrupt response, it is desirable to identify the interrupting source immediately.

When the INTR is activated, immediate identification is accomplished via a special cycle, during which the 80386 reads a number on the lower byte of its data bus. Such a number, ranging from 00h to FFh, is called a *vector number* and is provided typically by an interrrupt controller chip, the 8259A or equivalent. The interrupt number directs the 80386 to a particular memory-resident pointer, the *vector*, through which it fetches the first instruction of an interrupt-service routine.

When the NMI pin is activated, however, no special cycle is performed, and no vector is read, because NMI is automatically associated with interrupt number 02h. For that interrupt, vector 02h is dedicated to serve as the critical nonmaskable interrupt vector; upon NMI, the 80386 redirects control to the routine for interrupt number 02h.

Interrupt Vectors

In REAL mode, the *interrupt vectors* are complete addresses, in the style of 16-bit addressing: 16-bit selector and 16-bit offset. They appear as shown in Figure 6.1. An interrupt vector is the entry-point address of the routine used to service the interrupt. Thus, the interrupt vector redirects the 80386 to the interrupt-service routine.

Interrupt vectors also serve to redirect the 80386 in case of an exception being detected, as is discussed on page 72.

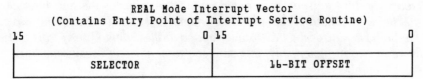

Figure 6.1 REAL **Mode Interrupt Vector Is a Complete Address (Full Pointer).**

Interrupt-Vector Table

All interrupt vectors are memory-resident, as mentioned, and constitute an array of vectors, called the **interrupt-vector table**. This table, beginning at linear address 0, consists of 256 vectors, indexed as vector 0 through vector 255, corresponding of course to the possible values of an interrupt vector number. *Important: Hardware interrupt vectors should be numbered in the range 32 through 255 only. Interrupt numbers 0 through 31 are reserved for Intel-designated exception categories.* Interrupt 32 therefore is redirected using the vector 32; interrupt 33 is redirected through vector 33; interrupt 34 through vector 34; and so on, up to interrupt 255. The interrupt vector table is depicted in Figure 6.2.

```
31              16 15            0

|  SELECTOR  255  |  OFFSET  255  |    Vector 255 at memory address 000007FCh

|  SELECTOR  254  |  OFFSET  254  |    Vector 254 at memory address 000007F8h

|  SELECTOR  253  |  OFFSET  253  |    Vector 253 at memory address 000007F4h

                  .                .
                  .                .
                  .                .

|  SELECTOR   2   |  OFFSET   2   |    Vector 2   at memory address 00000008h

|  SELECTOR   1   |  OFFSET   1   |    Vector 1   at memory address 00000004h

|  SELECTOR   0   |  OFFSET   0   |    Vector 0   at memory address 00000000h
```

```
This illustrates the location and size of the interrupt vector table in
REAL mode after reset. In fact, the LIDT instruction can be used in REAL
mode to relocate the base of the interrupt-vector table and set its limit,
but doing so and continuing to operate in REAL mode would create a
nonstandard REAL-mode environment.
```

Figure 6.2 REAL-**Mode Interrupt Vector Table.**

Note: The IBM Personal Computer architecture violates the above guideline, i.e., that hardware interrupts not use vector numbers 0 through 31. The PC Basic I/O System (BIOS) initializes the 8259A interrupt-controller chip to use vectors 8–15 for hardware interrupts. Potentially, this can lead to conflicting uses for various interrupt-vector numbers.

The interrupt-vector table is also used to redirect the 80386 in case of an exception being detected, is covered later in this chapter.

Executing Interrupt Routines

Interrupt routines are the programs executed when the 80386 redirects control through the interrupt-vector table. These are normally the programs that service the device causing an interrupt. A given routine, *n*, for interrupt or exception *n*, can be activated under hardware control or software control, as listed below:

Hardware Control Activating INTR and supplying vector n, if maskable interrupts are enabled (IF flag = 1). When a HIGH level on the INTR pin activates an interrupt routine *n*, the IF flag is reset to 0, preventing further activation of any routines by INTR until software sets the IF flag to 1. Activating NMI activates interrupt routine 2, regardless of the IF flag value.

When a rising edge on NMI activates interrupt routine 2, the IF flag is reset to 0, preventing activation of any routines by INTR. Furthermore, until the IRET instruction is executed (typically at the end of interrupt-service routine 2), another rising edge on NMI will not reactivate interrupt routine 2. This prevents a ragged rising edge from generating numerous nested invocations of the interrupt 2 routine. However, one rising edge of NMI is "remembered" if it occurs during the NMI service routine, activating the interrupt 2 routine again as soon as the first invocation completes (to be more precise, as soon as it executes an IRET instruction).

Compatibility Note: The 8086 and 8088 do not lock out further NMIs when the first NMI occurs. If for some reason you want the 80286 or 80386 also to accept further NMIs while in the NMI service routine, execute an IRET instruction early in the NMI routine. To execute IRET, yet stay in the NMI handler, first build a stack frame with three PUSH instructions so the IRET will "return" to the following instruction, as below:

```
NMI_ENTRY:      PUSHF
                PUSH    CS
                PUSH    NEXT_INSTR  ;push offset of instr following IRET.
                IRET
NEXT_INSTR:                         ;IRET "returns" to here.  More NMIs will
                                    ;be taken now if they occur.
```

```
    .                    ;body of NMI service routine
    .
    .
    IRET                 ;IRET at end of service routine.
```

Software Control Executing INT *n* instruction, regardless of IF flag state. When an INT *n* instruction activates an interrupt routine *n*, the IF flag is not affected; this allows a software-generated interrupt routine to be interrupted by a hardware-generated interrupt. This desirable arrangement maintains 80386 responsiveness to surrounding system hardware.

Interrupt Processing

Interrupt processing is the 80386's action of redirecting control to the interrupt-servicing routine. If INTR is activated, this includes reading an interrupt-vector number from the bus, saving the state of the current program, reading the appropriate interrupt vector, and branching to the location indicated by the interrupt vector. If the interrupt is signaled via NMI or if it is signaled via INTR while interrupts are enabled, then interrupt processing begins as soon as the current instruction is complete. If an INT *n* instruction occurs, then interrupt processing is performed by that instruction. Table 6.1 lists the steps for processing interrupts signaled on INTR or NMI or caused by the INT *n* instruction.

Table 6.1   Interrupt Processing Sequences.

INTR-initiated interrupts	NMI-initiated interrupts	INT *n*-initiated interrupts
1. Get vector number n from interrupt controller chip by performing two special cycles: "Interrupt Acknowledge" cycles.		
2. Push FLAGs on stack.	1. Push FLAGs on stack.	1. Push FLAGs on stack.
3. Push CS on stack.	2. Push CS on stack.	2. Push IP on stack.
4. Push IP on stack.	3. Push IP on stack.	3. Push IP on stack.
5. Reset IF to 0.	4. Reset IF to 0 and lock out further NMI.	
6. Read Interrupt Vector *n*. Put selector in CS and offset in IP.	4. Read Interrupt Vector 2. Put selector in CS and offset in IP.	3. Read Interrupt Vector *n*. Put selector in CS and offset in IP.
7. Begin execution at entry point (CS:IP).	5. Begin execution at entry point (CS:IP).	4. Begin execution at entry point (CS:IP).

Exceptions

Exceptions are *internal* CPU events. Exceptions occur when the 80386 detects a problem that prevents execution of its next instruction. Certain categories of exceptions are recognized, and each is assigned a fixed number *n*, in the range 0–31. That range is specifically reserved for exceptions; interrupts should not be assigned to vector numbers in that range.

In REAL mode, the 80386 recognizes several types of exceptions, listed below. In PROTECTED mode or in VIRTUAL 8086 mode, the 80386 recognizes additional types of exceptions, as described in Chapter 16.

As with an interrupt, a service routine is required to handle this condition. It is called the **exception-service routine** or sometimes the **exception-handler**. The interrupt vector table is used to redirect control to the exception-service routine, based on the number *n* assigned to the type of exception that occurred.

Recognition

When an instruction raises an exception, the exception is always recognized. There is no method of masking an exception, nor would masking be desirable.

Although exceptions are raised and recognized in the course of executing an instruction, the exception appears to have been taken at an instruction boundary, because the state of the 80386 is always preserved as it was *prior to* that instruction. Thus CS:IP points to the instruction (including any prefix bytes) that caused the exception. This is ideal for a service routine attempting to correct the exception, because it can resume the program merely by executing an IRET instruction at completion of the exception-service routine.

The 80386 in REAL mode recognizes twelve exception categories, the same ones an 80286 recognizes in REAL mode. Of the twelve exceptions, five of these exist on the 8086, two are dedictated for reporting coprocessor numeric errors, one is for reporting illegal opcodes, and four are for reporting various segment-limit violations. A summary is given in Table 6.2.

Table 6.2 Exception Vector Assignments in REAL Mode.

	Exception Number	Name (and Type)	Description	Detected in REAL Mode?	Also Detected by 8086/88?
	0.	Divide Error (fault)	Division by zero was attempted with DIV or IDIV instructions.	Yes.	Yes, however, 8086 CS:IP points to instruction after the DIV or IDIV.
	1.	Single Step (trap), Debug Register Breakpoint (fault or trap)	If the TF flag in FLAG is set to 1, this exception is taken after the next instruction. The Debug Registers can define breakpoints that also cause exception 1.	Yes.	Yes, the 8086 has only the TF flag. It doesn't have the Debug Registers.
Exceptions Also Detected by 8086/8088.	3.	Breakpoint Opcode (trap)	Single-byte breakpoint opcode (CCh) executed. The processor initiates exception 3.	Yes.	Yes.
	4.	INTO (trap)	If the OF overflow flag is set, the processor initiates exception 4.	Yes.	Yes.
	5.	BOUND (trap)	If a bounds violation is detected, the processor initiates exception 5.	Yes.	Yes.
	6.	Illegal Opcode (fault)	Unassigned opcodes cause the 80386 to initiate exception 6.	Yes.	No, the 8086 treats unassigned opcodes as NOPs.
	7.	Coprocessor Not Available (fault)	A coprocessor opcode, when the coprocessor is not present, causes the processor to initiate exception 7. Allows emulation of coprocessor instructions if the EM flag in CRO is reset to 0.	Yes, if the EM flag in CRO is reset to 0.	No, to emulate the coprocessor in 8086 systems, INT *n* instructions should be substituted for the coprocessor opcode. The INT *n* initiates exception *n* processing.

Table 6.2 Exception Vector Assignments in REAL Mode *(Continued).*

	Exception Number	Name (and Type)	Description	Detected in REAL Mode?	Also Detected by 8086/88?
	8.	Double Fault (fault)	While attempting to access an interrupt or exception routine, an exception is detected.	Yes, but requires atypical use of LIDT instruction to shorten limit of the interrupt table.	No.
	9.	Coprocessor Operand Limit Violation (fault)	An operand for the numeric coprocessor is partially beyond the limit (end) of the segment.	Yes, but only if software wraps operand around 64K limit.	No, the 8086 allows operands to wrap around to the beginning of the segment.
Exceptions Also Detected by 80286/80386 REAL Mode	12.	Stack segment exception (fault)	An operand in the stack segment (SS) is entirely or partially beyond the limit of the segment. Or stack is not present or wrong privilege level or not a data segment. Or several other reasons listed with exception 12 details.	Yes, but only if software wraps operand around 64K limit.	No, the 8086 allows operands to wrap around to the beginning of the segment.
	13.	General Protection exception in CS, SS, DS, ES, FS, or GS (fault)	An operand in CS, SS, DS, ES, FS, GS is entirely or partially beyond the limit of segment. Or segment is not present or wrong privilege level or not a data segment. Or several other reasons listed with exception 13 details.	Yes, but only if software wraps operand around 64K limit.	No, the 8086 allows operands to wrap around to the beginning of the segment.
	16.	Coprocessor Numeric Error (fault)	The 80386 ERROR# input was activated (presumably by the numeric coprocessor).	Yes, if the 80386 ERROR# input pin is activated by the 80387 ERROR# output.	No, the 8087 signals coprocessor numeric errors to the 8086 via the interrupt (through the 8259A typically, but through the NMI pin in personal computer architectures).

Since the 8086 recognizes just five categories of the 80386 REAL-mode exceptions, compatibility concerns may arise. The 80386-recognized exceptions are a superset of 8086 exceptions, the 80386 being more discerning than its predecessor. For all practical purposes, compatibility is maintained, since the additional exceptions 9, 12, and 13 (the limit violations) are evoked only by unusual 8086 programming practices (e.g., wrapping a multibyte operand around to the beginning of the segment) not found in working commercial programs. The addition of exception 7, the Coprocessor Not Available exception, is not a problem, because the 8086 technique for coprocessor emulation (see Table 6.2) also works fine on the 80386. The Coprocessor Numeric Error exception, 16, occurs only if the coprocessor ERROR# signal is connected to the 80386 ERROR# input pin; such a connection is not required, however, and 80386-based personal computers do not activate exception 16 since the coprocessor ERROR# output is sent to the processor NMI input, just as on the original 8088-based personal computers.

Exception Processing Detail

Additional detailed information about each exception category is provided in Chapter 16.

PART 3

FULL 32-BIT PROGRAMMING: SIMPLE PROTECTED MODE

The 80386 PROTECTED-mode architecture protects against the effects of program bugs and malicious programming. So complete are the protections, in fact, that a system using the protection architecture to its full extent may be more sophisticated than necessary or desirable for many applications. Therefore, this section is devoted to the so-called fundamentals of 32-bit PROTECTED-mode operation, those readily applicable to all 32-bit systems. This section includes information regarding a simple user/supervisor model in PROTECTED mode, and a code example for establishing such a model immediately from a processor reset is provided.

The fundamentals are really quite powerful in their own right. Consider what they can accomplish. With just a basic set of 80386 PROTECTED-mode features, a programmer can create a 32-bit system with 32-bit memory addressing, 32-bit data operations, paged virtual memory, and a two-level privilege scheme: user and supervisor.

Indeed, what we call the fundamentals of the 80386 exceed the full architecture of several other 32-bit processors, and these topics alone constitute enough material for this practical section on the PROTECTED mode. You should find this a valuable section for nearly all your 32-bit work with the 80386.

The topics delayed until the final sections are the VIRTUAL 8086 mode, 80386 hardware multitasking, and the built-in debugging features.

CHAPTER 7

MEMORY ADDRESSING
IN THE 32-BIT MODE

This chapter explains memory addressing in the 80386 32-bit mode, that is, when executing a 32-bit code segment in PROTECTED mode. The 32-bit addressing modes reflect the true power of the 80386. They provide a much more generalized and powerful environment for program execution than is available with the 16-bit addressing modes. For example, any general register can be used in the 32-bit addressing modes, and the index component of the address can be scaled by 1, 2, 4, or 8.

The convenience afforded by the generality of the 32-bit addressing forms greatly eases program development. 32-bit address formation can often occur without adding time to the instruction. The address-formation hardware is a major reason 80386 performance exceeds that of several other competitive microprocessors. Even the 80386 scaled-indexing mode adds no time to the execution of an instruction. The positive effect on performance is important, since memory addressing is part of nearly each instruction. Without belaboring the competitive aspects of other 32-bit processors, it is true that the 68020 or 32000 microprocessors require up to 15 clock periods to perform the more complex addressing combinations. Within 15 clock periods, the 80386 performs an average of two and a half complete instructions, including address calculations.

32-bit Addressing

In the 32-bit PROTECTED mode, an **effective address** is calculated as the sum of up to three 32-bit address components: base, displacement, and index. The effective address is therefore a 32-bit value. The general process of 32-bit addressing, including the scaled indexing, is shown in Figure 7.1.

The 32-bit effective address is considered an offset from the base of the current memory segment. Therefore, as the second step of any 32-bit address formation, a segment base is added to the effective address, forming a **32-bit linear address**. The segment base address is obtained from a **descriptor**, an 8-byte data block that describes the characteristics and location of each segment. Descriptors are a subject of Chapter 8.

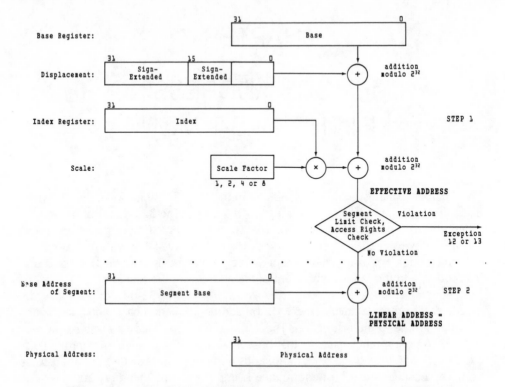

Figure 7.1   2-bit Address Calculation (In PROTECTED Mode, No Paging).

The 32-bit operating modes provide a linear, physical address space of 2^{32} bytes, in other words, four gigabytes. This is a direct result of 32-bit addressing, which generates a 32-bit linear address.

Introduction to Paging

The 80386 has built-in support for virtual memory through paging. Paging does not affect the addressing modes, which calculate an effective address. Paging, if enabled, is a *translation* process performed upon the linear address, prior to accessing memory. 32-bit addressing with paging is illustrated by Figure 7.2. As the figure

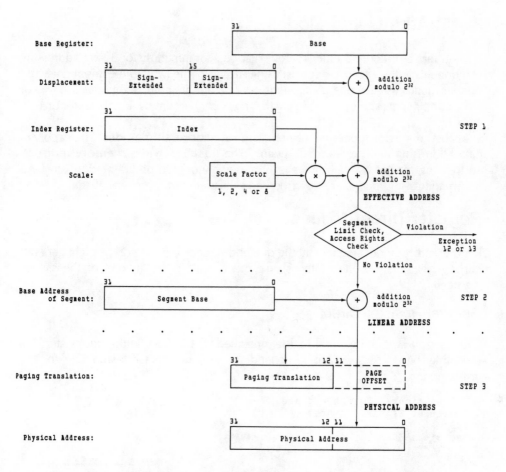

Figure 7.2   32-bit Address Calculation (In Protected Mode, Paging Enabled).

shows, page translation causes the upper 20 bits of effective address to be replaced with another 20-bit value. Replacement occurs as a function of the original 20-bit value, using a memory-resident **page table**. This chapter introduces paging, since it is related to the overall process of address translation. Paging is further described in Chapter 9. This chapter focuses on 32-bit address formation.

32-bit Addressing Modes

A wide range of address modes allows various combinations of 32-bit addressing components in the effective address, using subsets of the available components. The simpler modes use just one component, while the more complex modes use two or more components and may also scale the index component by a scale factor of 1, 2, 4, or 8.

Most addressing modes are **register indirect-addressing modes**. They apply to data addressing and program addressing. The 80386 provides **memory indirect-addressing modes** as well; however, these apply only to program addressing. All 32-bit addressing modes are described and illustrated in the pages ahead.

Register Direct Modes

Register direct modes specify that the operand is located in one of the eight general-purpose registers, in one of the six segment registers, or in one of the system registers.

General Register Direct

The operand is in the general register specified by the R/M field. The register size used may be 8, 16, or 32 bits, depending upon the data operand size for the instruction.

```
Calculation:        EA = genreg
Assembler Syntax:   genreg
MOD:                00
Register:           reg, r/m
```

Segment Register: Segreg

Segment Register Direct

The operand is in the segment register specified by the reg field. Note that this addressing mode does not use the MOD R/M byte. It instead uses a SREG field in the instructions that load or store the segment registers.

```
Calculation:        EA = segreg
Assembler Syntax:   segreg
Register:           SREG
```

General Register: Genreg

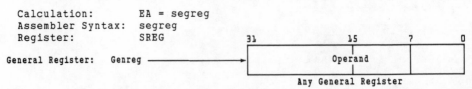

Immediate Modes

Immediate addressing specifies that the operand is contained in the instruction itself. The immediate-addressing mode can specify only a source operand, never a destination operand. The immediate operand may be a BYTE, WORD, or DWORD. The immediate-addressing mode is not specified by the MOD R/M byte; rather, certain opcodes implicitly specify use of immediate addressing for the source operand. The same instruction can therefore include the MOD R/M byte to specify its destination operand.

```
Calculation:        EA = # <data>
Assembler Syntax:   data
Opcode:             Certain opcodes implicitly specify that
                    the instruction uses immediate data.
```

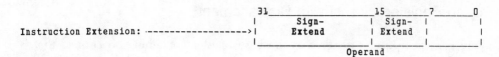

Register Indirect Modes

These addressing modes specify that the operand is in a memory segment and that the contents of one or more registers are used to calculate the effective address of the operand within the segment. The segment base address is then added to form the 32-bit linear address of the operand.

Base Register Indirect

Any general register except EBP can serve as the base register containing the address of the memory operand.

```
Calculation:        EA = (genreg)
Assembler Syntax:   (genreg)
MOD:                00
Base Register:      EAX, EBX, ECX, EDX, ESI, EDI, ESP
```

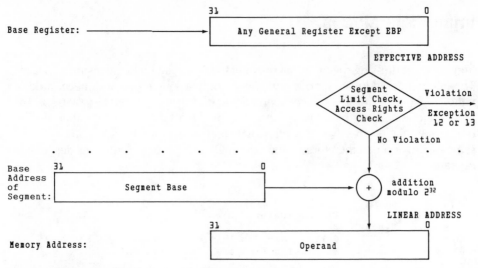

Base Register Indirect with Displacement

Any general register can serve as the base register containing an address that is added to a 32-bit displacement or a sign-extended 8-bit displacement. The sum forms the effective address of the memory operand. The segment base address is then added to form the 32-bit linear address of the operand.

```
Calculation:        EA = (genreg)
Assembler Syntax:   (genreg)
MOD:                01, 10
Base Register:      EAX, EBX, ECX, EDX, ESI, EDI, EBP, ESP
```

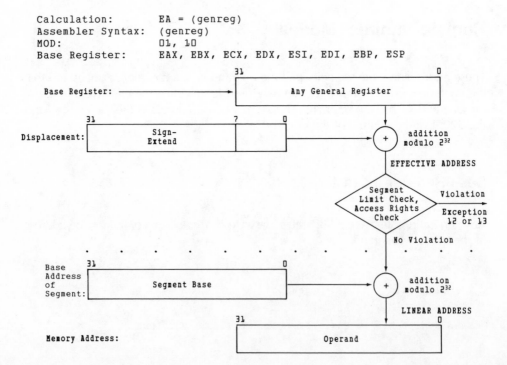

Base and Index Register Indirect

Register pairs made of any two general registers can serve as base and index registers containing addresses that are added to form the effective address of the memory operand. The index register may be scaled by 1, 2, 4, or 8. The segment base address is then added to form the 32-bit linear address of the operand.

```
Calculation:        EA = (genreg) + (genreg × scale)
Assembler Syntax:   (genreg) + (genreg × scale)
MOD:                00
Base Register:      EAX, EBX, ECX, EDX, ESI, EDI, ESP
Index Register:     EAX, EBX, ECX, EDX, ESI, EDI, EBP
```

Base and Index Register Indirect with Displacement

Register pairs of any general registers can serve as base and index registers containing addresses that are added to a 32-bit displacement or a sign-extended 8-bit displacement. The sum forms the effective address of the memory operand. The segment base address is then added to form the 32-bit linear address of the operand.

```
Calculation:       EA = (genreg) + (genreg × scale) + signextend(displacement)
Assembler Syntax:  (genreg) + (genreg) + constant
MOD:               01, 10
Base Register:     EAX, EBX, ECX, EDX, ESI, EDI, EBP, ESP
Index Register:    EAX, EBX, ECX, EDX, ESI, EDI, EBP
```

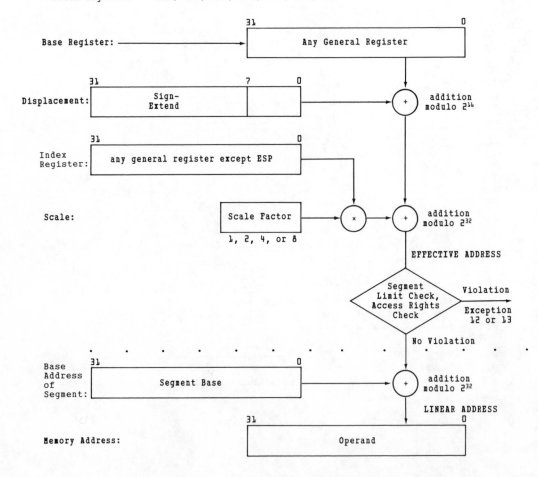

Displacement

The effective address is specified as an absolute 32-bit offset from the base of the segment. The displacement value is given in the instruction itself.

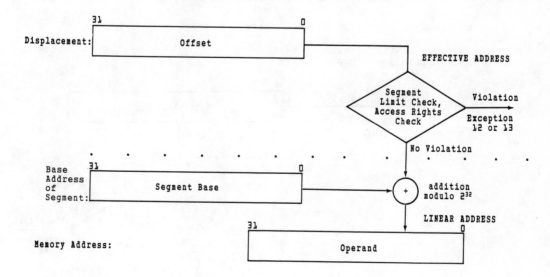

ESP Register Indirect with Predecrement

For instructions PUSH, PUSHA, CALL, and INT *n*, register ESP serves as the register containing the address of the memory operand. After ESP is used, it is incremented by the size of the data operand popped from the stack.

```
Calculation:        ESP = ESP - operand size;
                    EA = ESP
Assembler Syntax:   Implicit with PUSH, PUSHA, CALL, or INT n opcodes
Base Register:      ESP
```

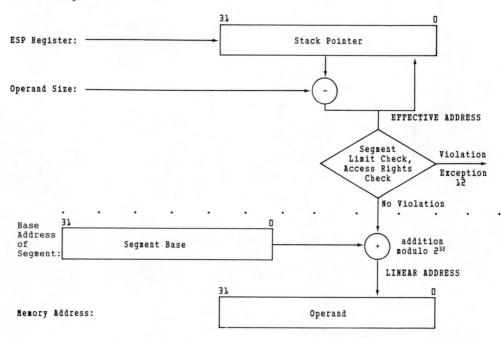

ESP Register Indirect with Postincrement

For instructions POP, POPA, RET, and IRET, register ESP serves as the register containing the address of the memory operand. After the ESP register is used, it is incremented by the size of the data operand just popped from the stack.

```
Calculation:        EA = ESP;
                    ESP = ESP + operand size
Assembler Syntax:   Implicit with POP, POPA, RET, or IRET opcodes
Base Register:      ESP
```

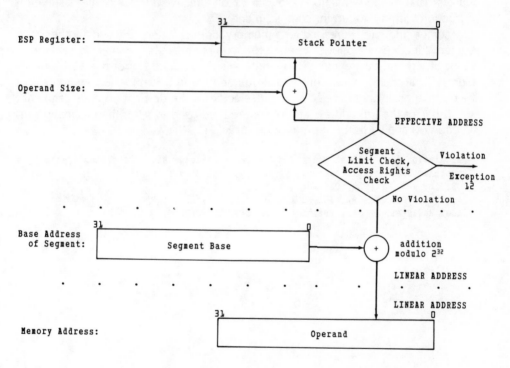

Memory Indirect Modes

The memory indirect forms of the JMP and CALL instructions use memory indirect addressing. The memory indirect addressing mode offers all the flexibility of the register indirect modes listed in the previous section.

Memory indirect addressing for a memory indirect JMP or CALL within the code segment functions as follows: The address components are summed to generate a 32-bit offset, and the segment base address is then added, to form a 32-bit linear address. That memory location holds the 32-bit effective address of the destination instruction within the current code segment.

Memory indirect addressing for a memory indirect JMP or CALL to another code segment functions as follows: The address components are summed to generate a 32-bit offset, and the segment base address is then added, to form a 32-bit linear address. That memory location holds a full address (the 32-bit effective address of the destination instruction and a 16-bit selector for the destination code segment). All 48 bits of the full address are loaded and are used to fetch the destination instruction, as shown in the illustration on page 91.

```
Calculation:        EA =[(genreg) + (genreg × scale) + signextend(displacement)]
Assembler Syntax:   ptr (genreg) + (genreg × scale) + constant
MOD:                00, 01, 10
Base Register:      EAX, EBX, ECX, EDX, ESI, EDI, EBP, ESP
Index Register:     EAX, EBX, ECX, EDX, ESI, EDI, EBP
```

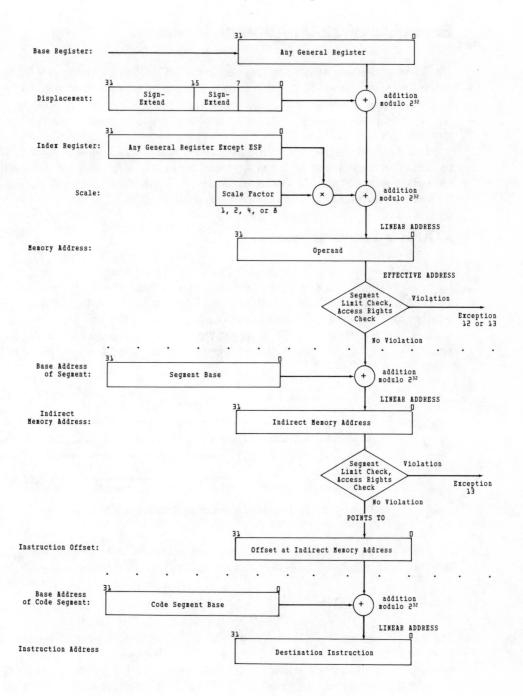

Base Register: — Any General Register

31   0

Displacement: — Sign-Extend | Sign-Extend

31   15   7   0

+ addition modulo 2^{32}

Index Register: — Any General Register Except ESP

31   0

Scale: — Scale Factor

1, 2, 4, or 8

×   + addition modulo 2^{32}

LINEAR ADDRESS

Memory Address: — Operand

31   0

EFFECTIVE ADDRESS

Segment Limit Check, Access Rights Check   Violation → Exception 12 or 13

No Violation

Base Address of Segment: — Segment Base

31   0

+ addition modulo 2^{32}

LINEAR ADDRESS

Indirect Memory Address: — Indirect Memory Address

31   0

Segment Limit Check, Access Rights Check   Violation → Exception 13

No Violation

POINTS TO

Instruction Offset: — Offset at Indirect Memory Address

31   0

Base Address of Code Segment: — Code Segment Base

31   0

+ addition modulo 2^{32}

LINEAR ADDRESS

Instruction Address — Destination Instruction

31   0

Encoding of 32-bit Address Modes

The 32-bit addressing modes are encoded in the MOD R/M byte and an S-I-B byte (Scale-Index-Base byte). 32-bit addressing that specifies either displacement only or a base register and displacement requires only the MOD R/M byte for encoding. 32-bit addressing that specifies a base and an index register also requires the S-I-B byte for encoding.

Either the source operand or the destination operand is a general register. The second operand may also be either a general register or a memory location. If the second operand is a memory location, the addressing mode is specified. To specify both operands, the MOD R/M byte contains three fields.

MOD R/M Encoding Byte

The MOD R/M byte follows the opcode byte(s) of 80386 instructions, as depicted in Figure 7.3. The MOD R/M byte is subdivided into three fields, as shown in the figure. A 3-bit REG field specifies the register operand. A 2-bit MOD field specifies whether the other operand is also a register operand; if so, the 3-bit R/M field specifies the other register operand. If, however, the MOD field indicates a memory operand, then the MOD field and R/M field together indicate the addressing mode to be used.

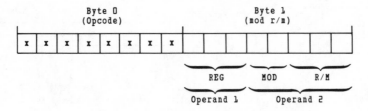

Figure 7.3   Two-operand Instruction with MOD R/M Byte.

Finally, if the MOD field indicates a memory operand and the R/M field is 100, then the next byte is the S-I-B byte, which indicates the addressing mode.

S-I-B Encoding Byte

The S-I-B (Scale-Index-Base byte) byte follows the MOD R/M byte, to encode the more sophisticated 32-bit addressing forms: those that use an index register with scaling. The S-I-B byte is subdivided into three fields. Figure 7.4 indicates scale (SS), index (INDEX) and base (BASE) fields. The SS field indicates a scaling factor, 1, 2, 4, or 8, for the index component. A general register (any register except ESP) is identified in the INDEX field. The BASE field identifies the general register (any, except EBP when there is no displacement) serving as the base component.

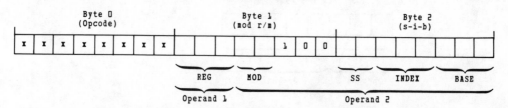

Figure 7.4   Two-operand Instruction with MOD R/M and S-I-B Bytes.

32-bit MOD R/M and S-I-B Encoding Tables

Table 7.1 defines the MOD R/M and S-I-B fields, including all the 32-bit memory-addressing modes. Note that all general registers are used in the 32-bit addressing modes. (ESP is implicitly used for memory addressing by the PUSH, POP, PUSHA, POPA, CALL, and INT *n* instructions.) The displacement can be specified as a 32-bit value or as an 8-bit value (sign-extended to 32 bits).

Table 7.1   Definition of REG MOD R/M and S-I-B Fields for 32-bit Addressing.

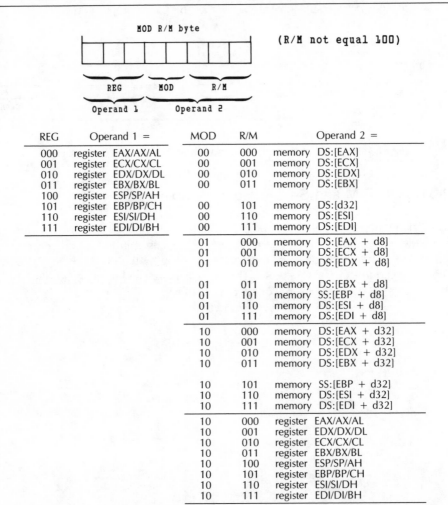

REG	Operand 1 =	MOD	R/M	Operand 2 =
000	register EAX/AX/AL	00	000	memory DS:[EAX]
001	register ECX/CX/CL	00	001	memory DS:[ECX]
010	register EDX/DX/DL	00	010	memory DS:[EDX]
011	register EBX/BX/BL	00	011	memory DS:[EBX]
100	register ESP/SP/AH			
101	register EBP/BP/CH	00	101	memory DS:[d32]
110	register ESI/SI/DH	00	110	memory DS:[ESI]
111	register EDI/DI/BH	00	111	memory DS:[EDI]
		01	000	memory DS:[EAX + d8]
		01	001	memory DS:[ECX + d8]
		01	010	memory DS:[EDX + d8]
		01	011	memory DS:[EBX + d8]
		01	101	memory SS:[EBP + d8]
		01	110	memory DS:[ESI + d8]
		01	111	memory DS:[EDI + d8]
		10	000	memory DS:[EAX + d32]
		10	001	memory DS:[ECX + d32]
		10	010	memory DS:[EDX + d32]
		10	011	memory DS:[EBX + d32]
		10	101	memory SS:[EBP + d32]
		10	110	memory DS:[ESI + d32]
		10	111	memory DS:[EDI + d32]
		10	000	register EAX/AX/AL
		10	001	register EDX/DX/DL
		10	010	register ECX/CX/CL
		10	011	register EBX/BX/BL
		10	100	register ESP/SP/AH
		10	101	register EBP/BP/CH
		10	110	register ESI/SI/DH
		10	111	register EDI/DI/BH

Table 7.1 Definition of REG MOD R/M and S-I-B Fields for 32-bit Addressing *(Continued).*

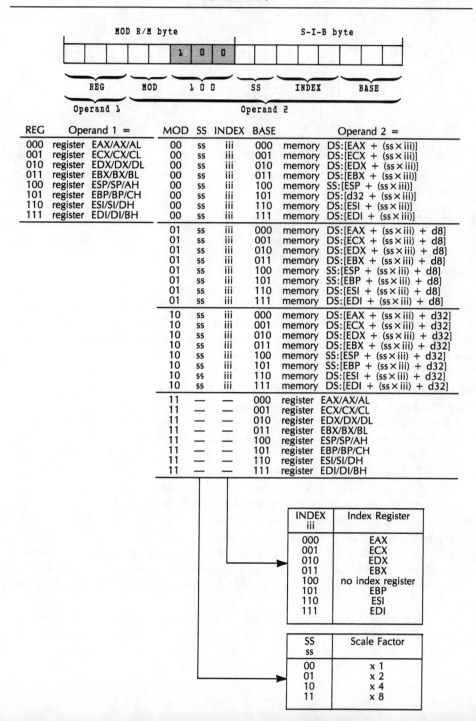

REG	Operand 1 =	MOD	SS	INDEX	BASE	Operand 2 =
000	register EAX/AX/AL	00	ss	iii	000	memory DS:[EAX + (ss × iii)]
001	register ECX/CX/CL	00	ss	iii	001	memory DS:[ECX + (ss × iii)]
010	register EDX/DX/DL	00	ss	iii	010	memory DS:[EDX + (ss × iii)]
011	register EBX/BX/BL	00	ss	iii	011	memory DS:[EBX + (ss × iii)]
100	register ESP/SP/AH	00	ss	iii	100	memory SS:[ESP + (ss × iii)]
101	register EBP/BP/CH	00	ss	iii	101	memory DS:[d32 + (ss × iii)]
110	register ESI/SI/DH	00	ss	iii	110	memory DS:[ESI + (ss × iii)]
111	register EDI/DI/BH	00	ss	iii	111	memory DS:[EDI + (ss × iii)]
		01	ss	iii	000	memory DS:[EAX + (ss × iii) + d8]
		01	ss	iii	001	memory DS:[ECX + (ss × iii) + d8]
		01	ss	iii	010	memory DS:[EDX + (ss × iii) + d8]
		01	ss	iii	011	memory DS:[EBX + (ss × iii) + d8]
		01	ss	iii	100	memory SS:[ESP + (ss × iii) + d8]
		01	ss	iii	101	memory SS:[EBP + (ss × iii) + d8]
		01	ss	iii	110	memory DS:[ESI + (ss × iii) + d8]
		01	ss	iii	111	memory DS:[EDI + (ss × iii) + d8]
		10	ss	iii	000	memory DS:[EAX + (ss × iii) + d32]
		10	ss	iii	001	memory DS:[ECX + (ss × iii) + d32]
		10	ss	iii	010	memory DS:[EDX + (ss × iii) + d32]
		10	ss	iii	011	memory DS:[EBX + (ss × iii) + d32]
		10	ss	iii	100	memory SS:[ESP + (ss × iii) + d32]
		10	ss	iii	101	memory SS:[EBP + (ss × iii) + d32]
		10	ss	iii	110	memory DS:[ESI + (ss × iii) + d32]
		10	ss	iii	111	memory DS:[EDI + (ss × iii) + d32]
		11	—	—	000	register EAX/AX/AL
		11	—	—	001	register ECX/CX/CL
		11	—	—	010	register EDX/DX/DL
		11	—	—	011	register EBX/BX/BL
		11	—	—	100	register ESP/SP/AH
		11	—	—	101	register EBP/BP/CH
		11	—	—	110	register ESI/SI/DH
		11	—	—	111	register EDI/DI/BH

INDEX iii	Index Register
000	EAX
001	ECX
010	EDX
011	EBX
100	no index register
101	EBP
110	ESI
111	EDI

SS ss	Scale Factor
00	x 1
01	x 2
10	x 4
11	x 8

CHAPTER 8

BASIC USE OF PRIVILEGE LEVELS
AND INTERRUPT SERVICE

This chapter describes the topics you need to know about 80386 PROTECTED-mode architecture when creating or using an 80386 32-bit system with a two-level user/supervisor protection model.

This covers 80386 use in 32-bit mode with a basic protection model, using just two of the four privilege levels available. The most-privileged level and the least-privileged level are the levels utilized for a simple two-level system; the two intermediate privilege levels are ignored.

The most-privileged level is assigned to the operating system. As such, it is named the supervisor level. It includes the system's control code, a supervisor program. The least-privileged level is available for user programs. This level provides for programs designed for a specific application, such as a database, a compiler, a word processor, or a spreadsheet. The 80386 PROTECTED-mode architecture protects the supervisor level from the effects of any program bugs, even malicious bugs, at the user level. The address space assigned to supervisor code and data is protected from direct read/write access by a user program.

The PROTECTED-mode interrupt structure is closely associated with the privilege levels. The interrupt structure makes possible transfers from one privilege level to another. It provides this function, of course, for vectoring hardware interrupts, but it can vector software interrupts as well.

Using software interrupts as a calling mechanism, as in PC-compatible applications, the supervisor contains service routines for user-level needs. Service routines activated by software interrupt instructions may perform system functions, such as peripheral input/output, memory allocation/deallocation, and so forth. User software can easily access the service routines by invoking them with INT n software interrupt instructions. Furthermore, use of the interrupt structure helps protect the supervisor level by limiting supervisor entry points to only those listed in the interrupt table.

NOTE: Call gates, discussed in Chapter 14, are a somewhat more powerful mechanism for user-to-OS linkage, since they are not limited in number and they allow autocopy of parameters to the supervisor stack.

Use of Memory Paging

This chapter concentrates primarily on the segment requirements of a simple 32-bit protected system. We should note that in such a system the memory paging system provides the needed protection of supervisor code and data.

In a very simple protected system, the memory paging system segregates the linear address space into user regions and supervisor regions. Each page of memory can be declared either as a user page or as a supervisor page with the 80386 paging system (see Chapter 9).

The paging system can also provide virtual memory capability. User programs can partially reside on disk, and the paging system is transparent to them (see Chapter 9).

Use of 32-bit Memory Segments for Simple PROTECTED Systems

In the PROTECTED mode, memory segments can be assigned attributes of privilege, base address, size, and usage. In a simple PROTECTED system, only a minimal number of segments, five in fact, need be assigned. In a two-level protection system, five memory segments fulfill the requirements of the PROTECTED-mode architecture. These five segments are

A. a supervisor-code segment, for code at the supervisor level
B. a supervisor-data segment, for the supervisor stack and data
C. a user-code segment, for code at the user level
D. a user-data segment, for user stack and data
E. a task-state segment, to hold the stack pointer for the supervisor stack when executing code at the user level

These segments fulfill PROTECTED-mode requirements that:

1. At least one code segment exist for each level of privilege established. In this case, there are a supervisor level and a user level, requiring two code segments.
2. At least one stack segment exist for each level of privilege established. In this case, two data segments must be created to hold the stacks. These same segments may be used also for other data.
3. A task state segment be present to hold the initial stack pointer for the supervisor privilege level when the processor is executing code at the user level.

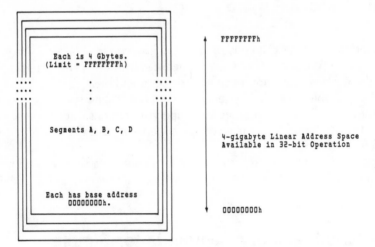

Figure 8.1   Coincident Segments A, B, C, and D for 32-bit Simple PROTECTED System.

The four code and data segments listed should each be declared as very large in size. In fact, they should be declared as 2^{32} bytes (4 gigabytes), so that each encompasses the entire 32-bit linear address space, as shown in Figure 8.1. Establishing large segments avoids memory-addressing limitations within the set of four segments listed above and eliminates any need for a user program to reload the segment registers during its operation. The large linear address space of the segments provides a "flat," 4 gigabytes environment in which the user program operates.

The task-state segment is a special segment just 104 bytes in size, as described later on page 111. The task-state segment may be positioned anywhere in the 4-gigabyte linear address space shown in Figure 8.1.

Segment Descriptors for Simple PROTECTED Systems

In REAL mode (Chapters 4 through 6), segment descriptors do not exist. In REAL mode, memory segments have only one attribute, a base address. Recall, however, that the base address in REAL mode is a direct function of the segment selector value multiplied by sixteen (shifted four bits to the left). The selector itself thus fully describes the REAL-mode memory segment.

Memory segments are more sophisticated in PROTECTED mode, however. Each possesses several attributes: an individual base address in the 32-bit linear address space (not directly a function of the selector value), an individual size, and individual access rights. These attributes are contained in a special datatype, the **segment descriptor**, recognized by the 80386 in PROTECTED mode.

In PROTECTED mode, segments are declared by listing the attributes in descriptors, one descriptor per segment, and grouping the descriptors together to form a memory-resident table named the **Global Descriptor Table** (GDT). Several descriptors and the GDT are further described in these sections. Other descriptors and other tables, not needed for a simple 32-bit system, are discussed in Chapter 14.

Segment Descriptor Format

Each descriptor is just eight bytes, two 32-bit DWORDS, yet contains all descriptive information concerning one memory segment: its base address, its size, and its access rights. Figure 8.2 illustrates a code-segment descriptor, and Figure 8.3 shows a data-segment descriptor. Part a in each figure shows the descriptor overall. In Part b, the **base-address** information is shaded; in Part c, the **limit** information; and in Part d, the **access-rights** information.

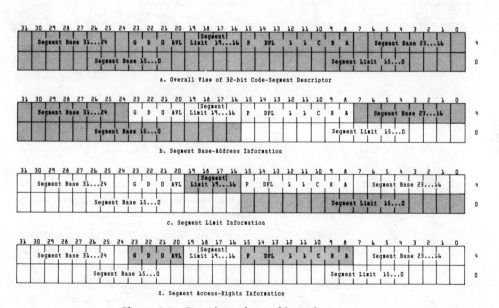

Figure 8.2   Descriptor for 32-bit Code Segment.

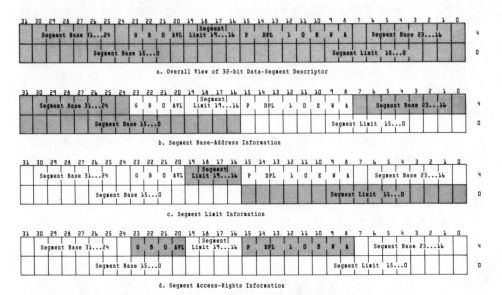

Figure 8.3   Descriptor for 32-bit Data Segment.

Definitions of the descriptor fields are as follows:

1. **Segment base address** is a 32-bit value defining the base address of the segment in the linear address space.

2. **Segment limit** is a 20-bit field defining the largest offset of the segment. The limit can be byte-granular or page-granular (4096-byte-granular), as controlled by the G bit of the descriptor.

3. **G (Granularity)** indicates whether the limit of the segment is byte-granular (G = 0) or page-granular (G = 1). If byte-granular, then the limit can be adjusted with byte resolution, because the field represents bits 19 . . . 0 of the maximum allowable offset, up to 1 megabyte. If page-granular, the limit can be adjusted with page resolution, because the field represents bits 31 . . . 12 of the maximum allowable offset, up to 4 gigabytes.

4. **D (Default)** indicates whether the segment is a 32-bit segment (D = 1) or a 16-bit segment (D = 0). If D = 1, the descriptor format for code segments and data segments is as shown in Figure 8.2 and Figure 8.3 respectively. If D = 0, the descriptor format is that used by 80286 PROTECTED mode for 16-bit segments, as covered in Chapter 14. The 16-bit code provides 32-bit data operand size and 32-bit address size by default. (80286 PROTECTED mode-compatible).

5. E (Expansion Direction), for data segments only, indicates whether the segment exists in the range of addresses from the segment base up to its limit, inclusive (E = 0), or from the maximum offset down to the limit, exclusive (E = 1). Most data segments, such as segments B and D on page 97, have 0 in this bit, for *expand up.* A data segment used only to hold a data stack, which grows downward towards lesser addresses, may find it useful to have 1 in this bit, for *expand down.*

6. B (Big), for data segments only and significant only if the segment is *expand down,* indicates the maximum offset of the segment. The maximum offset of an *expand-down* data segment is indicated as FFFFFFFFh (B = 1) or as 0000FFFFh (B = 0). B is a *don't care* for *expand-up* data segments.

7. Access Rights are several bits indicating the allowable forms of access to the segment, including the privilege level requirement, and the write and read protection. If usage of an operand within the segment is not consistent with the allowable forms of access, the 80386 generates a general-protection exception (exception 13) or a stack exception (exception 12) if a stack segment is involved.

7a. P (Present) indicates whether the segment is present in physical memory (P = 1) or not present (P = 0). This bit allows the declaration of many large segments, perhaps only a subset of which are wholly or partially present in physical memory at any one time. The paging system allows any segment to be loaded on a page basis; even if P = 1, the segment need not be entirely present.

7b. DPL (Descriptor Privilege Level) indicates the privilege level of the segment as a number, 0, 1, 2 or 3, in the following way:

DPL Field	Description		
00	Level 0	most-privileged	(supervisor, kernel)
01	Level 1		
10	Level 2		
11	Level 3	least privileged	(user)

The DPL of the current code segment indicates the *Current Privilege Level* (CPL) of operation. For example, if the processor is executing a code segment of DPL 00, it is executing at a CPL of 0, the most privileged level, the supervisor level.

7c. A (Accessed) indicates whether the segment has been accessed (A = 1) or not (A = 0) since the last time this bit of the descriptor was cleared to 0. If a system implements swapping of segments between memory and disk, this bit can be useful for determining segment usage. Typical simple systems swap pages, not segments, and this bit would not be of interest for such systems.

7d. **R (Readable)**, for code segments only, indicates whether the code segment is readable (R = 1) or not (R = 0). Code segments are of course always executable. The R attribute can provide extra security by forbidding software to read from the segment using the CS override prefix (see page 44 and Table 2.6).

7e. **C (Conforming)**, for code segments only, indicates whether the CPL changes when the segment is called from a level of lesser privilege (C = 0) or not (C = 1). If C = 1, then the code segment is said to be a conforming code segment, because the value of CPL does not change when this code segment is CALLed. Conforming code segments are very useful for library routines, allowing the routine to be called by a user-level program, but keeping the user program at user CPL. The conforming feature is a rather abstract concept of the PROTECTED-mode architecture, and, in a 32-bit simple protected system, all code segments are regular, i.e., not conforming.

7f. **W (Writable)**, for data segments only, indicates whether the data segment is writable (W = 1) or not (W = 0). Data segments are of course always readable. The W attribute can provide extra security by forbidding software to write to the segment. Among the uses for this specialized feature are reserving a segment for status information and protecting a publicly accessible database. In a simple 32-bit protected system, the data segment serves all purposes and contains the stack, among other things; it must therefore be writable.

GDT (Global Descriptor Table)

The Global Descriptor Table holds an array of segment descriptors. As shown in Figure 8.4, it is a memory-resident table, with its base and limit within the linear address space, at a location defined by the GDTR system register (see page 20 and Figure 2.8). The GDTR accepts a 48-bit operand comprised of a 32-bit base and 16-bit limit. Thus, the GDT base may be placed at any address within the linear address space; the limit (maximum offset) may extend to FFFF, holding up to 8192 descriptors, indexed 0 through 8191. Descriptor 0 is at the GDT base address.

Descriptor 0, specially defined as the **null descriptor**, is not used by the processor. It is safest to fill the null descriptor with eight BYTES of 00h.

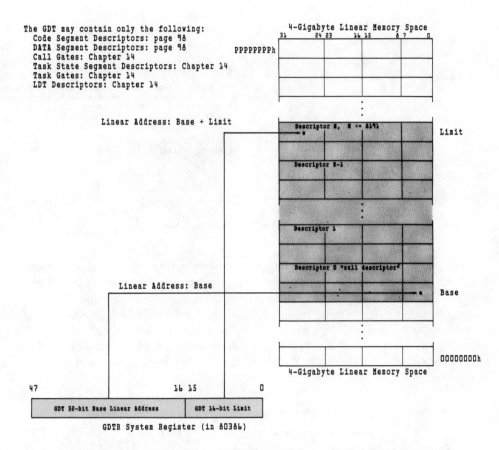

The GDT may contain only the following:
    Code Segment Descriptors: page 98
    DATA Segment Descriptors: page 98
    Call Gates: Chapter 14
    Task State Segment Descriptors: Chapter 14
    Task Gates: Chapter 14
    LDT Descriptors: Chapter 14

Figure 8.4 GDTR Register Locates the GDT in the Linear Address Space.

PROTECTED-Mode Selector Format

As Figure 8.5 indicates, a selector contains three fields in PROTECTED mode. The upper 13 bits comprise an index that selects one descriptor from the GDT when the Table Indicator (TI) bit of the selector is 0, indicating GDT. The TI bit and RPL bits both default to 0 for simple protected systems, as shown at bottom of Figure 8.5.

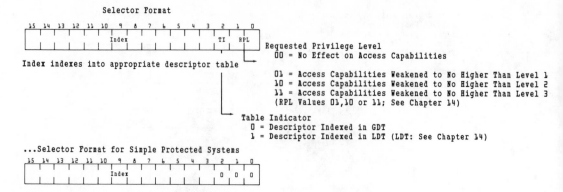

Figure 8.5 PROTECTED-**Mode Selector.**

In PROTECTED mode, loading a selector into a segment register causes the 80386 to access a segment *n*, described by descriptor *n*, where *n* is the upper 13 bits of the selector. The upper 13 bits of the selector act as an index into the table of descriptors (the GDT when the bit is 0). All instructions that move a value into a segment register (CS, SS, DS, ES, FS, GS) cause the 80386 to automatically reference a descriptor *n*, read the descriptor, and store the contents internally in the **descriptor cache**. One descriptor cache exists internally for each segment register, as depicted in Figure 8.6.

Segment Registers	Segment-Descriptor Cache (Hidden, Holds On-chip Copies of Segment Descriptors)		
CS	32-bit Linear Base Address of Segment	20-bit Limit (Byte- or Page-granular)	Other Attributes G D P CPL C R A
SS	32-bit Linear Base Address of Segment	20-bit Limit (Byte- or Page-granular)	G B P CPL E W A
DS	32-bit Linear Base Address of Segment	20-bit Limit (Byte- or Page-granular)	G B P DPL E W A
ES	32-bit Linear Base Address of Segment	20-bit Limit (Byte- or Page-granular)	G B P DPL E W A
FS	32-bit Linear Base Address of Segment	20-bit Limit (Byte- or Page-granular)	G B P DPL E W A
GS	32-bit Linear Base Address of Segment	20-bit Limit (Byte- or Page-granular)	G B P DPL E W A

Figure 8.6 Descriptor Cache Registers Associated with all Segment Registers.

The descriptor-cache registers retain a copy of the segment descriptor. This copy is used in all address calculations to provide the segment base address, as discussed in Chapters 4 and Chapter 7, and in PROTECTED mode to provide the segment limit and access rights used in the limit check and access-rights check. Placing the descriptor-cache registers on chip is critical to performance. They provide instant access to all the current segments.

Several important points may be gleaned from Figure 8.6. Note that the descriptor cache for CS and SS hold CPL, whereas the others hold DPL. This denotes that the code segment's DPL establishes CPL, and also that the DPL of the stack segment must always match CPL. These facts are critical even for a simple PRO-TECTED system.

Use of Software Interrupts

In a simple protected system, the user invokes supervisor routines using software interrupts, the INT *n* instructions. Interrupt numbers 32 through 255 are suitable for this purpose.

Interrupt structure is therefore an integral part of simple 32-bit protected systems. It is described in the following section. Following that, the design of multilevel systems is discussed.

Interrupt Structure in PROTECTED Mode

The PROTECTED-mode interrupt structure is highly analogous to the REAL-mode interrupt structure, described in Chapter 6. The similarity is striking in all respects:

1. As in REAL mode, software interrupts can be caused with the INT *n* instructions. Hardware interrupts signals arrive on input pins INTR (maskable) and NMI (nonmaskable). Upon receipt of an interrupt, control is redirected to a service routine through a memory-resident table containing the proper vectoring information.
2. The entry points for supervisor interrupt routines are contained within **interrupt gates** or **trap gates**. These gates are the counterpart of interrupt vectors in REAL mode. Interrupt gates are especially suited for vectoring hardware interrupts, whereas trap gates are ideal for vectoring software interrupts.
3. Interrupt gates and trap gates are listed together in a memory-resident array named the **Interrupt Descriptor Table** (IDT). The IDT is the counterpart of the interrupt-vector table recognized in REAL mode. The IDT is further described on page 108.

Interrupt Gates

The vectoring element especially designed for vectoring hardware interrupts in PRO-TECTED mode is an interrupt gate. Like its counterpart in REAL mode, the interrupt vector, the interrupt gate contains selector and offset. However, the selector and offset are embodied in an 8-byte descriptorlike element, an interrupt gate.

Each interrupt gate is just eight bytes, two 32-bit DWORDS, containing the full vectoring and protection information for one interrupt: a selector (which must be the selector of a code segment), an offset to the entry point of the code segment, and a privilege level assigned to this gate. Figure 8.7 illustrates an Interrupt Gate.

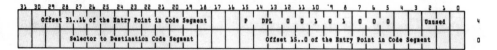

Figure 8.7   Interrupt Gate for Vectoring PROTECTED Mode Interrupts.

Definitions of the interrupt gate fields are as follows:

1.   **Selector to Destination Code Segment** identifies the code segment containing the interrupt-service routine. This selector must reference a code segment.

2.   **Offset of the Entry Point** identifies the entry point of the interrupt-service routine.

3.   **Access Rights** indicate the allowable forms of access to the gate, including presence and privilege-level requirements. If usage of the gate is not consistent with the requirements, the 80386 generates a general-protection exception (exception 13).

3a. **P (Present)** indicates whether the gate is available for use (P = 1) or not (P = 0). For successful vectoring, the gate must be present.

3b. **DPL (Descriptor Privilege Level)** indicates the privilege level of the gate. *A hardware interrupt may always vector through an interrupt gate if it is marked present, regardless of the gate's DPL.* DPL applies only to software interrupts (the INT *n*, INTO, BOUND instructions, and exceptions). DPL indicates the privilege level of the gate as a number, 0, 1, 2, or 3, in the following way:

DPL Field	Description
00	Level 0 most-privileged (supervisor, kernel)
01	Level 1
10	Level 2
11	Level 3 least privileged (user)

For a software interrupt or exception, the instruction using the interrupt must have a CPL at least as privileged as the DPL of the gate. For example, if the processor is executing at a current privilege level of 3, then software interrupts can only use interrupt gates with DPL = 3. Any other value of gate DPL (i.e., 2, 1, or 0) would indicate a greater privilege requirement, and successful vectoring would not occur. A general-protection exception (exception 13) would instead be generated.

Transfer of Control through Interrupt Gate

As control is transferred to an interrupt routine, via an interrupt gate, three DWORDS are pushed onto the stack: a copy of EFLAGS, a copy of CS padded with an upper WORD of 0000h, and a copy of EIP.

The IF flag of EIP is then cleared, disabling further interrupts until IF is again set under software control (IF is typically set at the beginning of the service routine).

The EIP register is then loaded from the offset field of the interrupt gate, and CS is loaded from the selector field of the interrupt gate. The 80386 also reads the descriptor corresponding to the selector field. In doing so, it loads in its code segment descriptor cache all descriptor information (base, limit, and access rights). The 80386 proceeds to fetch an instruction at offset EIP, the first instruction of the service routine.

Trap Gates

The vectoring element especially designed for vectoring software interrupts in PROTECTED mode, a **trap gate**, bears great similarity to the interrupt gate, described on pages 105 and 106. Each trap gate is just eight bytes, two 32-bit DWORDS, containing the full vectoring and protection information for one interrupt: a selector (which must be the selector of a code segment), an offset to the entry point of the code segment, and a privilege level assigned to this gate. Figure 8.8 illustrates a trap gate.

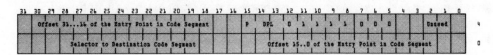

Figure 8.8   Trap Gate for Vectoring Protected-Mode Exceptions.

Definitions of the trap-gate fields are identical to those of the interrupt gate.

Transfer of Control through Trap Gate

Control transfer via a trap gate is identical to the transfer process through an interrupt gate, except that the IF flag in EFLAGS is not cleared. This maintains 80386 responsiveness to maskable hardware interrupts on the INTR pin, an arrangement especially suited to vectoring software interrupts.

IDT (Interrupt Descriptor Table)

The IDT is the counterpart of the interrupt-vector table recognized in REAL mode (See Chapter 6). The IDT holds only gates, not descriptors. Besides the interrupt gate and the trap gate, described in this chapter, the IDT may also be a gate type called the task gate. Task gates, not needed in the simple 32-bit protected system, are covered in Chapter 14.

The IDT holds an array of gates. As shown in Figure 8.9, it is a memory-resident table, with its base and limit mapped in the linear address space, at a location defined by the IDTR system register (see page 20 and Figure 2.8). The IDTR accepts a 48-bit operand comprised of a 32-bit base and 16-bit limit. Thus, the IDT base may be placed at any address within the linear address space; the limit (maximum offset) may extend to 7FFh, holding up to 256 gates, indexed 0 through 255. Gate 0 is at the IDT base address.

Uses of Privilege Levels

It stands to reason that, to implement reliable systems, code performing the most sensitive functions, such as input/output to a disk drive for instance, should be required to have a greater privilege level than code performing routine calculations. It also stands to reason that some data, containing, for example, user IDs and passwords, should be designated as high privilege (i.e., top secret). Generally, interaction with the supervisor must be controlled. The 80386 is designed to provide the necessary protection using its privilege mechanism.

Up to four privilege levels are available in the PROTECTED mode. Four levels provide adequate granularity for even the most sophisticated systems. However, minimal system planning allows utilizing two of the levels for a practical two-level user/supervisor design. In certain systems, you may want to use at least three levels, dedicating the lowest level for user application software and splitting the supervisor itself among two or more of the higher privilege levels.

It is never mandatory to use more than one of the privilege levels. You may find applications for which a single privilege level is entirely satisfactory. You may be requiring only the raw computing speed of the 80386. When only a single privilege level is used, however, it must be level 0, the most-privileged level, so that all instructions of the 80386 can be executed.

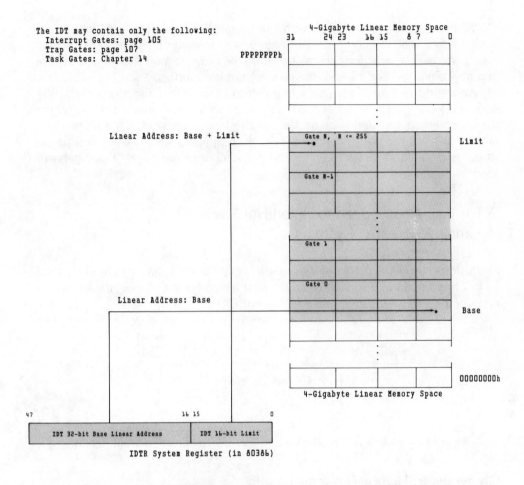

The IDT may contain only the following:
   Interrupt Gates: page 105
   Trap Gates: page 107
   Task Gates: Chapter 14

4-Gigabyte Linear Memory Space
31   24 23   16 15   8 7   0

PPPPPPPPh

Linear Address: Base + Limit

Gate N, N <= 255

Limit

Gate N-1

Gate 1

Gate 0

Linear Address: Base

Base

00000000h

4-Gigabyte Linear Memory Space

47   16 15   0

| IDT 32-bit Base Linear Address | IDT 16-bit Limit |

IDTR System Register (in 80386)

Figure 8.9   IDTR Register Locates the IDT in the Linear Address Space.

Interlevel Transfer Mechanism

This section describes transfers between privilege levels. These occur when the 80386 transfers control from one code segment at privilege level *n* to another code segment at level *m*. Such transfers are easily accomplished in one direction and then the other with single instructions, such as CALL (to higher privilege) and RET (back to lower privilege), or INT *n* (to higher privilege) and IRET (back to lower privilege). The 80386 PROTECTED-mode architecture, as described so far in this chapter, easily accommodates these transfers.

When control is transferred from one segment to another, new values are loaded into the 80386 code segment register and instruction pointer. That having been performed, instructions are fetched from the new location. Transfer of control to a new privilege level extends the concept one step further.

An **interlevel transfer** requires a new instruction stream *and* a new stack. Besides the loading of new CS and EIP values, as with a conventional transfer, the stack-segment register and stack pointer are also loaded with new values. The loading of CS:EIP *and* SS:ESP is consistent with each privilege level having its separate stack, as required to guarantee integrity of a stack area for use by the supervisor level.

INT *n* Instructions Used for Interlevel Transfer in Simple PROTECTED Systems

As illustrated by Figure 8.10, transfers to levels of greater privilege can be performed by INT *n* instructions to supervisor routines. At the end of the routine, transfer in the opposite direction is accomplished with the IRET instruction.

```
         Instruction              Privilege              Instruction
         to Transfer                Level                to Transfer
          "Upward"                                        "Downward"
       ───────────────────────────────────────────────────────────────

                            │    00   Supervisor Level    │
            INT n           │    01                       │       IRET
                            │    10                       │
                            │    11   User Level          │
```

Figure 8.10   Interlevel Transfer via Software Interrupt and Interrupt Return.

Gateways to Higher Privilege Levels

When a trap gate or interrupt gate is placed in the IDT as gate *n*, the INT *n* instruction vectors its selector and offset through the gate to the destination specified. The trap gate or interrupt gate provides *redirection* to a specific entry point, which may be at a higher privilege level or at the same level as the CPL of the INT *n* instruction.

Whether or not transfer to the entry point is permitted depends on a comparison of the CPL of the INT *n* instruction with the DPL of the gate. The normal comparison rule applies. If the CPL is as least as great as the DPL of the gate, then redirection through the gate occurs successfully. Otherwise a general-protection exception (exception 13) is generated (see Chapter 16 for more information on PROTECTED-mode exceptions).

The gate transparently adds a step of indirection to the process of reaching code in a higher privilege level. However, the gate thereby protects higher privilege code by permitting access only if the gate is present and by specifying the exact entry point into the privileged code.

Transparency to the User

Privilege level transfer is accomplished with simple INT *n* and IRET instructions. It is transparent to the user, since no special opcode is required.

Note: CALL instructions that reference CALL gates also accomplish privilege-level transfers in a transparent manner. CALL gates are discussed in Chapter 14. In this protected system, we simply use interrupt instructions.

The supervisor program controls which INT *n* instructions perform a level transfer by controlling the contents of gate *n* referenced by the instruction. For instance, if the destination is gate *k*, whose selector specifies a code segment of the same privilege as the CPL, the INT *k* instruction merely transfers control to the service routine (CS:EIP are loaded with new values). However, when an INT *q* instruction specifies a gate *q* whose selector specifies a code segment of higher privilege than the CPL, a level transfer automatically takes place (CS:EIP *and* SS:ESP are loaded with new values).

Correspondingly, the IRET instruction inspects the contents of CS in the supervisor stack frame, to determine the DPL of the return destination. If the DPL is the same as the CPL, transfer takes place without a level transfer (CS:EIP are loaded with new values). If the DPL is lower than the CPL, a level transfer to the lower level occurs (CS:EIP and SS:ESP are loaded with new values).

32-bit Task State Segment

The **task state segment**, TSS, is primarily used in multitasking systems, as covered in Part 5. In such systems, where the 80386 provides hardware support for many tasks, a 32-bit task state segment is created for each 32-bit task, to hold the register contents of a task when it is not the task currently being executed. For this reason, the 32-bit task state segment must be large enough to hold all necessary information concerning one task. For a 32-bit task, a 32-bit TSS must be at least 104 bytes in size.

Programmer Note: For a simple 32-bit protected system, the TSS is merely a parking spot for the SS:ESP supervisor stack pointer. It is just a segment to be declared with a descriptor in the GDT, in similar manner as the two code and two data segments needed for the simple system.

For a simple 32-bit protected system, the 32-bit TSS is nearly all zeros, corresponding to the fields unnecessary for a simple protected system. Nevertheless, the TSS must be at least 104 bytes in size, as shown in Figure 8.11. Its relevant fields are SS for level 0 and ESP for level 0. These two fields must indicate the initial SS:ESP used for the supervisor stack.

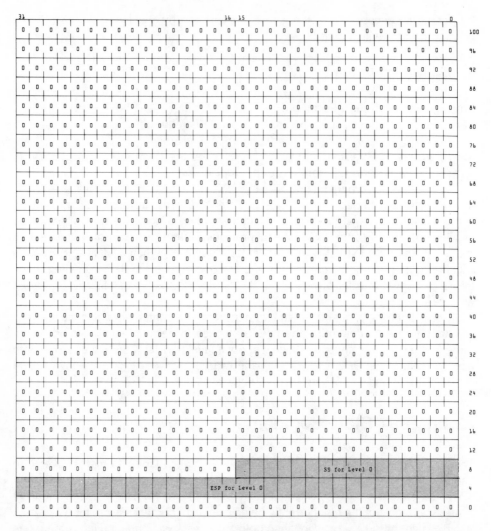

Figure 8.11 32-bit Task State Segment (TSS), Utilizing Only SS:ESP for Supervisor Stack.

TSS Descriptor

The 32-bit task state segment of Figure 8.11 is declared by placing a special descriptor in the GDT. Such a TSS **descriptor** is depicted in Figure 8.12. Definitions of the fields contained in a TSS descriptor are identical to the definitions in a code segment descriptor, except for:

B (Busy), which indicates if the task is currently busy (B = 1) or not (B = 0). For a simple protected system, this bit should be set to 1. Further details of the B field are found in Chapter 14.

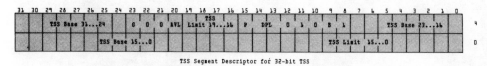

TSS Segment Descriptor for 32-bit TSS

Figure 8.12   Descriptor for 32-bit Task State Segment.

Initializing the TR (Task Register)

Finally, to activate the 32-bit TSS, the selector of the TSS descriptor must be loaded into a PROTECTED-mode register designed for that purpose, the **Task Register (TR)**.

The TR is initialized by writing a selector value to the register, using the LTR instruction. The selector used must reference a TSS descriptor, such as that illustrated in Figure 8.12, which contains the necessary base address and limit information. A descriptor-cache register associated with the TR register retains an internal copy of the TSS descriptor fields, as shown in Figure 8.13. Using the LTR instruction to load the LDT descriptor, the TSS can be located anywhere in the linear address space and can be as large as 64 Kbytes, as Figure 8.14 depicts.

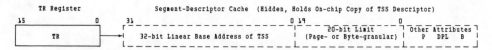

Figure 8.13   Descriptor-Cache Register Associated with TR Register.

Note that the TSS descriptor resides in the GDT. Therefore, it is necessary to create a GDT image and initialize the GDTR first. With the GDT established, the LTR instruction can be executed to load the TR, thereby locating the TSS.

A 16-bit TSS contains the following:
a fixed portion describing register contents;
optionally, additional storage beyond the
fixed portion but within the TSS limit

A 32-bit TSS contains the following:
a fixed portion describing register contents;
optionally, an I/O Permission Bitrap (Chapter 12);
optionally, additional storage before or after the
I/O Permission Bitrap but within the TSS limit

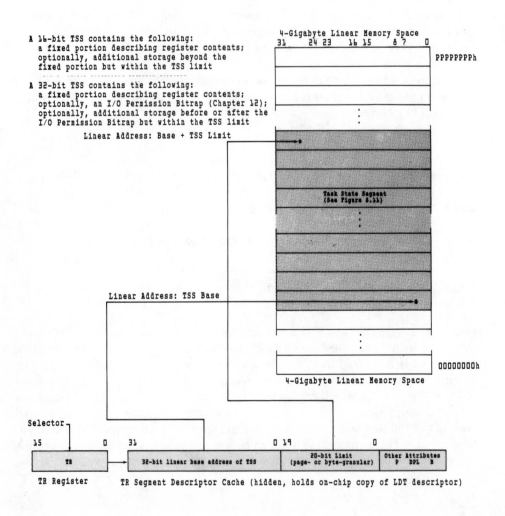

Figure 8.14 TR Descriptor Cache Locates the Simple TSS in the Linear Address Space.

CHAPTER 9

THE MEMORY PAGING SYSTEM

Sophisticated memory paging support is built into the 80386. The most publicized benefit of this is full support for demand-paged virtual memory. Virtual-memory support allows the programmer to use more memory space than is actually implemented with chips in the system. The *comprehensive* range of beneficial capabilities that the demand-paged memory-management unit (MMU) offers includes the following:

1. address protection for simple protected systems, such as those described in Chapter 8
2. demand-paged virtual memory, allowing the programmer a larger usable address space than is actually provided in system RAM
3. on-chip standardization of the operating system protection and virtual memory software
4. on-chip implementation to reduce bus loading and eliminate chip-to-chip delays
5. on-chip implementation that costs very little, using only approximately 10 percent of the silicon chip area, lowering the incremental cost of demand-paged virtual memory to practically nothing

The memory paging system can be enabled in PROTECTED-mode operation. Enabling or disabling paging is performed under software control from privilege level 0 only.

Page Structure

The page structure divides a 4-gigabyte linear address space into 1,048,576 pages of 4,096 bytes each. Figure 9.1 illustrates the concept of a paged memory space. The virtual address space is shown on the left, and the physical address space is shown on the right. The uniform size of all pages allows loading any required virtual page into any desired physical page, the key reason that paging is the commonly preferred technique for implementing virtual memory.

As Figure 9.1 shows, the *virtual* memory space is typically much larger than the *implemented* physical memory space, which is a result of physical and economic

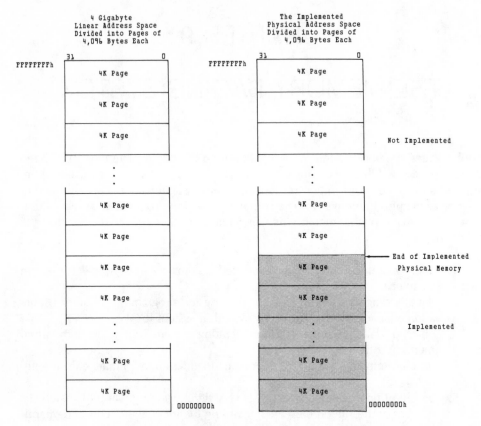

Figure 9.1   Paged Virtual Memory and Physical Memory.

constraints. Therefore, at any given time, only a fraction of all virtual memory pages are present in the physical memory. The pages not in memory are typically stored on a secondary storage device, such as a hard disk.

Demand paging, as paging is sometimes called, merely stresses the fact that a user program is unaware of the paging process. The term *paging* is synonymous with *demand paging*; both terms mean that a program can use the entire virtual address space as it wishes. The processor architecture generates an exception upon any attempt to access a page that is not present in memory. The exception allows a supervisor program to intervene as needed, transparently to the user program, to load all necessary pages as they are required by the user code. Under supervisor program control, the "old" RAM pages are saved to disk before the "new" pages are loaded into RAM.

Enabling/Disabling Memory Paging

Bit 31 of Control Register 0, Figure 9.2, controls the enabling/disabling of paging. This bit, the PG bit, enables paging when set to 1 and disables paging when reset to 0.

In PROTECTED mode, the MOV CR0,<ea> instruction, a machine-control instruction (see Table 3.9), is used to write into CR0. As this instruction can be executed only in PROTECTED mode, memory paging can be enabled and disabled only in that mode. Paging remains enabled during VIRTUAL 8086 mode (see Chapter 12), which is of course desirable, since it allows programs to run in VIRTUAL 8086 mode as part of a paged virtual-memory system.

Figure 9.2   PG Bit in Control Register 0.

Alignment of Page Boundaries with Segment Boundaries

Page boundaries occur at regular intervals of 4,096 bytes. *Segment boundaries* are entirely variable, depending upon the base and limit of individual segments. Strictly speaking, that is, segment and page boundaries are independent of each other and do not have to be aligned. Segments are defined by one set of tables, the GDT and the LDT, while pages are defined by another set, the page tables. For performance optimization, however, small segments (4,096 bytes or less) should be aligned so that each remains within one page. This applies, for example, to such small segments as the task state segment described in Chapter 8. Alignment within one page guarantees that loading a single page loads the entire segment.

Page-Privilege Levels Compared with Segment-Privilege Levels

The page-privilege levels are named *user* and *supervisor*. The segment-privilege levels are numbered 3, 2, 1, and 0. Level 3 is the user level. Levels 2, 1, and 0 are supervisor levels. Figure 9.3 illustrates the relationship of page privilege levels with segment privilege levels.

DPL Given in Segment Descriptor . . .		. . . Is Considered to Be Page Level:
Most Privileged	0	Supervisor
	1	Supervisor
	2	Supervisor
Least Privileged	3	User

Figure 9.3   Segment-Level and Page-Level Correspondence.

Page Translation Process

The paging process replaces the upper 20 bits of a 32-bit linear address, a **virtual page number**, with another 20-bit value, the **physical page number**. Paging is the final step of the address process, a step illustrated along with the general addressing mode descriptions, in Figures 4.2 and 7.2.

Translation Tables

The translated value, (i.e., the physical page number) is obtained from memory-resident translation tables. The 80386 is capable of automatically reading the translation tables when necessary, to translate the virtual addresses of memory operands.

The translation tables are arranged in a two-level hierarchy. The root-level table is the **page directory table**, or **page directory**, containing 1,024 entries, each of which points to a subordinate table. Therefore up to 1,024 subordinate **page tables** are supported.

Rather than having a single, linear translation table, a hierarchical arrangement avoids the commitment of reserving a large, contiguous range of linear addresses to hold the translation tables. The hierarchical arrangement also supports sparse mapping trees, where only several entries of the page directory point to page tables. The hierarchy allows protection attributes to be assigned in the page-directory entry, for 4-Mbyte granularity, or in the page-table entry, for 4-Kbyte (single-page) granularity.

Figure 9.4 illustrates the tables. Control register 3, CR3, anchors the table structure, since it points to the page directory table. Each entry of the page directory table points to a page holding a page table. In turn, each entry of a page table points to a physical memory page.

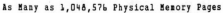

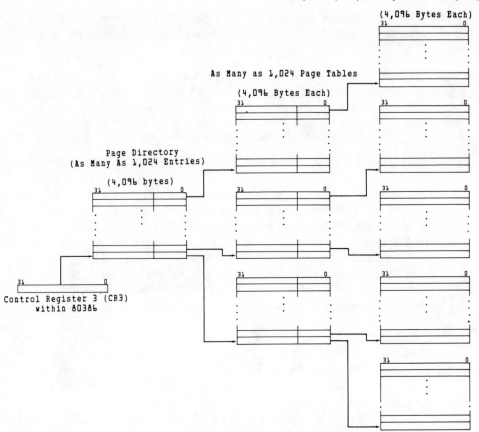

Figure 9.4   Structure of the Translation Tables.

Page Directory Entry

The page directory contains as many as 1,024 page-directory entries. Each entry points to a page table by indicating its physical base address and other information.

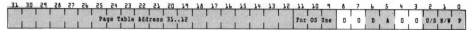

Page Directory Entry Points to Page Table and Lists Its Attributes.

Figure 9.5 Page Directory Entry.

A page-directory entry, illustrated in Figure 9.5, is defined as follows:

1. **Page Table Address** defines the upper 20 bits of a page table physical base address. Since a page table is page-aligned in physical memory, i.e., aligned to a 4,096-byte boundary, its lower 12 base address bits are 0.
2. **For OS Use** are three bits set aside for operating system use. The 80386 will never automatically alter these bits. An example use of these bits would be to store information about page-table aging. If these three bits are not sufficient to store all additional page-table information, the operating system should create a separate memory array to serve its information storage needs.
3. **D (Dirty)** indicates whether an operand has been written to any of the 1,024 pages of the page table (D = 1) or not (D = 0). If D = 1, then the copy of at least one of the pages held on disk is stale, and the supervisor program must write the appropriate memory page(s) back to disk before replacing those page(s) in memory.
4. **A (Accessed)** indicates whether at least one of the 1,024 pages has been read/written (A = 1) or not (A = 0). This bit is useful if the operating system is maintaining statistics on page usage.
5. **U/S (User/Supervisor)** generally indicates protection treatment assigned to the 1,024 pages described by the page table. For full interpretation, see Table 9.1.
6. **R/W (Read/Write)** generally indicates write protection for the 1,024 pages described by the page table. For full interpretation, the U/S bit must be considered also. See Table 9.1.
7. **P (Present)** indicates whether the page table is present in physical memory (P = 1) or not (P = 0).

The bit positions marked zero should be initialized as such when the Page Directory is created in memory. Those positions, which are not altered by the 80386, are reserved for use by future processors.

Page-Table Entry

The page table contains as many as 1,024 page-table entries. Each entry points to a memory page by indicating its physical base address and other information.

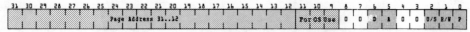

Page Table Entry Points to Page and Lists Its Attributes.

Figure 9.6   Page-Table Entry.

A page-table entry, illustrated in Figure 9.6, is defined as below. Note that its appearance and definition are very similar to a page-directory entry.

1. **Page Table Address** defines the upper 20 base address bits of the physical page. Since a page is page-aligned in physical memory, i.e., aligned to a 4,096-byte boundary, its lower 12 base address bits are 0.
2. **For OS Use** are three bits set aside for operating system use. The 80386 will never automatically alter these bits. An example use of these bits would be to store information about page aging. If these three bits are not sufficient to store all additional page information, the operating system should create a separate memory array to serve its information storage needs.
3. **D (Dirty)** indicates whether an operand has been written anywhere in the page (D = 1) or not (D = 0). If D = 1, then the copy of this page held on disk is stale, and the supervisor program must write this page back to disk before overwriting it in memory.
4. **A (Accessed)** indicates whether any location of the page has been read/written (A = 1) or not (A = 0). This bit is useful if the operating system is maintaining statistics on page usage.
5. **U/S (User/Supervisor)** generally indicates protection treatment assigned to the 1,024 pages described by the page table. For full interpretation, see Table 9.1.
6. **R/W (Read/Write)** generally indicates write protection for the page. For full interpretation, the U/S bit must be considered also. See Table 9.1.
7. **P (Present)** indicates whether the page is present in physical memory (P = 1) or not (P = 0).

The bit positions marked zero should be initialized as such when a page table is created in memory. Those positions, not altered by the 80386, are reserved for use by future processors.

Page Protection

In a page-directory entry, the user/supervisor and read/write bits are used to provide protection attributes for all the pages in a page table. The U/S and R/W bits in the first-level page-directory entry apply to all 1,024 pages described by that directory entry.

In a page-table entry, the U/S and R/W bits provide similar protection for a page. The U/S and R/W bits in a page-table entry apply only to the page described by that entry.

As shown in Figure 9.7, both levels of tables are used when paging occurs. Therefore, the protection that applies to a given page is *the more restrictive* of the U/S and R/W bits. By "more restrictive" is meant that the smaller value of the supervisor status and the read-only status, that is, the smaller value of [U/S : R/W], is the more restrictive value and therefore applies.

For an example page, if the U/S : R/W bits of its page-directory entry are 10 and the U/S : R/W bits of its page-table entry are 01, the more restrictive value is 01, in the page-table entry.

The more restrictive value applies the protection shown in Table 9.1.

Table 9.1   Protection Provided by U/S and R/W Bits.

U/S	R/W	Permitted Access from User Level (CPL = 3)	Permitted Access from Supervisor Level (DPL = 2, 1, or 3)
0	0	None	Read and Write
0	1	None	Read and Write
1	0	Read only	Read and Write
1	1	Read and Write	Read and Write

As the right column indicates, the supervisor can read and write all pages (i.e., the R/W bit affects only user access).

The segment-access rights also apply to any memory access. The most restrictive rights apply, whether they are segment rights or page rights. Notice that the execute-only protection is created only by the segment-access rights.

For instance, if data resides in a data segment marked read-only but in a page is marked read/write, then access to the data is read-only, because of the more restrictive segment access rights. A second example: if a code segment of level 3 is created but contains some pages marked as supervisor level, then when CPL = 3 only the code pages marked as user level can be executed. This second example is very typical of the 32-bit simple protected system in Chapter 8. The use of paging to protect simple systems is covered on page 124.

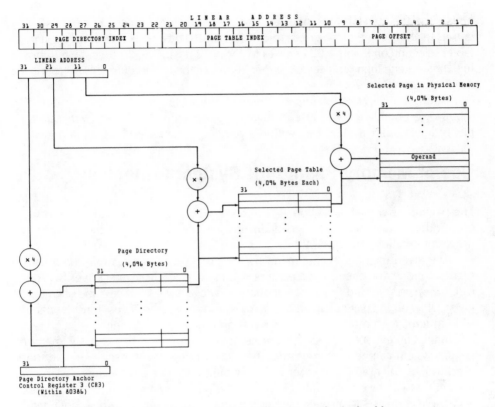

Figure 9.7   Translating a Linear Address to a Physical Address.

Translation Process: Detail

During the paging process, the upper 20 bits of a 32-bit linear address are replaced with 20 bits obtained from a page table. The 80386 thereby forms a new 32-bit address, the physical address, used to access the physical memory.

Figure 9.7 shows how portions of the linear address index into each level of the hierarchical translation tables, for translation of a linear address into a physical address. First, the upper 10 bits index into the page directory, selecting one of its 1,024 entries to choose one of the page tables. The next 10 bits index into the chosen page table, selecting one of its 1,024 entries to choose a page. The 20-bit page number of the chosen page then replaces the upper 20 bits of the linear address. This forms the 32-bit physical address.

Notice that all virtual-memory pages and physical memory pages are aligned to 4,096-byte boundaries. Because of this correspondence, the lower twelve address bits of linear address, the offset within a page, are unaffected by paging.

Use of Memory Paging for System Protection

The paging system lends itself to system protection because the page-directory entries and the page-table entries contain privilege information, on the U/S bit, and usage information, on the R/W bit.

Any given memory access made by the 80386 must successfully pass both a segment-protection check and a page-protection check. These checks verify that the CPL (see pages 98 and 99) is of adequate privilege level to access the segment of given DPL and the page of given U/S level. It also means the access must be permissible in terms of the segment-access rights and the page-R/W rights.

In the context of a simple 32-bit protected system, as in Chapter 8, the memory-paging system can be used to restrict the range of linear addresses available to the user. In particular, when the user code segment and user data segment each span the entire 4-gigabyte linear address range, the paging system can restrict the user-accessible addresses to a smaller area. The user's space can be further contained by marking various pages as supervisor pages (U/S = 0).

A final requirement applies to successful page access: the P (Present bit) in the page-directory entry and in the page entry must be set to 1, indicating a status of present. In a system using paging for protection but not for virtual memory, all P bits should be set to 1.

Use of Memory Paging for Virtual Memory

The 80386 paging system is easily used to provide virtual memory to the programmer. In a virtual-memory system, the P bit can be either 0 or 1, but it must always be an accurate indication of the in-memory/on-disk status of the virtual page. The operating system is responsible for accurately maintaining the P bits. They are never automatically changed by the 80386, although the 80386 automatically *references* the appropriate P bits for each memory access.

The bit forms the underpinning of paged virtual memory. For each memory access, the P bits in the page directory and in the page table are checked. If P equals 1 in the page directory and in the page table, the page is present, and address translation to the physical address occurs immediately. If either P bit equals 0, no memory reference is made. Instead, a *page fault* is detected, and the processor generates an exception. Exception 14 is assigned to the page fault condition. The 80386 design ensures that all page faults are *restartable*: therefore, the program causing the exception can be resumed after the needed page has been brought into physical memory and the translation tables have been updated with the physical page address and correct P-bit value.

Presence Requirements in a Virtual-Memory System

When the memory-paging system is used to provide virtual memory, most of the linear address space is not present in physical memory at any given time. However, certain critical code and data structures must be resident at *all* times, as described here and as listed in Table 9.2. These items must never be swapped to disk.

In a paged memory system, the page-directory table must remain present in physical memory at all times: a reasonable requirement because, as the first-level table, it is accessed whenever the translation tables are needed.

The complete service routine for the page-fault exception (exception 14), the service routine that brings necessary pages into the physical memory, must itself remain present in memory. Otherwise, no page could successfully be brought into physical memory without causing another page-fault exception. A similar line of thought applies to the other items required to remain in memory.

To initially invoke the page-fault service routine (exception 14 service routine), the IDT and GDT must be present in memory, since the IDT supplies the gate for vectoring the exception, and the GDT supplies the code and data descriptors for the service routine's code and data segments. The TSS must be present, since it supplies the stack pointer to the level 0 stack used by the service routine. The level 0 stack itself must therefore be in memory. Again for the same reason, the page table(s) used to translate linear addresses for the IDT, the GDT, the TSS, the level 0 stack, and the service-routine code and data segments must remain in memory. One page table could easily handle the address mapping for all these structures. The remaining page table(s) do not have to remain in memory; they can be paged to disk and the P bit of their page-directory entries can be reset to 0, indicating that they are not present in memory.

From an interrupt latency standpoint, however, it is highly desirable to maintain in memory all code for frequently used service routines.

From a general performance standpoint, it is highly desirable to maintain in physical memory as much of the frequently used other code and data as possible.

Table 9.2   Items Required to Be Memory-Resident.

Items Required to Remain in Memory	Reason
1. Page Directory	No way to indicate otherwise, since every access to the paging translation tables requires the page directory.
2. IDT	Required to successfully invoke the service routine for a page fault.
3. Page Table for IDT Addresses	Same as for item 2.
4. GDT	Same as for item 2.
5. Page Table for GDT Addresses	Same as for item 2.
6. TSS	Same as for item 2.
7. Page Table for TSS Addresses	Same as for item 2.
8. Stack for Level 0	Same as for item 2.
9. Page Table for Level 0 Stack	Same as for item 2.
10. Code for Page Fault Exception Handler	Required to successfully complete the service routine for a page fault (exception 14).
11. Data for Page Fault Exception Handler	Required to determine where page is stored on disk.
12. Page Table for Code and Data Segments of the Page Fault Exception Handler	Same as for item 2.

Note that the page tables listed as items 3, 5, 7, 9, and 12 can be the same page table.

The Translation Lookaside Buffer (TLB)

To speed the address translation process, the 80386 has on chip a fast cache memory containing recent address translations. This cache memory is the **Translation Lookaside Buffer (TLB)**, a term adopted from the mainframe computer architectures in which such caches were first implemented.

The on-chip TLB of the 80386 holds thirty-two translated-page values, corresponding to thirty-two virtual-page values. Any time a linear address is within one of those thirty-two virtual pages, the TLB can immediately supply the corresponding physical-page value for the translation. Accessing the TLB, which occurs automatically for every memory access, is called a *TLB lookup*. Because the TLB lookup requires only half a clock period, it greatly speeds the page-translation process. The TLB avoids frequent reference to the memory-resident translation tables. If the 80386 were without a TLB, it would have to reference the translation tables for each memory access.

Because it holds the thirty-two most recently translated values, the TLB supplies instant translation for approximately 98–99 percent of memory accesses. This is not an unexpected figure, since thirty-two pages cover 128K bytes. At any given time, most programs exhibit a characteristic *locality of reference* meaning that they

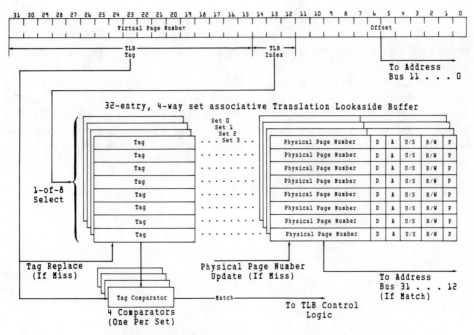

Figure 9.8   80386 TLB Organization.

perform most memory accesses within relatively narrow ranges of virtual addresses (usually well within a total of 128K). The locality principle allows the TLB to perform well.

If, however, a linear address is not within any virtual page mapped by the TLB, the 80386 automatically determines the physical-page value by referencing the memory-resident page directory and a page table, as shown in Figure 9.6. At the same time, the 80386 replaces one of its older TLB entries with this new translation information. Thus, the TLB stays current with recently performed page translations.

Organization of the TLB

The thirty-two entries of the TLB are arranged as four sets of eight entries each. This arrangement of four sets is commonly called a **four-way set associativity**. Associativity indicates that the cache sets operate in parallel, or in other words, simultaneously. For example, when a TLB lookup occurs, each set is simultaneously indexed by the three least-significant bits, bits [14, 13 and 12], of the virtual page number.

The indexed entries of each set are simultaneously compared with the current virtual address. If a match is found in any of the four sets, the TLB immediately supplies the physical page number from the set that matches. Figure 9.7 illustrates the TLB organization.

Statistically, the thirty-two-entry four-way associative organization provides a good chance that the needed translation will be found in the TLB. It provides a better performance, for example, than a single-set (direct-mapped) TLB of thirty-two entries. From an implementation standpoint, however, the four-way set associativity requires more logic on-chip: a separate comparator circuit for *each* set, as Figure 9.7 shows.

CHAPTER 10

INSTRUCTION DETAILS FOR

PROTECTED MODE

This chapter discusses the 80386 instructions as used in PROTECTED mode. All 80386 instructions are available in the PROTECTED mode.

In the PROTECTED mode, the 80386 may execute 32-bit code segments (with the default bit in the code-segment descriptor, D, equal to 1) or 16-bit code segments (D = 0). Use of 32-bit code segments provides full use of the 80386; 16-bit code segments provide full compatibility with 80286 PROTECTED-mode operation.

Operand sizes of 8 bits, 16 bits, and 32 bits are available. When the 80386 is executing 32-bit code segments, 32-bit addressing modes are used by default, as described in Chapter 7. When it is executing 16-bit code segments, 16-bit addressing modes are used by default, as described in Chapter 4.

When 16-bit code segments are executed, some of the new 80386 features are nevertheless available. Thus, strictly speaking, the 16-bit PROTECTED mode of the 80386 is a more capable environment than the PROTECTED mode of the 80286. The 80386 debug registers are available, and debugger utilities may utilize them for superior debugging power. Also available are the paging-test registers and control registers, used when preparing to enter the PROTECTED mode. Two new segment registers, FS and GS, provide increased programming efficiency. Bit-manipulation and double-shift instructions are available.

Instruction Availability

As mentioned, all 80386 instructions are available in PROTECTED mode. Compared to 80286 PROTECTED mode, twelve new instructions are available. New, full-displacement forms of the Jcc (Jump Conditional) instruction and a fully general form of the IMUL (Signed Multiply) instruction are available in 80386 PROTECTED mode. Table 10.1 lists the PROTECTED-mode additions, compared to the 80286 and other modes. These additional instructions allow new 80386 programs to execute more efficiently than 8086 or 80286 programs.

Table 10.1 Instruction Additions Compared to 8086.

80286 REAL-Mode Additions	80386 REAL-Mode Additions	80286 PROTECTED-Mode Additions	80386 PROTECTED-Mode Additions	Description
				Instructions for General Utility
BOUND	BOUND	BOUND	BOUND	Perform array bounds check
ENTER	ENTER	ENTER	ENTER	Create stack frame
IMUL #\<data>	IMUL #\<data>	IMUL #\<data>	IMUL #\<data>	Immediate signed multiply
INS	INS	INS	INS	String input instruction
LEAVE	LEAVE	LEAVE	LEAVE	Eliminate stack frame
OUTS	OUTS	OUTS	OUTS	String output instruction
POPA	POPA	POPA	POPA	Pop all general registers
PUSHA	PUSHA	PUSHA	PUSHA	Push all general registers
PUSH #\<data>	PUSH #\<data>	PUSH #\<data>	PUSH #\<data>	Push immediate data value
REP INS	REP INS	REP INS	REP INS	Repeated string input
REP OUTS	REP OUTS	REP OUTS	REP OUTS	Repeated string output
shift/rotate by count	shift/rotate by count	shift/rotate by count	shift/rotate by count	Shift/rotate by immediate count
	BT		BT	Bit test
	BTC		BTC	Bit test and complement
	BTR		BTR	Bit test and reset
	BTS		BTS	Bit test and set
	IMUL generalized		IMUL generalized	Signed multiply general register
	MOV CRn		MOV CRn	Move to/from control registers
	MOV DRn		MOV DRn	Move to/from debug registers
	MOV TRn		MOV TRn	Move to/from paging-test registers
	Jcc full display		Jcc full display	Jump conditional—full displacement
	Scc		Scc	Set Byte conditionally
	SHLD		SHLD	Double shift left
	SHRD		SHRD	Double shift right
				PROTECTED-Mode Instructions
CLTS*	CLTS*			Clear task-switched flag
LGDT*	LGDT*			Load GDTR register
SGDT*	SGDT*	SGDT	SGDT	Store GDTR register
LIDT*	LIDT*			Load IDTR register
SIDT*	SIDT*	SIDT	SIDT	Store IDTR register
LMSW*	LMSW*			Load machine status word
SMSW*	SMSW*	SMSW	SMSW	Store machine status word
		ARPL	ARPL	Adjust requestor privilege level
		LAR	LAR	Load access rights
		LSL	LSL	Load segment limit
		VERR	VERR	Verify for read
		VERW	VERW	Verify for write
				PROTECTED-Mode Level 0 Only
		CLTS	CLTS	Clear task-switched flag
		LIDT	LIDT	Load IDTR register
		LGDT	LGDT	Load GDTR register
		LMSW	LMSW	Load machine status word
		LLDT	LLDT	Load LDTR register
		LTR	LTR	Load TR register
			MOV CRn,\<ea>	Load control register n
			MOV \<ea>,CRn	Store control register n
			MOV TRn,\<ea>	Load test register n
			MOV \<ea>,TRn	Store test register n
			MOV DRn,\<ea>	Load debug register n
			MOV \<ea>,DRn	Store debug register n

*These PROTECTED-mode instructions are valid in REAL mode to allow initialization for PROTECTED mode.

Notice that certain PROTECTED-mode instructions can also be executed in the REAL mode. These instructions allow initializing the system for PROTECTED mode operation, as shown in Chapter 11. Once PROTECTED mode is established, many of these instructions can be executed only at privilege level 0, the most privileged level, because of their sensitive role in system programming.

Prefix Availability

All 80386 prefixes, listed in Figure 3.1, are available in PROTECTED mode.

PROTECTED-Mode Segment-Size Limit

In PROTECTED mode, the segment limit is determined by the descriptor contents. Code segments and data segments may either be 16-bit segments, having a maximum offset of FFFFh bytes, or 32-bit segments, having a maximum offset of FFFFFFFFh bytes. The D (Default) bit of the segment descriptor determines whether these are 16-bit segments (D = 0) or 32-bit segments (D = 1).

The segment limit requires that effective addresses generated in PROTECTED mode be less than or equal to the limit. In the case of multibyte operands, it therefore requires that the *entire* operand be at offsets less than or equal to the limit. In PROTECTED mode, attempted access to operands that lie entirely or partially beyond the segment limit causes a violation and generates an exception. (Segment-limit violations are further described in Chapter 16.) All operands should therefore lie within the defined segment limit.

CHAPTER 11

INITIALIZING SIMPLE PROTECTED 32-BIT SYSTEMS

This chapter provides a coding example to initialize the 80386 into 32-bit operation. The system environment is set up as a simple PROTECTED-mode system, as described in Chapter 8, with the four-gigabyte linear address space and a two-level protection scheme.

Objectives

With a minimum of code and data, the routine presented in this chapter initializes the 80386 to operate as a 32-bit processor. Therefore this routine enables the PROTECTED mode. Two privilege levels are utilized: the most-privileged level, for supervisor code and data, and the least-privileged level, for user code and data. The routine allows access to the full linear address space of four gigabytes.

Mechanics

The routine initializes several of the 80386 system registers to enable PROTECTED mode and reference the necessary descriptor tables, the GDT and IDT. Although there is no one single code sequence that must be used to initialize the 80386 for 32-bit operation, the important points should be well understood, so they can be incorporated into any given initialization routine. These points are listed below.

1. The routine is designed to execute immediately after a processor reset. For simplicity, this routine is designed to be EPROM-resident, and it begins execution at the reset address. At reset, the 80386 is in REAL mode, but the base of the code segment is initially preset to a FFFF0000h (64K from the top of the 4-gigabyte physical address space), a value beyond the normal 1-megabyte address range of REAL mode. The IP is preset to FFF0h, causing the initial fetch address to be FFFF0000h + FFF0h (code segment base address + IP value) = FFFFFFF0h in physical memory. Note that the code-

132

segment base address and the IP, as preset, allow the boot code in EPROM to be placed at the top of the 4-gigabyte physical memory. See Figure 11.1.

2. The first instruction is a JMP to the body of the routine. Since this example is designed to reside in a boot EPROM at the top of the physical address space, this JMP must be an intrasegment JMP (opcode E9h, direct jump within code segment), to avoid reloading the code-segment base address.

3. In the body of the routine, the 80386 system registers GDTR and IDTR are loaded with values that point to the two descriptor tables covered in Chapter 8, the GDT and IDT. Images of the GDT and IDT structures are also included in the boot EPROM (see Figure 11.2). *Important:* All the code and data descriptors in the EPROM images of the GDT must have the access bit set. The TSS descriptor must have the accessed bit set and the busy bit *reset*. *Note*: The GDT and IDT images can be copied to RAM if desired, allowing the tables to be altered as the system runs. For multitasking systems (not this example), such a step is actually required. For multitasking systems the tables must be located in RAM so the 80386 can properly control the busy bits of the several TSS descriptors existing in such systems.

4. Once the tables have been established, as above, the routine enables PRO-TECTED mode by loading a value into CR0 (Control Register 0, Figure 2.7), which sets the PE (Protection Enable) bit, bit 31. PROTECTED mode is now turned on, meaning that subsequent loads of a selector to a segment register will cause the 80386 to access the GDT, read the descriptor for the segment, and retain the descriptor information in an internal descriptor cache register (Figure 8.6). The selector loads can be accomplished via a MOV instruction or, for the CS register, via an intersegment JMP, CALL, INT *n*, RET, or IRET instruction.

5. The routine proceeds to initialize the 80386 descriptor cache for each segment register. The routine MOVes the selector for the supervisor data segment (selector = 0018h) to segment registers SS, DS, ES, FS, and GS. The selector value is such that it references the descriptor for a supervisor-level (level 0) data segment. By this action, the routine makes available a large supervisor data segment. As determined by the data-segment descriptor in the GDT, the data segment is a 32-bit segment, since the descriptor D bit is 1. The data-segment descriptor, which appears as shown in Figure 8.3, is listed as descriptor GDT 3 in Figure 11.2. This data-segment descriptor indicates a base address of 00000000h and a limit of maximum size of FFFFFFFFh. The supervisor data segment therefore spans the entire four-gigabyte linear address space. The SS, DS, ES, FS, and GS registers all describe the same maximum-size segment.

6. One final segment register remains to be loaded, the CS register. This is accomplished not by a MOV instruction (MOV to CS is not a legal opcode), but instead by a JMP instruction. Since the intention of the JMP instruction is to load a new selector value into CS, it is necessary to perform an *inter-*

segment JMP (opcode EAh, direct intersegment jump). An intersegment JMP instruction specifies the selector of the supervisor code segment (selector = 0010h) and the offset within that destination segment (offset = linear address of the instruction following this JMP). The code segment, as described by the code-segment descriptor in the GDT, is a 32-bit segment (D = 1). The code-segment descriptor, listed as descriptor GDT_2 in Figure 11.2, indicates a base address of 00000000h and a limit of maximum size of FFFFFFFFh. The supervisor code segment therefore spans the entire four-gigabyte linear address space.

The intersegment JMP instruction will use the selector value that references the descriptor for a supervisor-level (level 0) code segment. It will use an offset that specifies the destination relative to the newly loaded code segment. As described, the base of this code segment is 00000000h, so specifying an offset *n* will lead to destination address *n* within the four-gigabyte linear address space.

7. At the destination of the JMP instruction, it is desirable to have an instruction that initializes the supervisor stack. MOVing an initial value to the ESP register is all that is required.

Because the base address of all segments is specified as 00000000h and their limits are specified as FFFFFFFFh, this configuration is set up so the segment registers are little-used once the initialization routine is completed. A four-gigabyte linear space is made available for code and data.

8. The LTR instruction initializes the task register, pointing it to the TSS for this (the one and only) task. The TSS is required since the system allows a user/supervisor architecture. When executing code at the user level, the TSS stores the initial stack pointer (SS:ESP) for the supervisor level.

32-bit Supervisor Initialization Routine and Data

The program listing of Figure 11.1 is the code and data used to initialize the 80386 for 32-bit operation. The program performs all the steps described on pages 132–133.

The necessary data structures, Figure 11.2 includes an image of the GDT, with the null descriptor, the four segment descriptors mentioned on pages 98 and 99 and the TSS descriptor mentioned on page 111. For convenience, the selector values for the GDT descriptors are listed:

GDT Entry	Selector Value	Item
0	0000h	Null Descriptor
1	0008h	Task State Segment
2	0010h	Supervisor Code Segment
3	0018h	Supervisor Data Segment
4	0020h	User Code Segment
5	0028h	User Data Segment

The final necessary data structure is the image of the IDT, as covered on page 105. This is listed in Figure 11.2. Each entry of the IDT is a gate, not a selector, and is referred to by its position number in the IDT. For example, an INT *n* instruction will vector through gate *n* in the IDT.

This code and data enable the 80386 in 32-bit PROTECTED mode. Because the supervisor and user-code segment descriptors have D = 1, the 32-bit operand size and 32-bit address size are the defaults.

```
ASSUME      CS:INITIAL, DS:TABLEDATA

INITIAL     SEGMENT  PUBLIC AT 0F000h
            ORG      FFF0h
            ASSUME   CS: INITIAL, DS: NOTHING, ES: NOTHING
;
;  Begin from a reset condition.  Interrupts are disabled
;  after reset.
;

RES_ADR:    JMP      BODY               ;Intrasegment jump to body
                                        ; of initialization routine.

            ORG      0D000h

BODY:       LGDT     GDT_PTR            ;Load GDT register
                                        ; to locate GDT in
                                        ; linear address space.
                                        ; Here, GDT is based at linear
                                        ; address FFFFC000h, and holds 6
                                        ; entries (48 bytes), limit=002Fh.
            LIDT     IDT_PTR            ;Load IDT register
                                        ; to locate IDT in
                                        ; linear address space.
                                        ; Here, IDT is based at linear
                                        ; address FFFFC030h, and holds 256
                                        ; entries (2048 entries) the maximum
                                        ; size for the IDT, limit=07FFh.

            MOV      EAX, CR0           ;Prepare to alter CR0.
            OR       EAX, 00000001h     ;Set bit 0 (PE) in CR0 image.
            MOV      CR0, EAX           ;Enable PROTECTED mode.
```

Figure 11.1   32-bit PROTECTED **Mode Supervisor Initialization Code** *(Continued).*

```
;
;  Already in PROTECTED mode !
;
;  Now establish the large, 4 gigabyte data segments.
;
           MOV   AX,   0018h            ;0018h is selector for
                                        ; supervisor data segment.
           MOV   SS,   AX               ;Load segment selector in SS.
           MOV   DS,   AX               ;Load segment selector in DS.
           MOV   ES,   AX               ;Load segment selector in ES.
           MOV   FS,   AX               ;Load segment selector in FS.
           MOV   GS,   AX               ;Load segment selector in GS.

;
;  Now establish the large, 4 gigabyte code segment.
;
           JMP   DEST_OFFSET, DEST_SEL  ;Intersegment jump to load CS.
DEST:      MOV   ESP, 00400000h         ;Initialize ESP, typically to
                                        ; the top of physical memory.
                                        ; In this case, assuming 4 Mbyte
                                        ; physical memory, ESP is set to
                                        ; 0040000h (4,194,304 decimal).
                                        ; The stack grows downward.
;
;  Now establish the initial task state segment (the only TSS needed).
;  The TSS descriptor in EPROM must be marked "not busy" or a General
;  Protection exception (exception 13) will result from the LTR instruction
;  below.  The 80386 will write to the TSS descriptor marking it
;  "busy."  However, it doesn't check to be sure that the busy bit
;  became set, so having the GDT in EPROM is all right.
;
           LTR   SIMPLE_TSS_SEL
;
;  80386 32-bit supervisor/user initialization is complete
;

YOUR_SUPERVISOR:    ...                 ;your supervisor code begins here.
                    ...
                    ...

;
;  When the interrupt service routines are established, interrupts can
;  be enabled.  (Use STI instruction, for example.)
;

INITIAL    ENDS
```

Figure 11.1 *(Continued).*

```
INITIAL    SEGMENT  PUBLIC AT 0F000h

;
; Pointers defining the base address and size of the GDT and the IDT.
; These are used as operands of the LGDT and LIDT instructions, respectively.
;

           ORG      0BFF0h

GDT_PTR:   DW       002Fh          ;limit for 6 descriptor slots
           DW       C000h          ;base at FFFFC000h (bits 15:0)
           DW       FFFFh          ;base at FFFFC000H (bits 31:16)

IDT_PTR:   DW       07FFh          ;limit for up to 256 gates
           DW       C030h          ;base at FFFFC030h (bits 15:0)
           DW       FFFFh          ;base at FFFFC030h (bits 31:16)

           ORG      0C000h

GDT:                               ;Beginning of the GDT table.
GDT_0:                             ;Descriptor 0: Null descriptor. Not used.
           DD       00000000h      ;The null descriptor always in GDT
           DD       00000000h      ; slot 0, requires 8 bytes of 00h.

GDT_1:                   ;Descriptor 1: 32-bit Task State Segment (104 bytes)
           DW       0067h          ; limit 15..0  (limit 103 decimal).
           DW       8000h          ; base 15..0   (base is FFFF8000h).
           DB       FFh            ; base 23..16.
           DB       10001011b      ; access byte: 32-bit TSS, present,
                                   ; DPL=0, busy, accessed.
           DB       00000000b      ; granularity: byte, limit 19..16.
           DB       FFh            ; base 31..24.

GDT_2:         ;Descriptor 2: 32-bit Supervisor Code Segment (starts at 0 and extends
               ; for 4 gigabytes)
           DW       FFFFh          ; limit 15..0 (limit is FFFFF(FFF)hex).
           DW       0000h          ; base 15..0   (base is 00000000h).
           DB       FFh            ; base 23..16.
           DB       10011011b      ; access byte: 32-bit code segment,
                                   ; present, DPL=0, not conforming,
                                   ; readable, accessed.
           DB       10001111b      ; granularity: page,  limit 31..28.
           DB       FFh            ; base 31..24.

GDT_3:         ;Descriptor 3: 32-bit Supervisor Data Segment (starts at 0 and extends
               ; for 4 gigabytes)
           DW       FFFFh          ; limit 15..0 (limit is FFFFF(FFF)hex).
           DW       0000h          ; base 15..0   (base is 00000000h).
           DB       FFh            ; base 23..16.
           DB       10010011b      ; access byte: 32-bit data segment,
                                   ; present, DPL=0, expand up, writeable,
                                   ; accessed.
           DB       10001111b      ; granularity: page,  limit 31..28.
           DB       FFh            ; base 31..24.
```

Figure 11.2   GDT and IDT Images for Simple Protected 32-bit System *(Continued).*

```
GDT_4:                      ;Descriptor 4: 32-bit User Code Segment (starts at 0 and extends
                            ; for 4 gigabytes)
            DW      FFFFh           ; limit 15..0  (limit is FFFFF(FFF)hex).
            DW      0000h           ; base 15..0   (base is 00000000h).
            DB      FFh             ; base 23..16.
            DB      11111011b       ; access byte: 32-bit code segment,
                                    ; present, DPL=3, not conforming,
                                    ; readable, accessed.
            DB      10001111b       ; granularity: page,  limit 31..28.
            DB      FFh             ; base 31..24.


GDT_5:                          ;Descriptor 5: 32-bit User Data Segment (starts at 0 extends
                                ; for 4 gigabytes)
            DW      FFFFh           ; limit 15..0  (limit is FFFFF(FFF)hex).
            DW      0000h           ; base 15..0   (base is 00000000h).
            DB      FFh             ; base 23..16.
            DB      11110011b       ; access byte: 32-bit data segment,
                                    ; present, DPL=3, expand up, writeable,
                                    ; accessed.
            DB      10001111b       ; granularity: page,  limit 31..28.
            DB      FFh             ; base 31..24.


GDT_END:                            ;End of GDT table.


IDT:                                ;Beginning of the IDT table.
IDT_0:                              ;Gate 0: Trap Gate for Exception 0
            DW      XXXXh           ; offset 15..0 (points to entry pt).
            DW      0010h           ; selector 15..0 (refers to supervisor
                                    ; code segment).
            DB      00h             ; upper bits 000b, remainder unused.
            DB      11101111h       ; access byte: trap gate, present,
                                    ; DPL=3 (so user code can vector
                                    ; through the trap gate).
            DW      XXXXh           ; offset 31..16.


;
;  IDT Trap Gates 1 through 31 are the same as Trap Gate above, except
;  each gate may point to a unique entry point in the supervisor code
;  segment.
;
IDT_32:                             ;Gate 32: Interrupt Gate for
                                    ; Interrupt 32
            DW      XXXXh           ; offset 15..0 (points to entry pt).
            DW      0010h           ; selector 15..0 (refers to supervisor
                                    ; code segment).
            DB      00h             ; upper bits 000b, remainder unused.
            DB      11100101h       ; access byte: interrupt gate, present,
                                    ; DPL=3 (so user code can vector
                                    ; through the interrupt gate).
            DW      XXXXh           ; offset 31..16.
```

Figure 11.2 *(Continued).*

```
IDT_33:                                 ;Gate 33: Interrupt Gate for
                                        ; Interrupt 33
        DW      XXXXh                   ; offset 15..0 (points to entry pt).
        DW      0010h                   ; selector 15..0 (refers to supervisor
                                        ; code segment).
        DB      00h                     ; upper bits 000b, remainder unused.
        DB      11100101h               ; access byte: interrupt gate, present,
                                        ; DPL=3 (so user code can vector
                                        ; through the interrupt gate).
        DW      XXXXh                   ; offset 31..16.

;
;  IDT Interrupt Gates 34 through 255 are the same as Interrupt Gates above,
;  except each gate may point to a unique entry point in the supervisor
;  code segment.
;
IDT_END:                                ;End of the IDT Table.

INITIAL   ENDS
```

Figure 11.2 *(Continued).*

```
TABLEDATA  SEGMENT

TSS:                                    ;Beginning of the Task State Segment.
                                        ;This TSS is designed for the 32-bit
                                        ; simple protected system.  Most of its
                                        ; fields are zero since the simple
                                        ; system does not perform hardware
                                        ; multitasking, the operation which
                                        ; fully utilizes the TSS.
        DD      00000000h               ; back link selector
        DD      00400000h               ; ESP for level 0 (same as ESP initial-
                                        ; ization used in code (Figure 11.1).
        DW      0000h                   ; unused.
        DW      0018h                   ; selector for supervisor data segment
                                        ; that is used for supervisor stack seg.
        DD      00000000h               ; SS for level 1 (unused for this since privilege
                                        ; level 1 is unused.).
        DD      00000000h               ; ESP for level 1 (unused for this since privilege
                                        ; level 1 is unused.).
        DD      00000000h               ; SS for level 2 (unused for this since privilege
                                        ; level 2 is unused.).
        DD      00000000h               ; ESP for level 2 (unused for this since privilege
                                        ; level 2 is unused.).
        DD      00000000h               ; CR3 storage (unused for this since paging is not
                                        ; enabled).
        DD      00000000h               ; EIP storage (unused for this).
        DD      00000000h               ; EFLAGS storage (unused for this).
        DD      00000000h               ; EAX storage (unused for this).
        DD      00000000h               ; ECX storage (unused for this).
        DD      00000000h               ; EDX storage (unused for this).
        DD      00000000h               ; EBX storage (unused for this).
```

Figure 11.3   TSS Image for Simple Protected 32-bit System *(Continued).*

```
         DD     00000000h     ; ESP storage (unused for this).
         DD     00000000h     ; EBP storage (unused for this).
         DD     00000000h     ; ESI storage (unused for this).
         DD     00000000h     ; EDI storage (unused for this).
         DW     0000h         ; unused.
         DW     0000h         ; ES storage (unused for this).
         DW     0000h         ; unused.
         DW     0000h         ; CS storage (unused for this).
         DW     0000h         ; unused.
         DW     0000h         ; SS storage (unused for this).
         DW     0000h         ; unused.
         DW     0000h         ; DS storage (unused for this).
         DW     0000h         ; unused.
         DW     0000h         ; FS storage (unused for this).
         DW     0000h         ; unused.
         DW     0000h         ; GS storage (unused for this).
         DW     0000h         ; unused.
         DW     0000h         ; LDTR storage (unused for this).
         DW     0000h         ; upper 15 bits unused, lowest T bit
                              ; for trapping (unused for this).
         DW     FFFFh         ; I/O Permission Bitmap pointer
                              ; (unused for this).


TSS_END:                     ;End of the TSS.


TABLEDATA  ENDS
```

Figure 11.3 *(Continued).*

32-bit User Code and Data

User code is written as appropriate for the problem or application to be served.

Initially Dispatching a User-level Program

When the supervisor code is intended to dispatch a user program (i.e., begin execution of a user level program), control must be transferred with a RET or IRET instruction, much the same as a service routine terminates with an IRET instruction. However, since the user code has not actually called the supervisor level, the supervisor code must construct a stack frame on its stack.

The stack-frame requirements before executing the RET or IRET are depicted in Figure 11.4. Note that the stack frame shown must be the only frame on the supervisor stack when the RET or IRET is executed. This requirement allows the supervisor stack to be reestablished using the SS and ESP values contained in the TSS (see Figure 11.3).

Establishing the User Data Segment

The only consideration particularly needing mention occurs just before the supervisor dispatch of the user code. It is necessary that the supervisor MOVe the selector for the user-data segment to each segment register DS, ES, FS, and GS. The selector value is such that it references the descriptor for a user-level (level 3) data segment. By this action, the routine makes available a large user-data segment. As described by the data-segment descriptor in the GDT, the data segment is a 32-bit segment, since the descriptor D bit is 1. The data-segment descriptor appears as shown in Figure 8.3 and is listed as descriptor GDT_5 in Figure 11.2. This data segment descriptor indicates a base address of 00000000h and a limit of maximum size of FFFFFFFFh. The user-data segment therefore spans the entire four-gigabyte linear address space. The SS, DS, ES, FS, and GS registers all describe the same maximum-size segment.

The SS register is loaded with the selector to the user-data segment during the RET or IRET instruction used to dispatch the user program. The RET or IRET detects the privilege-level transition as it POPs the destination CS value from the stack frame. The destination CPL is determined in the lowest two bits of the CS selector. Upon reading a destination CPL value different from the current CPL, the 80386 detects that a level transition is intended. Because a separate stack is to be used at the destination privilege level, the 80386 therefore continues to POP more information from the stack, namely the destination ESP value and the destination SS selector.

Taking these considerations into account, an example of supervisor code appropriate for dispatching a user program is shown in Figure 11.5. The example builds a stack frame, loads DS, ES, FS, and GS with the selector to the user-data segment, and executes an IRET instruction to perform the dispatch. Note that the advantage of this approach is allowing the user code to be entirely unconcerned with the segment registers; the user data segment is accessible from the moment the user code begins execution. It would be possible, of course, to allow the user code to load the data-segment selector, but that is a clumsier approach, since it requires the user code to "know" the exact selector value needed.

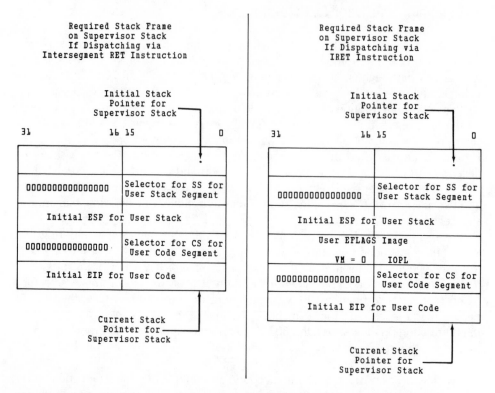

Figure 11.4 32-bit Supervisor Stack Frame Requirements Prior to Dispatching User Program.

```
;
; create a stack frame pointing to the user stack and code
;
        PUSHF                               ;Place EFLAGs on stack.
        SUB     ESP, 16                     ;Adjust ESP to accommodate remainder
                                            ; of the stack frame.
        MOV     [ESP+12], USER_STK_SEL     ;Build supervisor stack frame
        MOV     [ESP+8],  USER_STK_PTR     ; as shown in Figure 11.4 (left
        MOV     [ESP+4],  USER_CODE_SEL    ; illustration for RET instruction).
        MOV     [ESP],    USER_INSTR_PTR
        MOV     ESP, EBP
;
; establish user data segment in all data segment registers
;
        MOV     AX, USER_DATA_SEL          ;Selector for user data segment
        MOV     DS, AX                     ;Load segments DS, ES, FS, GS to
        MOV     ES, AX                     ; establish user data segment.
```

Figure 11.5 Supervisor Code to Dispatch User-level Program *(Continued)*.

```
        MOV     FS, AX
        MOV     GS, AX
;
;  now dispatch user-level (level 3) program
;
        IRET                            ;Dispatch user program per stack
                                        ; frame information.
```

Figure 11.5 *(Continued).*

When the user code subsequently invokes a service routine in the supervisor code, the supervisor routine should PUSH on its stack the values of any segment register it will use and, correspondingly at the end of the service routine, POP the original user-selector values back into the segment registers before executing an IRET to the user level.

PART 4

Virtual 8086 MODE

The VIRTUAL 8086 mode is a simple mechanism that allows a PROTECTED-mode supervisor program at privilege level 0 to dispatch an 8086 program, such as IBM Personal Computer programs, at the user level. The VIRTUAL 8086 mode therefore allows new 80386 systems, running 32-bit software, access to the large base of established PC software. With the VIRTUAL 8086 mode, 8086 software is executed in a manner subordinate to a PROTECTED-mode supervisor program at privilege level 0.

Simply because of its usefulness, the VIRTUAL 8086 feature is a likely addition to many 32-bit 80386 systems. Appendix G lists an actual, tested supervisor program that runs PC-DOS in VIRTUAL 8086 mode on any 80386 personal computer.

CHAPTER 12

THE VIRTUAL 8086 MODE

The previous chapter ended with coverage of how the 80386 supervisor level can dispatch a 32-bit user-level PROTECTED-mode program. In related fashion, the VIRTUAL 8086 mode is a simple mechanism that allows the supervisor level to dispatch an *8086 program* at the user level.

The 8086 programs dispatched, by utilizing VIRTUAL 8086 mode, can be any 8086 object code. It can be a single 8086 application program or even an 8086 operating system. The distinction does not matter, since all code executed in the VIRTUAL 8086 mode is assumed to be 8086 code. The VIRTUAL 8086 mode is completely 8086-compatible, in the same manner as 80386 REAL mode is 8086-compatible.

The Meaning of VIRTUAL 8086

Given the similarity of the REAL mode and the VIRTUAL 8086 mode, one must examine the distinction. In REAL mode, the 8086 program actually has control of the entire 80386, including the enabling/disabling of interrupts and the use of input/output instructions. In the VIRTUAL 8086 mode, the 8086 program is essentially *fooled* into "thinking" it has control of the entire 80386, although in fact the PROTECTED-mode supervisor has control over interrupts and input/output.

All virtual 8086 programs are executed at privilege level 3. This differs from REAL mode, which implicitly executes as if at privilege level 0 (all I/O is allowed, interrupts can be enabled/disabled). The lesser privilege of VIRTUAL-mode programs allows the PROTECTED-mode supervisor to retain ultimate control of the system.

When a VIRTUAL 8086 program is executing, at privilege level 3, most instructions proceed exactly as in the 8086-compatible REAL mode. However, instructions that attempt to view or alter the interrupt-flag bit or to perform input/output, cause a general-protection exception (exception 13), returning control to the supervisor program. The supervisor determines which instruction caused the exception and then appropriately emulates that instruction. The supervisor finally executes an IRET instruction to resume the 8086 program being executed in VIRTUAL 8086 mode. VIRTUAL mode operation continues at full speed until reaching the next restricted instruction.

Dispatching VIRTUAL 8086 Mode

Short of performing a task switch, a topic delayed until Chapter 15, the only way to dispatch (or resume) VIRTUAL 8086 mode is via an IRET instruction at privilege level 0. The technique is similar to the dispatch of a PROTECTED-mode user-level program, as shown in Figure 11.5. To dispatch a VIRTUAL 8086 mode program, however, the programmer sets the VM bit in the EFLAG image on the stack. The EFLAG images VM bit must be set to 1.

The IRET involved must be executed in PROTECTED mode at privilege level 0 because only at that level can that VM bit actually be set to 1 inside the 80386. At any lesser privilege level (1, 2, and 3), the VM bit remains 0, even if an EFLAG image on the stack contains a VM image of 1. The IRET must be in a 32-bit code segment (or in a 16-bit code segment with a operand-size prefix), so a 32-bit value is loaded into EFLAG. The VM bit occupies bit 17, within the upper word of EFLAG.

If, as the privilege level 0 IRET instruction reads the stack frame, it detects that the EFLAG image has VM = 1, the 80386 recognizes the intent to enter VIRTUAL 8086 mode. Therefore it assumes that the appropriate stack frame has been prepared, as shown in Figure 12.1.

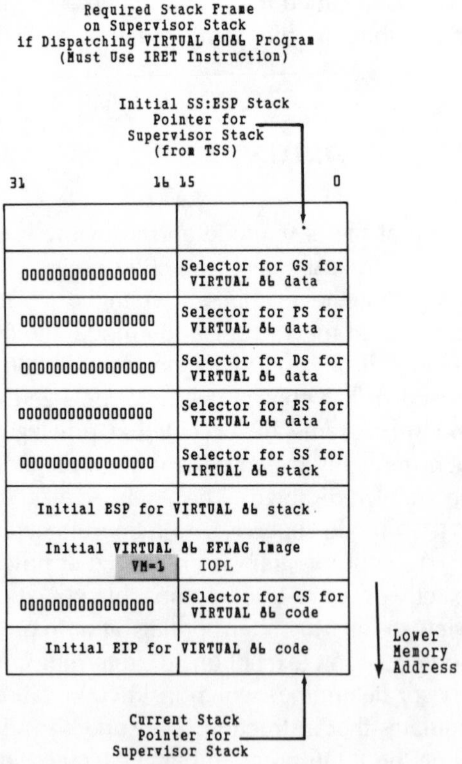

Figure 12.1   32-bit Supervisor Stack Frame Requirements Prior to Dispatching VIRTUAL 8086 Mode Program.

In the stack frame, the register values are those that will be initially used by the VIRTUAL 8086 program dispatched. The upper 16 bits of EIP and ESP should be zeros, as appropriate for 16-bit VIRTUAL 8086 operation. The stack-frame selector values for CS, SS, ES, DS, FS, and GS are read by the 80386, and segment-base addresses are generated as 16 times the selector values, the normal use of selector values by an 8086. The segment-base addresses are stored in the 80386 descriptor-cache register.

The 80386 then automatically establishes segment limits of FFFFh for each VIRTUAL 8086 segment, in accordance with 8086 characteristics, and stores the 64K limit in its internal descriptor-cache registers. The 80386 also establishes access rights in accordance with 8086 operation and stores them in its internal descriptor-cache registers. All VIRTUAL 8086 segments are given access rights for readability and writability. The segment limit and access rights are not altered during VIRTUAL 8086 mode.

Details of Entering VIRTUAL 8086 Mode via IRET Instruction

When the EFLAG image in the stack frame is set to 1, the level-0 IRET instruction will enter VIRTUAL 8086 mode with the following steps (assuming the NT bit in the EFLAG image is reset to 0 to avoid a task switch):

1. Read the EFLAGS image from the stack, SS:[ESP + 8], into the EFLAGS register. If the EFLAGS image has VM set to 1, this will set VM in the 80386.
2. POP off the VIRTUAL 8086 mode instruction-pointer CS:EIP. EIP is POPped first, then a 32-bit word is POPped that contains CS in the lower 16 bits. If VM equals 1, the load of CS will be performed as a REAL-mode segment load.
3. Increment the ESP register by 4 to bypass the EFLAGS image that was POPped in Step 1.
4. If VM equals 1, load the VIRTUAL 8086 mode segment registers ES, DS, FS, and GS from stack locations SS:[ESP + 8], SS:[ESP + 12], SS:[ESP + 16] and SS:[ESP + 20], respectively, where the new value of ESP stored in Step 3 is used. Since VM equals 1, these segment-register loads will be performed as REAL-mode segment loads.
5. POP the VIRTUAL 8086 mode stack pointer SS:ESP from the stack. ESP is POPped first, followed by 32 bits containing SS in the lower 16 bits. Since VM equals 1, the load of SS will be performed as a REAL-mode segment load.
6. Begin (or resume) execution of the VIRTUAL 8086 program as a level 3 program.

Operation in VIRTUAL 8086 Mode

In VIRTUAL 8086 mode, the data-operand size and address size default to 16 bits, as in the REAL mode. The few 80386 features available in REAL mode, such as the additional prefixes and the additional segment registers, FS and GS, are also available in the VIRTUAL 8086 mode.

Segment-register loads are handled as in REAL mode: the selector value is multiplied by 16 and directly establishes the base address of the segment, which the 80386 stores in its internal descriptor-cache register for the segment. Just as in REAL mode, the segment limit and access rights are not affected by segment-register loads: they remain as FFFFh and readable/writable, respectively.

Instruction Trapping in VIRTUAL 8086 Mode

Depending upon the IOPL level during VIRTUAL 8086 mode, established in bits 13 and 12 of the EFLAG image of the IRET stack frame, certain 8086 instructions will cause an exception. Since the VIRTUAL 8086 program is executed as a privilege-level 3 program, IOPL values of 2, 1, or 0 have a restrictive effect upon certain instructions during VIRTUAL 8086 mode.

If IOPL is 2, 1, or 0, the CLI, STI, PUSHF, POPF, and INT *n* instructions cause a general-protection exception (exception 13) when they occur during VIRTUAL 8086 operation. If the PROTECTED-mode supervisor establishes one of these IOPL values, the VIRTUAL 8086 program is forbidden from directly viewing or altering the interrupt flag. An IOPL value of 3 allows the VIRTUAL 8086 program to execute these instructions unhindered.

In similar manner, the IN, INS, REP INS, OUT, OUTS, and REP OUTS instructions will cause a general-protection exception (exception 13) unless the I/O permission bitmap permits I/O to the specific I/O address involved. The I/O permission bitmap allows very specific control of I/O, allowing I/O to be controlled on a port-by-port basis. The bitmap, an optional extension to each 32-bit TSS, is illustrated in Figure 12.3. To summarize, *note that, during VIRTUAL 8086 operation, IOPL does not affect the ability to execute I/O instructions. The I/O permission bitmap has sole control over I/O permission during VIRTUAL 8086 mode.*

Short of performing a task switch, the general-protection exception (exception 13) must be handled by an interrupt gate or trap gate that points to a privilege level 0 code segment (i.e., to the supervisor level). When such an exception occurs, the supervisor code emulates the instruction, advances the stack frame's EIP past the instruction just emulated, and executes an IRET to resume the VIRTUAL 8086 program.

Of course, the PROTECTED-mode instructions executable only at privilege level 0 are not available in the VIRTUAL 8086 mode. Attempts to execute these instructions cause a general-protection exception (exception 13). However, as a practical matter, existing 8086 programs do not attempt to execute such instructions, since those opcodes and the PROTECTED-mode registers are not implemented on the 8086.

Leaving VIRTUAL **8086 Mode**

The 80386 leaves VIRTUAL 8086 mode only on receipt of an exception (such as one due to a sensitive instruction) or an interrupt. These events vector via a trap gate or an interrupt gate to a privilege-level 0 code segment for service. All exceptions and interrupts are vectored through the PROTECTED-mode IDT, not through the 8086-style interrupt table.

The privilege-level 0 stack after an interrupt during VIRTUAL 8086 mode is shown in Figure 12.2, at left. This is of course exactly the same as Figure 12.1, since an IRET instruction is used in both cases to dispatch the VIRTUAL 8086 program.

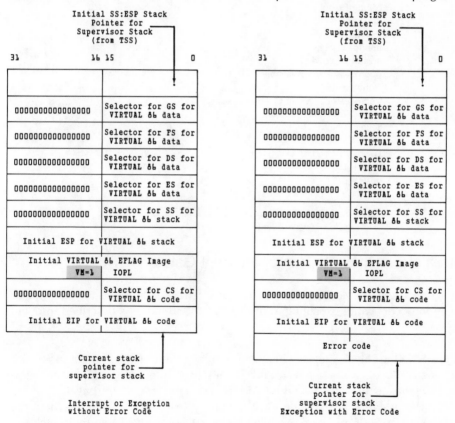

Figure 12.2   Privilege level 0 stack after Interrupt or Exception during VIRTUAL **8086 Mode.**

The privilege-level 0 stack after an exception during VIRTUAL 8086 mode is also shown in Figure 12.2. Depending on the exception type, the stack may appear with or without an error code. Any given exception number behaves consistently; either it always PUSHes an error code or it never does, as summarized in Table 12.1. Generally, exceptions that refer to specific segments PUSH an error code. The exception for page faults also PUSHes an error code. More information on exceptions and interrupts, including the exact format of the error code, is the topic of Chapter 16.

Table 12.1 Exception Error Code Summary.

Exception Description	Number (Decimal)	Error Code
Divide Error	0	No
Debug Exceptions	1	No
Breakpoint	3	No
Overflow	4	No
Bounds Check	5	No
Invalid Opcode	6	No
Coprocessor Not Available	7	No
Double Fault	8	Yes*
Coprocessor Segment Overrun	9	Yes
Invalid Task State Segment	10	Yes
Segment Not Present	11	Yes
Stack Exception	12	Yes
General Protection Exception	13	Yes
Page Fault	14	Yes
(reserved)	15	n/a
Coprocessor Numeric Error	16	No
(reserved)	17–31	n/a

*Error code is always 0000000h

Details of Exit through Trap or Interrupt Gates

The action taken by the 80386 for a trap or interrupt gate when an interrupt or exception occurs while executing in the VIRTUAL 8086 mode is described in detail below.

1. Save the EFLAGS register in a temporary register to PUSH on the supervisor stack later. Reset the VM and TF bits to 0 internally, and, if the interrupt/exception is serviced by an interrupt gate, reset IF to 0 also.
2. The interrupt or trap gate must perform a level switch from 3, where the VIRTUAL 8086 program executes, to level 0, so an IRET can redispatch the VIRTUAL 8086 mode program at the end of the service routine. The process involves a stack switch to the level 0 stack found in the TSS for privilege-

level 0 (See Figure 12.3). Save the VIRTUAL 8086 mode SS and ESP registers in temporary storage to PUSH in a later step. The segment register load of the level 0 SS is performed as a PROTECTED-mode segment load, since the VM bit was reset above.

3. Onto the level 0 stack, PUSH in order GS, FS, DS, and ES. Each of these registers is PUSHed as a 32-bit quantity to keep the stack aligned. The upper 16 bits of each value are 0. Then load these four registers with null selectors (0) internally, to prevent use of the old values by the level-0 routine.

4. PUSH the SS register as a 32-bit value, upper 16 bits 0. PUSH the 32-bit ESP register.

5. PUSH the 32-bit EFLAGS register saved internally in Step 1.

6. PUSH the CS register as a 32-bit value, upper 16 bits 0. PUSH the 32-bit EIP register.

7. Load the new CS and EIP from the interrupt or trap gate. The segment-register load of CS will be performed as a PROTECTED-mode segment load, since the VM bit was reset above. Begin execution of the level-0 service routine in PROTECTED mode.

The I/O Permission Bitmap in VIRTUAL 8086 Mode

The input/output instructions (IN, INS, REP INS, OUT, OUTS, REP, and OUTS) are *not* IOPL-sensitive in the VIRTUAL 8086 mode. Rather, these instructions become automatically sensitive to the *I/O Permission Bitmap*, an optional component of the 32-bit task- state segment. The I/O permission bitmap is shown in Figures 12.3 and 12.4.

As Figure 12.3 illustrates, the I/O permission bitmap is a bit map contained in a 32-bit task state segment. The size of the map and its location in the TSS segment are variable. It begins in memory at Bit_Map_Offset in the TSS. The 16-bit value Bit_Map_Offset 15 . . . 0 is found at offset 102 (decimal) in the fixed portion of the 32-bit TSS, as shown in Figure 12.3. Bit_Map_Offset should have a value of 104 (decimal) or greater to avoid conflict with the fixed portion of the TSS. From its base offset (Bit_Map_Offset), the I/O permission bitmap continues for 8K bytes or until the TSS limit, whichever is less.

Due to the use of a pointer to the base of the I/O permission bitmap, the bit map may be located anywhere within the TSS or may be ignored completely by pointing the Bit_Map_Offset beyond the limit of the TSS segment. By adjusting the TSS limit to truncate the bit map, only a small lower portion of the 64K I/O space need have an associated bit map. This eliminates the commitment of 8K of memory, while allowing the fully general case if desired.

Each bit in the bit map represents the I/O permission for a BYTE-wide port in the I/O space, from port 0 to port 66535. If a bit is 0, I/O to the corresponding BYTE-wide port can occur in VIRTUAL 8086 mode without generating an exception. If a bit is 1 or if the corresponding bit is beyond the limit of the TSS segment, the attempted I/O instruction causes a general protection exception (exception 13).

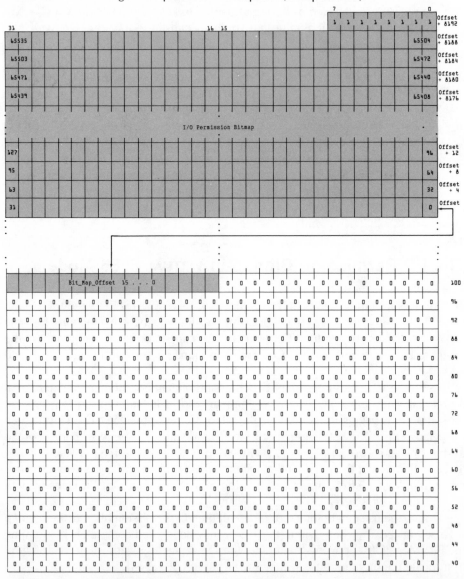

Figure 12.3   32-bit TSS for Simple Protected Systems with Complete I/O Permission Bitmap *(Continued)*.

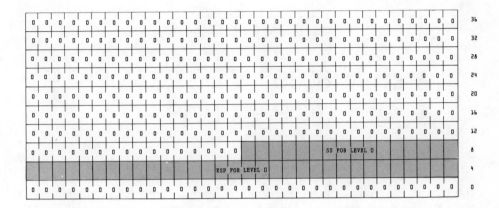

Figure 12.3 *(Continued).*

For a WORD-wide I/O port, both of the corresponding bits must be 0 for the I/O to occur successfully; for a DWORD-wide I/O port, all four of the corresponding bits must be 0 for the I/O to occur successfully.

To correctly implement the I/O permission bitmap, a byte of FFh is required beyond the last byte of I/O mapping information. The FFh byte must be within the TSS segment limit. The FFh byte is required because the 80386 internal algorithm reads *two* bytes of the I/O bit map whenever referencing the bit map.

Figure 12.4 presents an example I/O permission bitmap. As the 0 bits correspond to BYTE-wide I/O ports where I/O is permitted, this figure illustrates accessible ports 2–9, 12, 13, 15, 20–24, 27, 33, 34, 40, 41, 48, 50, 52, 53, 58–60, 62, 63, and 96–127.

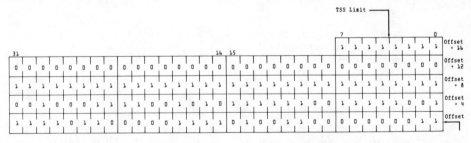

Figure 12.4   Example 16-byte I/O Permission Bitmap.

CHAPTER 13

VIRTUAL 8086 MODE EXAMPLE
FOR PC-DOS

The VIRTUAL 8086 mode allows any 8068 software to be executed within a 80386 PROTECTED mode. As Table 13.1 lists, a host of practical functions can result from the VIRTUAL 8086 mode, and as this example actually demonstrates, PC-DOS can be the software executed in VIRTUAL 8086 mode, on any 80386-based personal computer. The example, dispatched as a command in a PC-DOS environment, lends itself to experimentation by any programmer with access to an 80386-based personal computer.

Table 13.1   Practical Functions of VIRTUAL 8086 Supervisors.

1. Create multiple DOS environments for multitasking and background processing.

2. Transparently to DOS, simulate paging hardware of EMS and EEMS expanded memory boards, providing EMS/EEMS compatibility on 80386-based systems without additional paging hardware.

3. Support dissimilar 8086 operating systems simultaneously, for example PC-DOS and CP/M.

4. Support 8086 operating system(s) under Protected 32-bit operating system, for example, PC-DOS under UNIX.

This example software is a simple PROTECTED mode supervisor program activated from the keyboard by name, as a DOS command. In other words, the example supervisor program is run as a typical application from the DOS prompt. As the software executes, it causes the 80386 to enter a PROTECTED mode task at privilege level 0, and then RETurns control to PC-DOS in VIRTUAL mode at privilege level 3. From the DOS user's standpoint, Figure 13.1, DOS continues to behave as normal, proving the point that VIRTUAL 8086 mode allows the 8086 software to function compatibly even though the 80386 host computer is, ultimately, under the control of a PROTECTED mode supervisor program at privilege level 0.

1. PC-DOS prompt on 80386-based personal computer.

2. User types name of VIRTUAL 8086 supervisor program.

3. Supervisor program completes in fraction of a second. DOS prompt returns as DOS resumes but now 80386 is running in VIRTUAL 8086 mode. User notices no difference.

Figure 13.1   VIRTUAL 8086 Mode, Properly Utilized, is User-Transparent.

The example explores the mechanism of establishing the PROTECTED mode environment, a prerequisite for beginning PROTECTED mode operation. As soon as the supervisor program begins execution, it creates a Global Descriptor Table, an Interrupt Descriptor Table, and a Task State Segment including an I/O Permission Bitmap to be used by the 80386 in PROTECTED mode. For a simple supervisor program, the I/O Permission Bitmap is filled with 1's allowing unrestricted input/output to all ports. Having established these necessary data structures, the supervisor enables the PROTECTED mode.

The PROTECTED mode environment created by the example supervisor is a task. Its main purpose is to resume DOS as a VIRTUAL 8086 mode program. Naturally, the memory used for the newly-created GDT, IDT, and TSS must not be overwritten when DOS continues, so DOS is resumed by this supervisor executing a RET instruction to the entry point of the DOS interrupt routine for "Terminate But Stay Resident in Memory" (interrupt 39). The Terminate But Stay Resident routine prevents DOS from re-allocating memory where the PROTECTED mode supervisor resides.

Details of the RETurn to the Terminate But Stay Resident routine are quite interesting. In immediate preparation for the RETurn, the supervisor fabricates on the DOS stack a stack frame as if the program has just signaled a "Terminate But Stay Resident" interrupt 39 from REAL mode. For this purpose, the supervisor places a frame of six bytes (FLAG, CS and IP) on the DOS stack. The exact values are not important, since the routine is that for program termination. DOS will adjust the DOS stack pointer to free the six bytes of stackspace.

The supervisor then actually resumes DOS, running in VIRTUAL 8086 mode, beginning with the entry point of DOS interrupt 39. For maximum speed, the RETurn is performed simply as an interlevel RET instruction; there need be no separate task for the VIRTUAL 8086 program. To perform this initial RET to VIRTUAL 8086 mode conveniently, the supervisor places the CS and IP values for the interrupt 39 routine into a stack frame on the privilege level 0 stack, initializes the SS and SP stack images to point to the DOS stack, sets the VM flag bit of the EFLAG image in the stack and executes a RET instruction to accomplish the level transfer and begin VIRTUAL 8086 mode execution. DOS therefore resumes with the first instruction of the Terminate But Stay Resident routine, and as far as DOS can discern, the interrupt routine was invoked in normal fashion, by an INT 39 instruction from an application program in REAL mode.

Once the supervisor program has caused DOS to resume (in VIRTUAL 8086 mode of course), this example supervisor executes only for brief instances thereafter. Specifically, the supervisor executes for a brief moment each time a hardware or software interrupt occurs, but it executes merely to direct execution to the DOS routine for the interrupt that occurred. It performs this in much the same manner as when activating the Terminate But Stay Resident routine to initially start DOS in VIRTUAL 8086 mode. The only distinction is that the FLAG, CS and IP values placed on the DOS stack must be accurate, since DOS will use those values when returning from the interrupt service routine.

Listing of the VIRTUAL Mode Supervisor

The listing in Appendix G is a complete, fully verified example for enabling the PROTECTED mode, and running a program, DOS, in VIRTUAL 8086 mode. This code can be assembled using an 8086-style assembler since the few PROTECTED mode opcodes required have been defined using DB statements.

Enhancement Options

The example supervisor establishes a PROTECTED mode "base camp of operations" to which additional features can be added. For example, 80386 page tables, as described in Chapter 9, can be created and paging subsequently enabled.

On 80386-based personal computers, a very practical use of 80386 paging capabilities is in *simulating* the paging hardware built onto the extended memory boards (EMS or EEMS boards) available for 8088- or 80286-based PC's. The paging hardware contained on such boards are controlled by registers addressed as I/O ports. By using the 80386 I/O Permission Bitmap to prevent I/O to those addresses, attempted I/O to the control registers of those boards will cause a General Protection fault (exception 13 fault) to interrupt routine 13 of the PROTECTED mode supervisor.

The service routine in the supervisor can emulate the mapping function of an EMS or EEMS card by appropriately adjusting the 80386 page tables. Such a routine maps the required physical memory to the logical addresses assigned to the extended memory cards. With an approach like that, DOS applications can continue using extended memory without the need for external paging hardware.

Although perfectly well supported by the 80386 hardware, providing *multiple* Virtual 8086 environments becomes a significantly more complex job for the supervisor software. Input/output and interrupts must be managed by the supervisor to avoid conflicts or deadlock among the multiple 8086 environments. A more complex supervisor program, especially if it were managing multiple Virtual 8086 environments, would probably take more sophisticated actions than shown by the example code of Appendix G, which merely reflects interrupts. The sophisticated actions typically serve to coordinate the access to peripheral devices being used by two or more independent 8086 environments.

PART 5

PROTECTED MODE IN MORE DEPTH

The basic use of the 80386 for a simple protected 32-bit system was covered in Part 3. Part 4 then described the innovative and exciting VIRTUAL 8086 mode. Yet, as capable as those functions are, the 80386 offers additional interesting features.

This section pushes ahead to cover the more advanced and more intricate features of the 80386, including:

- A complete exposition of the descriptor tables and their contents
- The built-in support for multitasking and task switching
- A complete coverage of interrupt and exception handling
- The extensive debugging facilities built into each 80386

These features complete our picture of the 80386 architecture. The in-depth look at descriptor tables and their contents leads into coverage of the built-in multitasking capabilities. The interrupt and exception chapter is an essential reference for understanding all the operations of the 80386. Finally, the debug features available for 16-bit or 32-bit programs, REAL or PROTECTED mode, are of interest to all programmers.

CHAPTER 14

DESCRIPTOR TABLES
AND THEIR CONTENTS

This chapter contains a complete exposition of the 80386 descriptor tables and their contents. Chapter 8 introduced descriptors, gates, and descriptor tables of a simple protected 32-bit system. However, several other types of descriptors, gates, and descriptor tables are also recognized. This chapter summarizes and comprehensively describes the purpose and format of all descriptors and gates.

Purpose of Segment Descriptors

Segment descriptors for code and data describe, in a compact notation "understood" by the 80386, the essential segments existing in the memory—that is, code and data segments. Code segments and data segments are given separate descriptor types, since only code segments are executable and since, for proper system protection, a different set of attributes is desired for executable code than for data.

Providing descriptors for task-state segments (TSS) allows multiple TSSs to exist, a feature that allows 80386 support for multitasking. The currently active task is indicated by the selector currently in the task register (TR) and the TSS descriptor referenced by that selector value. This is further described in Chapter 15.

In similar manner, providing descriptors for local descriptor tables (LDT) allows multiple LDTs to exist. This lets each task in the 80386 multitasking architecture have its private local address space. The currently active local address space is indicated by the selector currently in the LDT register (LDTR) and the LDT descriptor referenced by that selector value.

Purpose of Gates

Gates provide only *redirection* of control to a feature in the address space, such as to a certain code segment or to a certain task. Call gates, trap gates, and interrupt gates specify an *entry point* into a code segment; task gates reference a *task*. Specifying a gate as the operand of an instruction results in control being redirected to the destination specified by the gate. The redirection function is needed in its own right, for there is often a need to create multiple entry points referencing a given segment or a given task.

Gates placed in the IDT allow the specified entry points to be accessed via the processor's hardware interrupt mechanism or via software interrupt instructions: INT *n*, INTO, BOUND instructions, and exceptions. For that purpose, the trap gate and the interrupt gate refer to a code segment within the current task, that is, using the GDT and the current LDT. The task gate refers to a task-state segment and requires the 80386 to perform an automatic task switch to reach the destination task (see Chapter 15).

Gates placed in the GDT or LDT allow entry points to be accessed using CALL instructions. For that purpose, call gates refer to a code segment within the current task. Task gates refer to a task-state segment; the 80386 performs an automatic task switch to reach the destination task (see Chapter 15).

Segment Descriptor Types and Formats

Segment descriptors are special 8-byte datatypes required in PROTECTED mode. They describe the base address, size, and attributes of segments. There are four types of segment descriptors: **code-segment descriptors**, **data-segment descriptors**, **task-state-segment descriptors**, and **local-descriptor-table descriptors**. The purpose of each type is further described on page 163.

All descriptors bear certain similarities with each other. The internal format of all descriptors contains a base address, a limit value, and other attribute information.

As for segments themselves, both 16-bit and 32-bit segments are provided for code segments, data segments, and task-state segments. The descriptors for code segments contain a default (D) bit, indicating whether the segment is a 16-bit segment (D = 0) or a 32-bit (D = 1) segment. When D equals 0, the entire upper word of the descriptor should be 0, in conformance with the definition of the format for a 16-bit descriptor. Code-segment and data-segment descriptors have a B (big) bit, which can be set to indicate a large segment size; 32-bit data descriptors typically have B equal to 1, indicating support for segment sizes up to four gigabytes. The descriptors for task-state segments distinguish 32-bit TSSs from 16-bit TSSs.

Taking into account the various segment types, 16-bit sizes and 32-bit sizes, there are seven descriptor formats, for:

    32-bit code segments
    16-bit code segments
    32-bit data segments
    16-bit data segments
    32-bit task state segments
    16-bit task state segments
    local descriptor tables

Figures 14.1 through 14.4 illustrate all descriptors.

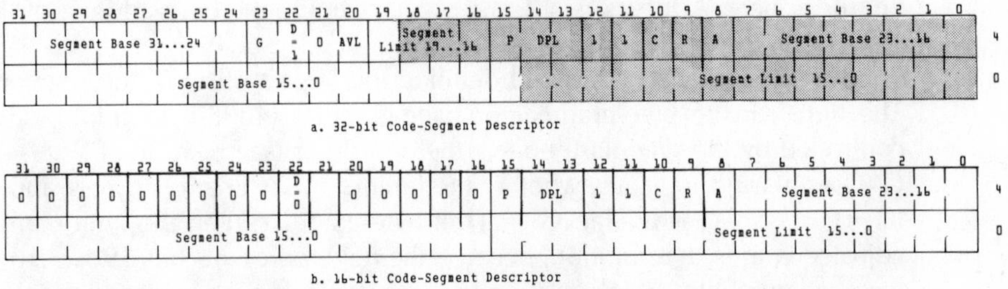

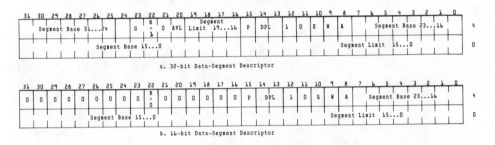

a. 32-bit Code-Segment Descriptor

b. 16-bit Code-Segment Descriptor

Figure 14.1 Descriptors for 32-bit Code Segments and 16-bit Code Segments.

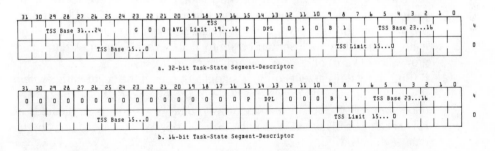

a. 32-bit Data-Segment Descriptor

b. 16-bit Data-Segment Descriptor

Figure 14.2 Descriptors for 32-bit Data Segment and 16-bit Data Segments.

a. 32-bit Task-State Segment-Descriptor

b. 16-bit Task-State Segment-Descriptor

Figure 14.3 Descriptors for 32-bit and 16-bit Task State Segments.

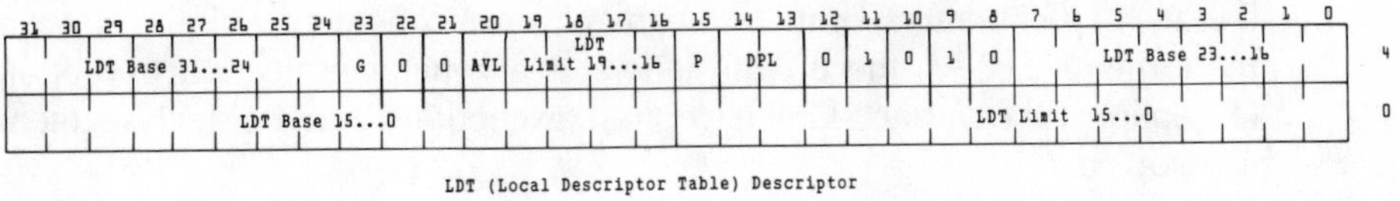

LDT (Local Descriptor Table) Descriptor

Figure 14.4 Descriptor for LDT (Local Descriptor Table).

Definitions of the Descriptor fields are as follows:

1. **Segment Base Address** is a 32-bit value defining the base address of the segment in the linear address space.
2. **Segment Limit** is a 20-bit field defining the largest offset of the segment. The limit can be byte-granular or page-granular (4096-byte-granular), as controlled by the granularity bit of the descriptor (see next item).
3. **G (Granularity)** indicates whether the limit of the segment is byte-granular (G = 0), or page-granular (G = 1). If byte-granular, then the limit can be adjusted with byte resolution, because the field represents bits 19 . . . .10 of the maximum allowable offset, up to 1 megabyte. If page-granular, the limit can be adjusted with page resolution, because the field represents bits 31 . . . 12 of the maximum allowable offset, up to 4 gigabytes.
4. **D (Default)** indicates whether the segment is a 32-bit segment (D = 1) or a 16-bit segment (D = 0). If D equals 1, the descriptor format for code segments and data segments is as shown in Figure 8.2 and Figure 8.3 respectively. If D equals 0, the descriptor format is that used by 80286 PROTECTED mode for 16-bit segments, as covered in Chapter 14. By default 32-bit code provides 32-bit data-operand size and 32-bit address size. By default, 16-bit code provides 16-bit data-operand size and 16-bit address size (80286 PROTECTED mode-compatible).
5. **E (Expansion Direction)**, for data segments only, indicates whether the segment exists in the range of addresses from the segment base up to its limit, inclusive (E = 0), or from the maximum offset down to the limit, exclusive (E = 1). Most data segments (such as segments B and D on page 97) have 0 in this bit, for *expand up*. A data segment that supports a dynamically expandable stack should be set to 1, for *expand down*. A data stack grows downward, of course, toward lesser addresses.
6. **B (Big)**, for data segments only, is significant only if the segment is *expand down*. B indicates the maximum offset of the expand-down segment. The maximum offset of an expand-down data segment is indicated as FFFFFFFFh (B = 1) or as 0000FFFFh (B = 0). B is a *don't care* for *expand up* data segments.
7. **Access Rights** indicate the allowable forms of access to the segment, including the privilege-level requirements and the write and read protection. If usage of an operand within the segment is not consistent with the allowable forms of access, the 80386 generates a general protection exception (exception 13) or a stack-fault exception (exception 12) if the stack segment is involved.
7a. **P (Present)** indicates whether the segment is present in physical memory (P = 1) or not present (P = 0). This bit allows the declaration of many large segments, perhaps only a subset of which are completely or partially present in physical memory at any one time. The paging system allows any

segment to be loaded on a page basis. Even if P = 1, the segment need not be entirely present. Many pages of a virtually present segment could actually be out on disk.

7b. **DPL (Descriptor Privilege Level)** indicates the privilege level of the segment as a number, 0 through 3, in the following way:

DPL Field	Description
00	Level 0 most-privileged (supervisor, kernel)
01	Level 1
10	Level 2
11	Level 3 least-privileged (user)

The DPL privilege level of the current code segment indicates the *Current Privilege Level* (CPL) of operation. For example, if the processor is executing a code segment of DPL 0, it is executing at a CPL of 0, the most-privileged level, the supervisor level.

7c. **A (Accessed)** indicates whether the segment has been accessed (A = 1) or not (A = 0) since the last time this bit of the descriptor was reset. A system that implements segment swapping can use this bit to determine segment usage. Typical simpler systems swap pages, not segments, and this bit would not be of interest on such systems.

7d. **R (Readable)**, for code segments only, indicates whether the code segment is readable (R = 1) or not (R = 0). Code segments are of course always executable. The R attribute can provide extra security by forbidding software to read from the code segment using the CS override prefix (see page 44 and Figure 3.1). This can prevent user piracy of object code resident in memory.

7e. **C (Conforming)**, for code segments only, indicates whether the CPL changes when the segment is called from a level of lesser privilege (C = 0) or not (C = 1). If C equals 1, then the code segment is said to be a conforming code segment, because the value of CPL does not change when this code segment is CALLed. Conforming code segments are probably the most abstract concept of the PROTECTED-mode architecture. In a simple protected 32-bit system, all code segments are regular, i.e., not conforming.

7f. **W (Writable)**, for data segments only, indicates whether the data segment is writable (W = 1) or not (W = 0). Data segments are of course always readable. The W attribute provides security by prohibiting any changes to the data. This specialized feature is applicable, for example, to segments containing important status information or to a publicly accessible data base. In a simple protected 32-bit system, the data segment serves all purposes and contains the stack, among other things; the data segment in a very simple system must therefore be writable.

Gate Types and Formats

Gates are special eight-byte datatypes required in PROTECTED mode as redirection devices or vectoring devices. There are four types of gates, with each type performing a slightly different form of redirection. The four types of gates are **call gates**, **trap gates**, **interrupt gates**, and **task gates**. The specific purpose of each, which is covered further on page 163-164, is generally indicated by the name.

The overall format of all gate types is identical, containing in each case a *selector*, referencing either a code-segment descriptor or a TSS descriptor, an *offset value*, determining the entry point (initial EIP value) into the selected segment, and *usage information*. Note that the task gate contains an offset field, which is not used since the referenced TSS supplies the EIP value.

Distinctions are made between 16-bit gates and 32-bit gates in the cases of call, trap, and interrupt gates, in that the two types of gate have different attribute fields.

Taking into account the various gate types, 16-bit sizes, and 32-bit sizes, there are seven gate formats for:

32-bit call gates
16-bit call gates
32-bit trap gates
16-bit trap gates
32-bit interrupt gates
16-bit interrupt gates
task gates

Figures 14.5 through 14.8 illustrate all gates.

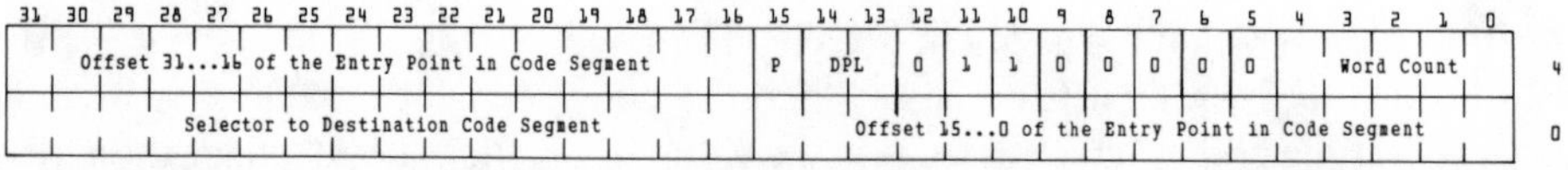

a. Call Gate to 32-bit Code-Segment Descriptor

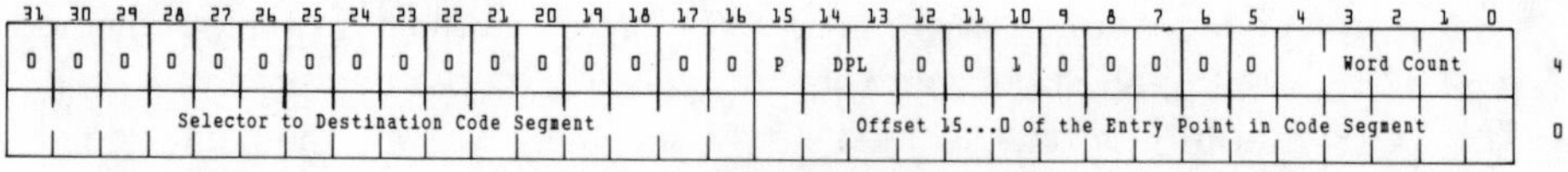

b. Call Gate to 16-bit Code Segment Descriptor

Figure 14.5 32-bit and 16-bit Call Gates.

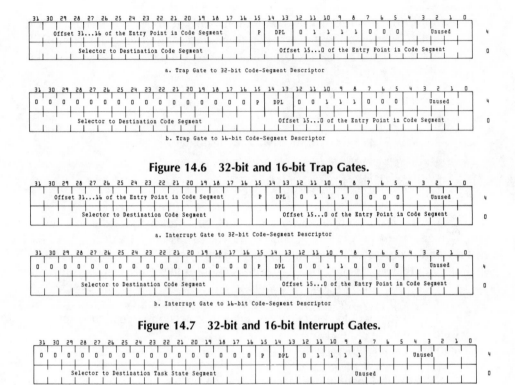

Figure 14.6 32-bit and 16-bit Trap Gates.

Figure 14.7 32-bit and 16-bit Interrupt Gates.

Figure 14.8 Task Gate for 32-bit or 16-bit TSS.

Definitions of the call gate, trap gate, and interrupt gate fields are as follows:

1. **Selector to Destination Code Segment** identifies the code segment containing the destination routine. This selector must reference a code segment.
2. **Offset of the Entry Point in Code Segment** identifies the entry point within the destination routine.
3. **Access Rights** are several bits indicating the allowable forms of access to the gate, including presence and privilege-level requirements. If usage of the gate is not consistent with the requirements, the 80386 generates a general-protection exception (exception 13) or a stack exception (exception 12) if the stack segment is involved.
3a. **P (Present)**, indicates whether the gate is available for use (P = 1) or not (P = 0). For successful vectoring, the gate must be present.
3b. **DPL (Descriptor Privilege Level)**, indicates the privilege level of the gate. *A hardware interrupt may always vector through a trap or interrupt gate if it is marked present, regardless of the gate's DPL.* DPL applies only to CALL

instructions for a call gate and to software interrupts (the INT *n*, INTO, BOUND instructions, and exceptions) for trap gates or interrupt gates. DPL indicates the privilege level of the gate as a number, 0, 1, 2 or 3, in the following way:

DPL Field	Description
00	Level 0 most-privileged (supervisor, kernel)
01	Level 1
10	Level 2
11	Level 3 least-privileged (user)

For a CALL instruction, a software interrupt, or an exception, the instruction using the gate must have a CPL at least as privileged as the DPL of the gate. For example, if the processor is executing a code segment of DPL 3 (i.e., it is executing at a current privilege level of 3), a CALL instruction in that code can use only call gates of DPL 3, and software interrupts can use only trap or interrupt gates of DPL 3. Any other value of gate DPL (i.e., 2, 1, or 0) would indicate greater privilege, and successful vectoring would not occur. A general-protection exception (exception 13) would instead be generated.

Definitions of the task gate fields are as follows:

1. **Selector to Destination Task State Segment** identifies the task state segment containing the destination routine. This selector must reference a task-state segment (either 32- or 16-bit TSS). The task gate contains no offset field, since the TSS itself contains the EIP value to be used.
2. **Access Rights** indicate the allowable forms of access to the gate, including presence and privilege-level requirements. If usage of the task gate is not consistent with the requirements, the 80386 generates a general-protection exception (exception 13) or a stack exception (exception 12) if a stack segment is involved. If the task-state segment itself is not correct, the 80386 generates an exception 10.
2a. **P (Present)**, indicates whether the task gate is available for use (P = 1) or not (P = 0). For successful vectoring, the gate must be present.
2b. **DPL (Descriptor Privilege Level)** indicates the privilege level of the gate. A *hardware interrupt may always vector through a task gate if it is marked present, regardless of the gate's DPL.* DPL applies only to software interrupts (the INT *n*, INTO, BOUND instructions, and exceptions). DPL indicates the privilege level of the gate as a number, 0, 1, 2, or 3, in the following way:

DPL Field	Description
00	Level 0 most-privileged (supervisor, kernel)
01	Level 1
10	Level 2
11	Level 3 least-privileged (user)

For a software interrupt (or exception), the instruction using the interrupt must have a CPL at least as privileged as the DPL of the gate. For example, if the processor is executing a code segment of DPL 3 (i.e., it is executing at a current privilege level of 3), a software interrupt instruction in that code can use only task gates of DPL 3. Any other value of DPL (i.e., 2, 1, or 0) would indicate greater privilege, and successful vectoring to the task would not occur. A general-protection exception (exception 13) would instead be generated.

Descriptor Tables

Descriptor tables are memory-resident arrays, containing in each element a descriptor or a gate. The 80386 supports three types of descriptor tables: *the global-descriptor table*, *the local-descriptor table*, and *the interrupt-descriptor table*.

Two of these tables, the GDT and LDT, contain descriptors and gates that describe the address space; they describe, for example, the existing segments and tasks. The descriptors and gates placed in these tables can be referenced using selectors. Recall that the GDT sets up a simple protected 32-bit system. The LDT was not needed for a simple system, because its use is closely tied to 80386 multitasking and to providing a local address space for an individual task, as discussed in Chapter 15.

The third table, the IDT, contains gates only; it serves to vector exceptions and interrupts to their appropriate service routines. The gates in this table are referenced via interrupt numbers, from 0 through 255.

Given the large numbers of descriptors, gates, and tables, the allowed placements of each should be clearly spelled out. That, fortunately, is precisely the purpose of Table 14.1, which summarizes the allowed contents of each descriptor table.

The GDT and LDT both can hold code-segment and data-segment descriptors, and they both can contain call and task gates. However, because an LDT is designed merely to provide a task's local address space, the GDT is the only table allowed to contain the special descriptors for task-state segments and LDTs. The IDT can contain only gates, for the purpose of vectoring interrupts and exceptions. The gates it can contain are interrupt, trap, and task gates, but *not* call gates.

Table 14.1   Allowable Contents of Descriptor Tables.

	GDT (Global Descriptor Table)	IDT (Local Descriptor Table)	IDT (Interrupt Descriptor Table)
Descriptors	Code-Segment Descriptors (32- and 16-bit) Data-Segment Descriptors (32- and 16-bit) Task-State Segment Descriptors (32- and 16-bit) Local-Descriptor Table Descriptor	Code-Segment Descriptors (32- and 16-bit) Data-Segment Descriptors (32- and 16-bit)	
Gates	Call Gate (to 32- and 16-bit Code Segments) Task Gate	Call Gate (to 32- and 16-bit Code Segments) Task Gate	Task Gate Trap Gate (to 32- and 16-bit Code Segments) Interrupt Gate (to 32- and 16-bit Code Segments)

System Registers for Locating the Descriptor Tables

An area of memory is known to contain a descriptor table when one of the 80386 PROTECTED-mode registers, listed in Table 14.2, is initialized with a base address and a limit referencing that memory area.

Table 14.2   System Registers for the Descriptor Tables.

80386 System Register	Function
GDTR	Locates and Limits the Global Descriptor Table (GDT)
LDTR	Locates and Limits the Local Descriptor Table (LDT)
IDTR	Locates and Limits the Interrupt Descriptor Table (IDT)

Initializing the GDTR and IDTR

The GDTR and IDTR are the only PROTECTED-mode registers loaded with linear addresses. These registers therefore serve as anchors locating the PROTECTED-mode descriptor-table structure.

The GDTR and IDTR are initialized in a similar manner. A linear base address and a limit are written into each register, using the LGDT and LIDT instructions, respectively. These instructions specify a 16-bit limit value, allowing a table size of up to 64 Kbytes, and a 32-base address, allowing the base location to be anywhere within the linear address space.

Figures 14.9 and 14.10 show the tables so located.

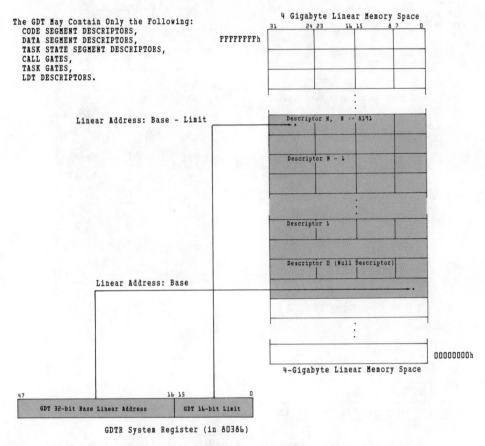

Figure 14.9   GDTR Register Locates the GDT in the Linear Address Space.

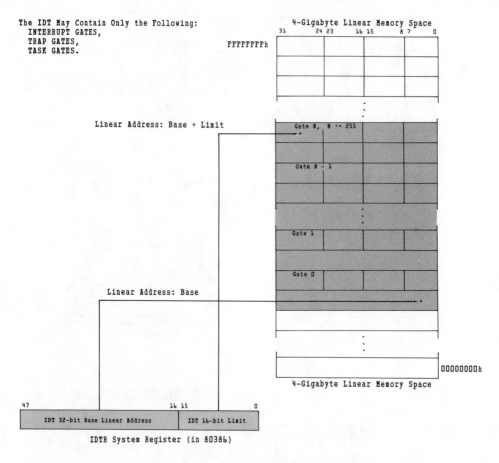

Figure 14.10   IDTR Register Locates the IDT in the Linear Address Space.

Initializing the LDTR

The LDTR is initialized by writing a selector value to the register, using the LLDT instruction. The selector must reference an LDT descriptor, such as that illustrated by Figure 14.4, which contains the necessary base address and limit information. A descriptor-cache register associated with the LDTR register retains an internal copy of the LDT descriptor fields, as shown in Figure 14.11. By using the LLDT instruction to load the LDT descriptor, the LDT can be located anywhere in the linear address space and can be as large as 64 Kbytes, as Figure 14.12 depicts.

The LDT descriptor resides in the GDT. Therefore, it is necessary to create a GDT image and initialize the GDTR first. With the GDT established, the LLDT instruction can be executed to load the LDTR, thereby locating the LDT.

Figure 14.11   Descriptor Cache Register Associated with LDTR Register.

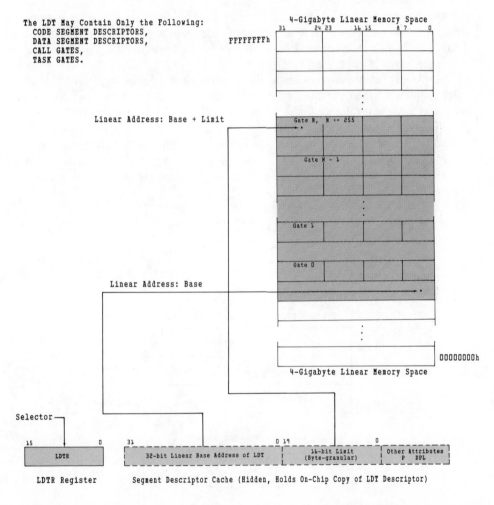

Figure 14.12   LDT Descriptor Cache Locates the LDT in the Linear Address Space.

Use of Gates for Redirection

Redirection via Call Gates

Call gates can be placed only in the GDT and LDT. Redirection via a call gate is performed with any *inter*segment CALL instruction (opcode 9Ah) that specifies a call gate as its destination. The selector of the call gate is used in the instruction's destination operand. Such a CALL instruction can lead either to another code segment at the current privilege level or to another code segment at a level of higher privilege. Thus, a call gate can extend the capabilities of the intersegment CALL instruction to reach segments at *greater privilege levels*.

CALL instructions always leave the address of the following instruction on a stack, so that a RETurn instruction can continue the main routine. This concept remains in force even if a call gate is specified by the CALL instruction.

When a call gate redirects control to a segment at the current privilege level, the CS and EIP are PUSHed onto the stack at the current level. When the call gate redirects control to a level of greater privilege, both stack and instruction addresses are PUSHed onto the stack at the destination (greater) privilege, as illustrated by Figure 14.13.

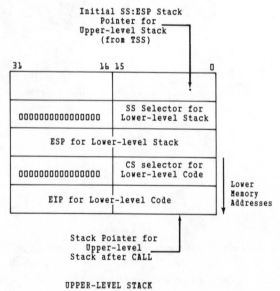

Figure 14.13   32-bit Upper-level Stack after CALL from Lower Level through Call Gate.

Redirection via Call Gate with Parameter Autocopy

Suppose the calling program places parameter values on its stack before performing an intersegment CALL instruction that references a call gate. If the call gate transfers control to a segment at a higher level, then the parameters are not on the stack being used by the called routine. The called routine can be coded to read the parameters from the lower-level stack. However, a more convenient solution is to activate the **parameter autocopy** option available with every call gate.

The call gate, as Figure 14.5 shows, includes a **word count** field that accepts values 0 through 31. The word count, n, of a 32-bit call gate instructs the 80386, if a privilege transition occurs due to the call-gate vectoring, to copy n DWORDS from the lower-level stack to the upper-level stack. Hence, the called routine finds the appropriate number of parameters on its stack. Figure 14.14 illustrates the autocopy of parameters from a lower-level stack to the destination, upper-level stack.

At the end of the called routine, it should execute a RET n instruction, where n, the number of bytes to be removed from the stack, must be identical to the number of bytes autocopied by the call gate. The specified number of bytes is removed from the lower-level stack as the RETurn occurs. The upper-level stack is assumed to be empty after the RETurn to the lower level occurs. That is, after the RETurn, the initial SS:ESP value stored in the TSS again defines the top of upper-level stack the next time that stack is required.

The parameter autocopy feature is inactive if the word count is zero. Be certain to write zeros into the word-count field if the parameter autocopy is not desired with a particular call gate.

Vectoring via Trap Gates and Interrupt Gates

Trap gates and interrupt gates can be placed only in the IDT. Redirection via a trap or interrupt gate can be performed with any software interrupt instruction (INT n, INTO, BOUND instructions), exceptions, or hardware interrupts. Redirection for the interrupt or exception n occurs through the gate at the numeric position n of the IDT. Such a gate leads to another code segment at either the current privilege level or a higher privilege level. Thus, a trap gate or interrupt gate extends the capabilities of the software interrupt instructions to the reaching of segments at *greater privilege levels*.

A trap gate and interrupt gate have the same stack effects as a call gate. When one of these gates redirects control to a level of greater privilege, both stack and instruction addresses are PUSHed onto the stack at the destination (greater) privilege, as illustrated by Figure 14.15. No parameter autocopy feature is provided, however.

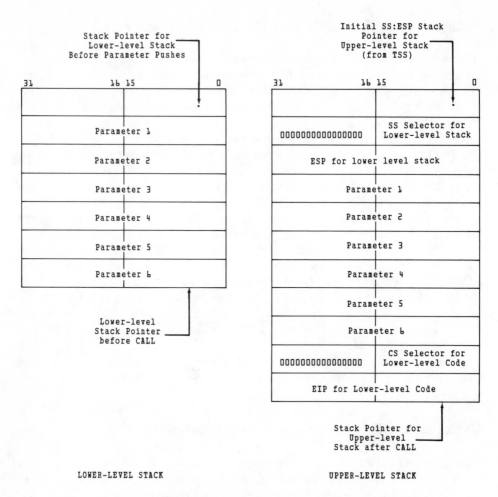

Figure 14.14   32-bit Lower- and Upper-level Stacks after CALL from Lower Level through Call Gate with Parameter Autocopy.

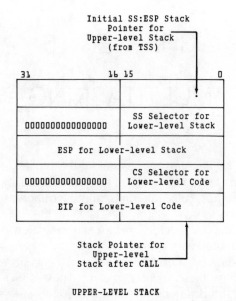

Figure 14.15 **32-bit Upper-level Stack after Software or Hardware Interrupt at Lower Level through Trap or Interrupt Gate.**

Redirection or Vectoring via Task Gates

Task gates can reside in the GDT, LDT, or IDT. When placed in the GDT or LDT, a task gate can be referenced with an intersegment CALL instruction. When placed in the IDT, it can be referenced with a software interrupt instruction, an exception, or a hardware interrupt.

With either manner of reference above, whenever a task gate is referenced, it causes the 80386 to perform an automatic task switch, which is the topic of Chapter 15.

CHAPTER 15

MULTITASKING

This chapter covers the multitasking features of the processor, which include the ability to support many tasks and to switch from one task to another, using ordinary instructions, such as jumps, calls, interrupts, and interrupt returns. Each task, as defined on the 80386, has its own unique task state and its own virtual address space.

Although the 80386 architecture has a clear definition of what constitutes a **task**, the word is often used with a much more general meaning. As associated with computing, the word *task* often brings to mind such concepts as "job" or "user" or "application window on the computer screen." These concepts may or may not correspond to the 80386 definition of a task. An 80386 task is a very definite and concrete entity that is closely tied to the 80386 architecture. Each 80386 task possesses an individual *virtual address space* and a unique *task state*.

Whether or not an 80386 system assigns an actual 80386 task to each "job," "user," or "application window on the computer screen" depends upon whether each such item needs a separate state and an individual virtual address space. If so, the 80386 architecture supports those needs with its multitasking features. If, however, not all items need true individuality, the operating system can share a single state and virtual address space among several items, without making excessive use of the multitasking features.

Even if one does not assign a separate 80386 task to each application program, a typical system will consist of several tasks, because of the inherent tendency to raise the level of robustness above that of single-task systems. For instance, certain tasks typically contain the exception-handling routines for the exceptions that report a serious system error has occurred.

Task Virtual Address Space

A complete virtual address includes a segment selector and an offset. The selector format in PROTECTED mode, as shown in Figure 15.1, contains a TI (Table Indicator) bit, indicating whether the desired descriptor is in the GDT (TI = 0) or in the currently active LDT (TI = 1). The currently active LDT is the one associated with the currently executing task.

The provision for giving each task access to the GDT and to its own LDT allows each task access to the global objects (segments, tasks, etc.) of the virtual address

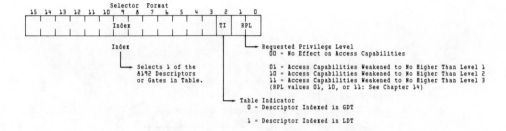

Figure 15.1 PROTECTED-Mode Selector.

space, identified by descriptors in the GDT, and to the objects in its local address space, identified by descriptors in the LDT. As mentioned, the TI bit in the selector format supports this provision.

Task State

Each task in an 80386 system exists by virtue of its **task-state segment**, the area of memory that holds the task's register state and other information. Without a task-state segment, a task does not exist, since no separate state or address space is defined. The TSS, in a fixed format, holds the task's *register state* and related information, such as its initial stack pointers for privilege levels 2, 1, and 0, its value for the LDTR, and its I/O permission bitmap.

A 32-bit TSS, as shown in Figure 15.2, holds the state of the full 32-bit register set, which includes not only the 32-bit extensions of the eight general registers but also the new data-segment registers, FS and GS. The 32-bit TSS also includes a pointer to a bit array, the I/O permission bitmap. Each 32-bit TSS includes a T bit for debugging purposes that allows trapping immediately upon entry to the task. See Chapter 17 for a further description of built-in 80386 debugging features.

For comparison, Figure 8.11 illustrated the 32-bit TSS contents when making only minimal use of the TSS structure. In that case, for a simple system not making use of multitasking, the TSS was utilized merely to hold the initial stack pointer for the privilege level 0 stack. The remaining TSS fields were filled with zeros.

A 16-bit TSS, as shown in Figure 15.3, is the 80286-compatible TSS. It holds the state of only the 16-bit register set used on the 80286 and has no I/O permission bitmap.

TSS Descriptor

A given 32-bit TSS or 16-bit TSS is declared by placing a special descriptor in the GDT. Such TSS **descriptors** are depicted in Figure 15.4.

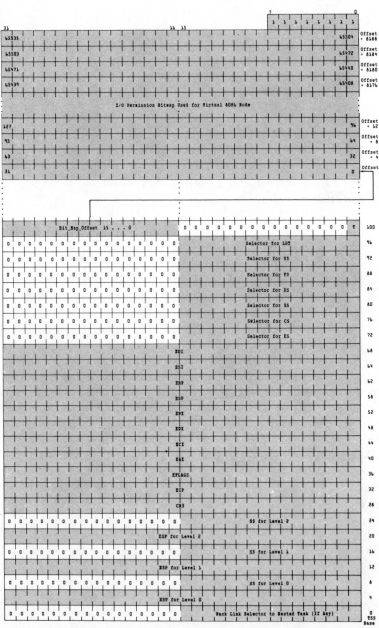

Figure 15.2 32-bit Task State Segment, Including I/O Permission Bitmap.

Definitions of the fields contained in TSS descriptors are covered thoroughly in Chapter 14. The fields are largely identical to the definition of a code-segment descriptor, *except* for the addition of one bit:

B (Busy), indicates whether the task is currently busy (B = 1) or not (B = 0). For a simple protected system, this bit should be set to 1. Further details of the B field and the busy concept are found on pages 186-187.

TSS descriptors are allowed only in the GDT. Therefore, by scanning the GDT for TSS descriptors, the number of tasks can easily be determined: 1 task for each TSS descriptor.

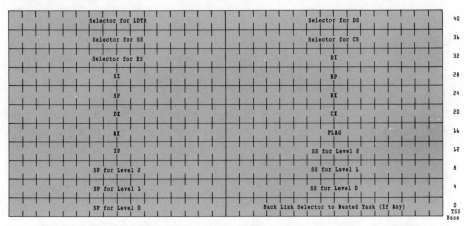

Figure 15.3   16-bit Task State Segment (Never Has I/O Permission Bitmap).

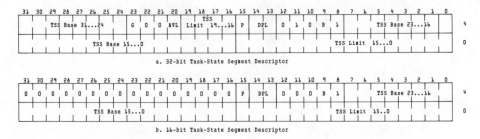

Figure 15.4   Descriptors for 32-bit and 16-bit Task-State Segments.

Figure 15.5   Task Gate for 32-bit or 16-bit TSS.

Task Gates

Task gates may be placed in any descriptor table: GDT, LDT, or IDT. A task gate holds a selector of a TSS descriptor in the GDT and thus acts as a redirection mechanism leading to a task.

Just a single task gate format exists, as shown by Figure 15.5. This same gate can refer to either a 32-bit or a 16-bit TSS, since only the TSS selector is needed from the task gate. Note that a task gate contains no offset value for the entry, as do the 32-bit call gate and the 16-bit call gate. For a task gate, the offset is determined by the initial EIP value, as stated in the TSS itself, so the task gate need not contain an offset value.

Task Transfer

One of the most powerful 80386 features is the ability to transfer between tasks using ordinary instructions; this is often termed *task switching*. The 80386 allows a task switch to be performed by using the intersegment control transfer instructions: intersegment JMP, intersegment CALL, the interrupt instructions INT 3, INT *n*, INTO and BOUND, and IRET. *The instructions themselves are no different.* A task switch is performed by the 80386 merely by specifying the selector of a 32-bit TSS, a 16-bit TSS, or a task gate in the destination field of the instruction.

The tasks involved in a task switch are termed the *outgoing task* and the *incoming task*. The TSS of the current task is specified by the system register **task register** (**TR**) of the 80386. The TSS of the incoming task is specified by the instruction performing the task switch.

The 80386 saves the register context of its outgoing task in the current TSS, as indicated by register TR, then uses the TSS of the incoming task, as indicated by the task switch instruction, as the source of new register context.

Items saved in an *outgoing 32-bit TSS* are the contents of:

Eight 32-bit general registers
Six segment registers
EFLAG register

Items saved in an *outgoing 16-bit TSS* are the contents of:

Eight 16-bit general registers
Four segment registers (CS, SS, DS, and ES only)
FLAG register

Items picked up from an *incoming 32-bit TSS* are the contents of:

Eight 32-bit general registers
Six segment registers
EFLAG register
LDTR contents to establish task's LDT (its own address space)
CR3, to establish task's page directory (its own page tables)
T-bit, to determine if an immediate debug trap is requested

Items picked up from an *incoming 16-bit TSS* are the contents of:

Eight 16-bit general registers
Four segment registers (CS, SS, DS, and ES only)
EFLAG register
LDTR contents to establish task's LDT (its own address space)

As indicated in the above lists, the incoming task picks up a new value for the LTDR and CR3, indicating that each task can use a unique LDT and a unique Page Table Directory. It is not expected that a task would change these values, however, so those two registers are not stored back into the TSS upon suspension of the task.

Transfer through Task-State Segments

Task transfer through a TSS is the most direct transfer path, since the selector of the TSS is specified directly. However, the software performing the task switch must have adequate privilege to use the task-state segment directly.

Transfer through Task Gates

Task transfer through a task gate accomplishes the same result as transfer directly through a TSS. The transfer is accomplished by specifying the selector of the task gate, which in turn holds the selector of the TSS itself. Indirection through the task gate adds about 15 clock periods to the transfer time, but the architectural advantages of utilizing task gates often make this the preferred method of effecting a task switch. These advantages include allowing the task gate a larger DPL than that of the TSS itself and allowing lower-level software to cause the task switch. Task gates can also be placed in tables other than the GDT, a distinct advantage over the TSS itself. Placing a task gate in the IDT allows interrupts and exceptions to cause a task switch. Placing a task gate in an LDT allows only the task(s) using that LDT to perform a switch to the specified task. Direct use of the TSS in the GDT, the table available to all tasks, is prevented by assigning the TSS a very small DPL, typically 0, so only level 0 code can access it.

Task Nesting

At any given time, only one task and the tasks activated from within it are *busy*. Busy tasks are so indicated by the B bit in every descriptor for a TSS. Table 15.1 illustrates the behavior of the B bit, which is automatically manipulated by the 80386 as it switches tasks.

The B bit is controlled as follows:

Table 15.1   Behavior of Task Busy Bit.

Instruction Used to Perform Task Switch	Effect on Busy Bit of Outgoing Task	Effect on Busy Bit of Incoming Task
Intersegment JMP	Reset to 0. JMP does not cause the incoming task to be nested, so the outgoing task becomes *not busy*.	Set to 1. The incoming task always becomes *busy*.
Intersegment CALL	Stays set to 1. CALL creates a nested task situation where the incoming task is nested within the current task. The current task stays *busy* expecting an IRETurn from the incoming task.	Set to 1. The incoming task always becomes *busy*.
Hardware Interrupts and Software Interrupt Instructions (INT 3, INT *n*, INTO, BOUNDS)	Same as intersegment CALL.	Same as intersegment CALL.
IRET Instruction	Reset to 0. The IRET instruction indicates termination of the current task. The IRET indicates the task was a nested task and that it is now complete, so it is marked *not busy*.	Remains 1. The incoming parent remains *busy*, as it was while the child task was executing.

The *back-link* field of the TSS supports task nesting, as occurs when another task becomes busy and activated via a call or interrupt instruction (CALL, INT 3, INT *n*, INTO, or BOUND). In such a case, the parent task (the task that was executing prior to the current task), is identified by placing the selector of its TSS in the back-link field of the incoming TSS.

The IRET instruction allows a task switch back to the parent task. When the **nested task** (NT) bit in the EFLAG register is set, the IRET instruction performs a task switch back to the parent task, identified by the back-link field of its TSS. Note that IRET performs its normal action when NT equals 0 in EFLAG. The TS bit NT bit in register CRO are controlled automatically by the 80386 during task-switch operations. Under software control, the NT bit can be changed only at privilege-level 0, preventing alteration by low-privilege software. See Table 15.2.

Table 15.2 Behavior of TSS Back-link Field and EFLAG NT Bit.

Instruction Used to Perform Task Switch	Effect on Back Link of Outgoing Task	Effect on Back Link of Incoming Task	Effect on EFLAG NT (Nested Task) Bit
Intersegment JMP	Unchanged.	Set to null selector. Since this task was accessed via JMP, no IRETurn to previous task is expected.	Reset to 0. The incoming task is not nested.
Intersegment CALL	Unchanged.	Set to TSS selector of outgoing task. That establishes the nested relationship between tasks, so an IRET instruction can cause a switch back to the previous task.	Set to 1. The incoming task is nested.
Hardware Interrupts and Software Interrupt Instructions (INT 3, INT *n*, INTO, BOUNDS)	Unchanged.	Same as intersegment CALL.	Set to 1. The incoming task is nested.
IRET Instruction	Unchanged.	Unchanged. If the incoming parent task is a nested task, let that relationship stand.	Loaded per EFLAG image in TSS of the incoming parent task.

CHAPTER 16

INTERRUPTS AND EXCEPTIONS IN
Protected AND Virtual 8086 MODE

This chapter describes the 80386 as it handles interrupts and exceptions in the PRO-TECTED mode and in the VIRTUAL 8086 mode.

This chapter also describes the interrupt inputs and the interrupt-descriptor table (IDT), the PROTECTED-mode vectoring mechanism. The coverage of these items is similar to the real-mode description in Chapter 6.

Each type of exception is described. This chapter provides the *comprehensive* discussion of each exception type, going beyond the descriptions in Chapter 6. For each exception, the description includes its causes in PROTECTED mode, its limited set of causes (if any) in REAL mode or VIRTUAL 8086 mode, and important connections between the exception and all other aspects of the 80386 architecture. Under-standing these connections allows the programmer to write routines that can handle exceptions under worst-case conditions.

It should be mentioned that 80386 response to interrupts and exceptions in PRO-TECTED mode is largely the same as in REAL mode. Because of this, useful back-ground can be found in Chapter 6. The PROTECTED-mode distinctions include several additional exception types that are detected in protected mode, as well as use of the PROTECTED-mode IDT rather than the REAL-mode vector table.

Interrupts and Exceptions

Interrupts and exceptions both suspend the present operation of the 80386 and redi-rect its execution to the service routine for the interrupt or exception routine. The distinction between interrupts and exceptions is in their differing points of origin. Interrupts originate from important *external events* signaled to the 80386 on dedi-cated pins, whereas exceptions originate from conditions or problems the 80386 *internally detects*.

The 80386 response to interrupts and exceptions in PROTECTED mode or VIRTUAL 8086 mode is identical. In either case, the 80386 handles the event in PROTECTED mode (termination of VIRTUAL 8086 mode upon receipt of an interrupt or exception was discussed in Chapter 12). From this point forward in this book, the description of interrupts and exceptions in PROTECTED mode will also apply to VIRTUAL 8086 mode, unless otherwise mentioned.

Recognition of Interrupts and Exceptions

As in the REAL mode, interrupts and exceptions are recognized at instruction boundaries, after one instruction has completed execution but before the next instruction has begun. This simplifies the progammer's work, especially when dealing with exceptions, since the programmer is spared the nuances of 80386 internal temporary registers and pipeline stages. The 80386 performs all required maintenance and housecleaning internally and takes the interrupt or exception cleanly at an instruction boundary.

At a single instruction boundary, several interrupts and exceptions can be active simultaneously. Simultaneous events are discussed at the end of this chapter, on pages 223 and 224.

Interrupts

Interrupts provide a hardware mechanism allowing the 80386 to deal with its outside environment, which usually involves a variety of external events happening at unpredictable intervals. The occurrence of such events can be signaled to the 80386 on either of two pins: INTR (maskable INTeRrupt pin) or NMI (Nonmaskable Interrupt pin). These two input pins of the 80386 are dedicated for interrupt signaling.

The INTR pin indicates an active interrupt when driven to a HIGH level. It is a software-maskable signal, enabled when the EFLAG IF bit is set to 1 and disabled when the EFLAG IF bit is cleared to 0.

The NMI pin indicates an active interrupt when driven by a rising edge, and it does not require that the level remain HIGH for any sustained period. NMI is not software maskable; it is always enabled. NMI is typically reserved for the most critical interrupts, typically only interrupts that signal fatal conditions, such as power failure or noncorrectable memory failure.

Interrupt Hardware

Within 80386 systems, many peripheral devices, such as disks, timers, printers, and others, activate interrupts. Such common interrupts are typically directed to the 80386 INTR pin. Since there is only a single INTR pin, interrupts from many devices are ORed via logic to form a single INTR signal is shared by many devices. To achieve quick interrupt response, it is desirable to identify the interrupting source immediately.

When the INTR is activated, immediate identification is accomplished via a special cycle, during which the 80386 reads a number on the lower byte of its data bus. Such a number, ranging from 00h to FFh, is called a *vector number* and is provided typically by an interrupt-controller chip, the 8259A or equivalent. The interrupt number directs the 80386 to a particular memory-resident redirection device, the gate, through which the 80386 fetches the first instruction of an interrupt-service routine.

When the NMI pin is activated, however, no special cycle is performed, and no vector is read. No vector is read because NMI is automatically associated with interrupt number 02H. For that interrupt, vector 02h is dedicated to serve as the critical nonmaskable interrupt vector; upon NMI, the 80386 redirects control to the routine for interrupt number 02H.

Interrupt-Descriptor Table

All interrupts are vectored through a memory-resident array of gates, the IDT. This table begins at the linear address indicated by the **interrupt-descriptor table register**, IDTR. The table consists of up to 256 gates, indexed as gate 0 through gate 255, corresponding of course to the possible values of an interrupt vector number. *Important: Hardware interrupt vectors should be numbered in the range 32 through 255 only. Interrupt numbers 0 through 311 are reserved for Intel-designated exception categories.* Interrupt 32 therefore is redirected using gate 32, interrupt 33 is redirected through gate 33, interrupt 34 through gate 34, and so on, up to interrupt 255. The interrupt-descriptor table is depicted in Figure 16.1.

Note: The IBM Personal Computer architecture violates the above guideline, i.e., that hardware interrupts not use vector numbers 0 through 31. The PC Basic I/O System (BIOS) initializes the 8259A interrupt-controller chip to use vectors 8–15 for hardware interrupts. Potentially, this can lead to conflicting uses for various interrupt vector numbers.

The IDT may contain interrupt gates, trap gates, and task gates. Interrupt gates and trap gates redirect control to a code segment within the current task, the difference being that interrupt gates cause IF to be reset to 0, while trap gates do not affect TF. Refer to Chapter 8 for further information on the uses of these gate types in the IDT. Task gates redirect control to an entirely different task, as indicated by the gate, and execution begins at the CS:EIP location indicated by the task's TSS. Refer to Chapter 15 for further coverage of transfers through task gates.

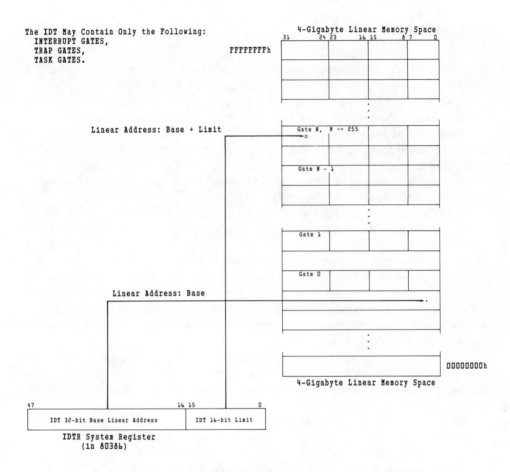

Figure 16.1   Protected- Mode Interrupt-Descriptor Table.

Gate Privilege for Interrupt Vectoring

When a hardware interrupt occurs, the DPL of the gate referenced is *not* of concern. The DPL of the gate is not checked for hardware interrupts; interrupts always have access to the gate for redirection to the correct interrupt routine or task.

Note this constraint on the use of interrupt gates and trap gates, however: if the referenced gate is an interrupt gate or a trap gate, then the DPL *of the destination code segment* is of concern and must be less than or equal to the CPL, so that an IRET instruction can be used at the end of the routine to return control to the interrupted program. (If the referenced gate is a task gate, then the privilege level of the servicing code is *not* constrained by the CPL when the interrupt occurs, since there is never any relation between the privilege level of code in *separate* tasks.)

Exceptions

An exception is a condition preventing completion of the next instruction. It is a condition that the 80386 internally detects. Insofar as the exception prevents completion of the next instruction, it is a *problematic condition*. Yet the exception condition may be a type that is servicable with an *exception-handling routine*.

Each type of exception has been assigned an exception number in the range 0–31, the range reserved by Intel for assignment to exceptions. The 80386 recognizes fifteen exception types, with a specific exception number assigned to each. The remaining exception numbers are not currently used, but they remain reserved for assignment in future Intel processors.

Several exception types are detectable by the 80386 in PROTECTED mode. Exceptions can arise from the segmentation checks, from the paging checks, or for miscellaneous causes, such as invalid opcodes or debug exceptions. Table 16.1 lists all fifteen exception types, summarizing the cause of each.

For comparison, Table 16.1 also shows a strict listing of the exceptions detectable in REAL mode. The table takes a very strict view, meaning that some quite bizarre REAL-mode code is needed to intentionally invoke exceptions 8, 9, 12, and 13 in REAL mode. A realistic listing of exceptions likely to occur in REAL mode would include only 0, 1, 3, 4, 5, 6, 7, and 16.

The occurrence of several exception types is actually anticipated if the system uses the virtual-memory features, performs multitasking, or emulates the coprocessor. For instance, in a virtual-memory system, a page-fault exception (exception 14) occurs from time to time. If a system performs multitasking or emulates the 80287 or 80387 math coprocessor, the coprocessor-not-available exception (exception 7) can occur when a coprocessor opcode is about to be executed.

Fault Exceptions versus Trap Exceptions

Any given exception can be attributed to a particular instruction. Depending upon the exception type, however, it may be signaled either immediately before or immediately after the responsible instruction. When signaled immediately before the instruction, the exception is termed a **fault**; when signaled immediately after the instruction, the exception is termed a **trap**.

Most exceptions, especially those caused by conditions preventing instruction execution, are signaled as faults, before the instruction executes. The only exceptions signaled as traps, after the instruction, are certain debug exceptions (TF single-step flag and data breakpoints) and exceptions caused by a task switch, where the problem is due to the incoming task and the task switch has already occurred.

Table 16.1   Exception Vector Assignments in PROTECTED Mode.

	Exception Number	Name (and Type)	Description	Also Detected in REAL Mode? (See also Table 6.2)	Also Detected by 8086/88?
Exceptions Also Detected by 8086/8088	0	Divide Error (fault)	Division by 0 was attempted with DIV or IDIV instructions.	Yes.	Yes, however, 8086 CS:IP points to instruction after the DIV or IDIV.
	1	Single Step (trap), Debug Register Breakpoint (fault or trap)	If the TF flag in FLAG is set to 1, this exception is taken after the next instruction. The Debug Registers can define breakpoints that also cause exception 1.	Yes.	Yes, the 8086 has only the TF flag. It doesn't have the Debug Registers.
	3	Breakpoint Opcode (trap)	Single-byte breakpoint opcode (CCh) executed. The processor initiates exception 3.	Yes.	Yes.
	4	INTO (trap)	If the OF overflow flag is set, the processor initiates exception 4.	Yes.	Yes.
	5	BOUND (trap)	If a bounds violation is detected, the processor initiates exception 5.	Yes.	Yes.
Exceptions Also Detected in 80286/80386 REAL Mode	6	Illegal Opcode (fault)	Unassigned opcodes cause the 80386 to initiate exception 6.	Yes.	No, the 8086 treats unassigned opcodes as NOPs.
	7	Coprocessor Not Available (fault)	A coprocessor opcode, when the coprocessor is not present, causes the processor to initiate exception 7. Allows emulation of coprocessor instructions if the EM flag in CR0 is reset to 0.	Yes, if the EM flag in CR0 is reset to 0.	No, to emulate the coprocessor in 8086 systems, INT *n* instructions should be substituted for the coprocessor opcode. The INT *n* initiates exception *n* processing.
	8	Double Fault (fault)	While attempting to access an interrupt or exception routine, an exception is detected.	Yes, but requires atypical use of LIDT instruction to shorten limit of the interrupt table.	No.
	9	Coprocessor Oper- and Limit Violation (fault)	An operand for the numeric coprocessor is partially beyond the limit (end) of the segment.	Yes, but only if software wraps operand around 64K limit.	No, the 8086 allows operands to wrap around to the beginning of the segment.
	12	Stack segment exception (fault)	An operand in the stack segment (SS) is entirely or partially beyond the limit of the segment, or stack is not present, or wrong privilege level, or not a data segment, or several other reasons listed with exception 12 details.	Yes, but only if software wraps operand around 64K limit.	No, the 8086 allows operands to wrap around to the beginning of the segment.

Table 16.1   Exception Vector Assignments in PROTECTED Mode *(Continued).*

	Exception Number	Name (and Type)	Description	Also Detected in REAL Mode? (See also Table 6.2)	Also Detected by 8086/88?
Exceptions Also Detected in 80286/80386 REAL Mode	13	General-Protection exception in CS, SS, DS, ES, FS, or GS (fault)	An operand in CS, SS, DS, ES, FS, GS is entirely or partially beyond the limit of the segment, or segment is not present, or wrong privilege level, or not a data segment, or several other reasons listed with exception 13 details.	Yes, but only if software wraps operand around 64K limit.	No, the 8086 allows operands to wrap around to the beginning of the segment.
	16	Coprocessor Numeric Error (fault)	The 80386 ERROR# input was activated (presumably by the numeric coprocessor).	Yes, if the 80386 ERROR# input pin is activated by the 80387 ERROR# output.	No, the 8087 signals coprocessor numeric errors to the 8086 via the interrupt (through the 8259A typically, but through the NMI pin in personal computer architectures).
Exceptions Detected Only in Protected Mode	10	Invalid Task-State Segment (fault or trap)	The 80386 detected an error in the contents of a TSS when performing a task switch. If the TSS of the outgoing task has an error, this exception is taken as a fault. If the TSS of the incoming task has an error, this exception is taken as a trap.	No, there is no automatic task switch ability.	No, there is no automatic task switch ability.
	14	Page Fault (fault)	Paging is enabled, and a needed page is not present or has wrong privilege or wrong access rights.	No, paging cannot be enabled in REAL mode.	No, 8086 has no paging feature.

Recognition of Exceptions

When an instruction raises an exception, the exception is always recognized. There is no method of masking an exception, nor would masking be desirable.

Although exceptions are raised and recognized in the course of executing an instruction, the exception appears to the user to have been taken at an instruction boundary, because the state of the 80386 is always preserved as it was *prior to* the instruction. Thus, for fault exceptions, where the exception is taken before the responsible instruction, CS:EIP points to the instruction (including any prefix bytes) that caused the exception. This is the ideal case for a service routine that attempts to correct the exception, because it can resume the program merely by executing an IRET instruction as the last instruction of the exception service routine.

Restartability of Exceptions

A faulting 80386 instruction or coprocessor instruction is fully restartable for all exception types *except* for the coprocessor operand limit violation (exception 9) and, under a certain condition, the invalid task-state segment exception (exception 10). With proper operating system design, these rather obscure cases are easily avoidable, yielding complete system restartability. The condition required to cause the coprocessor operand limit violation exception is so obscure and awkward that the operating system can easily prevent its occurrence. See Chapter 16 for details. The invalid task-state segment exception is not restartable if caused by a *partially-not-present* TSS for the destination task of a task switch. The operating system can prevent this condition by not letting page boundaries fall across the fixed portion of any TSS (the fixed portion is the portion referenced during a task switch). See Chapter 16 for details. The condition of a *completely-not-present* TSS is, of course, restartable.

In summary, the 80386 hardware exceeds the restartability requirements of practical operating systems.

Error Codes for Exceptions

In PROTECTED mode, the exception types that relate to a specific segment or gate cause an **error code** to be PUSHed onto the stack of the exception-handler routine or task. It should be noted that, in REAL mode, no exception types PUSH an error code, not even those types that generate an error code during PROTECTED mode. Neither does any interrupt generate an error code.

The error code PUSHed in PROTECTED mode is a 32-bit value when the exception-handling code is in a 32-bit code segment, and it is a 16-bit value when the exception-handling code is in a 16-bit code segment. It is anticipated, of course, that nearly all new PROTECTED-mode software will be comprised of 32-bit code. In either case, only 16 bits of the error code carries significant information. For all exceptions other than the double-fault exception (exception 8) and page-fault exception (exception 14), Figure 16.2 illustrates the error-code formats. It also shows how an error code is merely padded with 16 undefined bits when pushed onto a 32-bit stack. There are also instances when the error code pushed is merely 0, UUUU0000h (see instruction-set details, Appendix B).

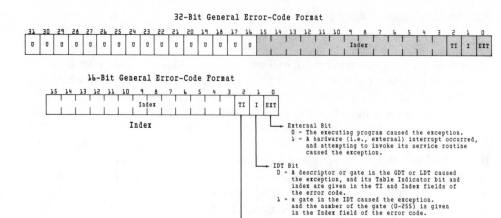

Figure 16.2   32-bit and 16-bit General-Format Error Codes.

The error-code format resembles that of a selector. It contains an index field and a TI bit. However, the least-significant-bit positions, rather than containing the RPL of a selector, contain an I bit and an EXT bit:

1.   The EXT (External) bit is set to 1 if an event external to the program caused the exception. An external event is an interrupt that caused an exception (fault) as the 80386 attempted to transfer control to the interrupt-handling routine. Once the first instruction of the handler executes, subsequent exceptions caused by the handling routine are of course *internal* (software-caused) exceptions. The EXT bit is reset to 0 if the executing software is responsible for the exception.

2.   The I (IDT) bit is set to 1 if the index portion of the error code refers to a gate in the IDT. This is the case if a gate in the IDT is responsible for the exception (for example, if the referenced gate is marked *not present* (P = 0) or is not a gate at all). The I bit is reset to 0 if the index portion of the error code refers to an item in the GDT or LDT.

3.   The TI (Table Indicator) bit is meaningful only when I equals 0, indicating that the index portion refers to the GDT or LDT. In that case, TI indicates whether the index refers to the GDT (TI = 0) or to the LDT (TI = 1), just as TI is defined in a PROTECTED-mode selector.

The above is applicable to all exception error codes other than the double-fault exception (exception 8) and the page-fault exception (exception 14). For exception

8, the error code is simply all zeros. For the page-fault exception, the error code, illustrated in Figure 16.3, is designed to meet the needs of the page-fault handler. See Figure 16.3 for details.

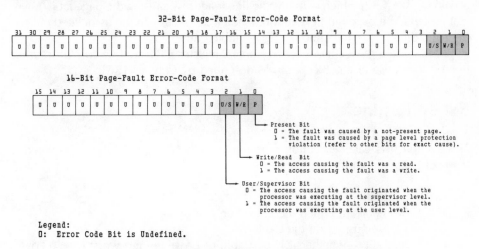

Figure 16.3   32-bit and 16-bit Page-Fault Error-Codes.

Table 16.2   Protected Mode Error-Code Summary.

Number	Exception	Error Code on Stack of Exception Handler in PROTECTED Mode?
0	Divide Error	No
1	Debug Exceptions	No
3	Breakpoint Instruction	No
4	INTO Instruction If Overflow	No
5	BOUND Instruction If Bounds Violation	No
6	Invalid Opcode	No
7	Coprocessor Not Available	No
8	Double Fault	Yes, but error code is all zeros.
9	Coprocessor Operand Segment Overrun	Yes, as in Figure 16.2.
10	Invalid Task State Segment	Yes, as in Figure 16.2.
11	Segment Loaded into CS, DS, ES, FS, or GS Is Not Present	Yes, as in Figure 16.2.
12	Segment Loaded into SS Is Not Present, or SS Limit Violation	Yes, as in Figure 16.2.
13	General Protection Violation	Yes, as in Figure 16.2.
14	Page Fault—Not Present or Usage Error	No, error information is in register CR2.
16	Coprocessor Numeric Error	No, execute FNSTENV instruction (Store Coprocessor Environment instruction) to get pointer to failing numeric instruction.

Note: No error codes are generated in REAL mode.

Other Error Information

For a page-fault exception (exception 14), useful error information is provided in 80386 register CR2, which contains the linear address causing the page fault. Given that address, the page-fault exception handler can reference the associated entry in the page directory, page table, and page table entry.

For the debug exceptions (exception 1), register DR6 contains useful information on the cause of the exception, as described by Chapter 17.

Exception List

This section lists each exception type individually. Each exception is covered in terms of six pertinent topics:

- Description
- 80386 modes in which the exception can occur
- Error code pushed on the stack
- Restartability—whether it is desirable or possible, and worst-case recovery scenarios
- Any subtle differences from the 8086/8088
- Comments—any other connected concepts information, or useful tips

EX 0 <div style="text-align:center">Divide Error</div> **EX 0**

Exception 0: Divide Error

Description: This exception, taken as a fault, is detected when the DIV or IDIV instruction attempt division by zero or when the DIV or IDIV quotient (result) overflows its destination operand. Since the exception is taken as a fault, the instruction pointer points to the failing divide instruction.

Active modes: REAL, PROTECTED, VIRTUAL 8086. REAL-mode vectoring uses vector 0 of the REAL-mode interrupt-vector table. PROTECTED-mode or VIRTUAL 8086-mode vectoring uses gate 0 in the PROTECTED-mode interrupt-descriptor table (IDT).

Error code pushed in PROTECTED **mode:**   None.

Restartability: The instruction causing this exception is restartable. Of course, restarting the instruction will again generate the exception unless the divide operands are adjusted. Therefore, a good strategy in dealing with this exception is to report the error and terminate the failing program.

Difference from 8086/8088:   On the 8086/8088, this exception is taken as a trap. Therefore, on the 8086/8088, the instruction pointer points at the *following* instruction, a less useful situation. Having the 80286/80386 take this exception as a fault gives the exception handler more useful information, namely, the pointer to the failing instruction itself. This exception occurs infrequently, so the change made to improve 80286/80386 handling of this exception results in little or no incompatibility.

Exception 1:   Debug

Description: This exception occurs when any of the debug breakpoints (for instruction execution, data, or task switch) is triggered or if the TF (single-step) flag bit
is set. This exception is taken as a fault for instruction execution breakpoints but as a
trap for data breakpoints, task switch breakpoints, and trap flag (TF) trap.

The debug status register, debug register 6 (DR6), allows this debug-exception
handler to easily determine why it was invoked. The debug-status register contains
single-bit flags for each type of possible event invoking this exception. Note below
that some of these events are faults (exception is taken immediately prior to executing an instruction that causes the debug exception), while other events are traps
(exception is taken after the instruction that caused the debug exception).

The debug-exception handler can be invoked as a result of one of the following
events, as indicated in register DR6:

1. **Debug Register 0 (DR0) Breakpoint**, taken as a fault if it is a code
   breakpoint, as a trap if it is a data breakpoint
2. **Debug Register 1 (DR1) Breakpoint**, taken as a fault if it is a code
   breakpoint, as a trap if it is a data breakpoint
3. **Debug Register 2 (DR2) Breakpoint**, taken as a fault if it is a code
   breakpoint, as a trap if it is a data breakpoint
4. **Debug Register 3 (DR3) Breakpoint**, taken as a fault if it is a code
   breakpoint, as a trap if it is a data breakpoint
5. **Single-step instruction trap**, caused by setting the TF bit in EFLAG, taken
   as a trap after one instruction executes
6. **Task switch trap**, caused by setting the T bit in the TSS of a task, taken as a
   trap, in the context of the incoming task
7. **Fault**, due to attempted read or write access to any of the debug registers at
   a time when GD equals 1 in DR7. This indicates that an in-circuit emulator,
   such as ICE-386, is currently using the debug registers for its purposes.

For complete information on using the 80386 debug registers, refer to Chapter
17.

Active modes: REAL, PROTECTED, VIRTUAL 8086. REAL-mode vectoring uses vector 1 of the REAL-mode interrupt-vector table. PROTECTED-mode or VIRTUAL 8086-
mode vectoring uses gate 1 in the PROTECTED-mode interrupt-descriptor table (IDT).

Error code pushed in PROTECTED mode: None.

EX 1   Debug   **EX 1**

Restartability: All occurrences of this exception are restartable. The RF (Resume Flag) allows the instruction at the breakpoint address to be restarted without immediately generating another debug-exception fault.

Difference from 8086/8088:   The behavior of the TF when single-stepping an INT 3, INT *n*, INTO, or BOUND instruction is different on the 80286/80386 from the 8086/8088. When executing these instructions, the 80286/80386 reset TF after the original EFLAG image is PUSHed on the stack; this is a security feature that prevents an application program from causing a single-step through an operating-system software interrupt routine. The 8086/8088 do not reset TF for these instructions. Implication: a debugger written for the 8086/8088 but run on the 80286 or 80386 will not single-step through interrupt routines; rather, it will run completely through the routine and through the next instruction of the main program. To remedy this, an 80286/80386 debugger using the TF to perform single-stepping should emulate the activity of any interrupt instruction that it encounters. Emulation requires building the stack frame as the interrupt instruction would and taking the next instruction from the entry point of the interrupt routine.

Comments: If using the 80386 debug registers to trap data references, use the data breakpoint feature, then enable the exact data breakpoint match feature to be assured that the breakpoint will be taken.

Exception 3:   Breakpoint Instruction

Description: This exception is generated if the single-byte INT 3 instruction is executed (opcode CCh). The vectoring to the exception handler is considered part of the INT 3 instruction. Therefore the exception is considered to be taken as a trap, and the instruction pointer is left pointing to the instruction *following* the INT 3.

Active modes: REAL, PROTECTED, VIRTUAL 8086. REAL-mode vectoring uses vector 3 of the REAL-mode interrupt vector table. PROTECTED-mode or VIRTUAL 8086-mode vectoring uses gate 3 in the PROTECTED-mode IDT.

Error code pushed in PROTECTED mode: None.

Restartability: Since this exception is taken as a trap, the INTO instruction has already completed. The program can be resumed from the instruction following INT 3.

Difference from 8086/8088:   None.

Comments: This exception is the only way to generate instruction execution breakpoints on the 8086/8088 or 80286. Thus this exception provides compatibility for existing 8086/8088 or 80286 debugger programs run on the 80386.

EX 4   Interrupt if Overflow Set   **EX 4**

Exception 4: INTO Instruction if Overflow Flag (OF) Is Set

Description: This exception is generated if, when the INTO instruction is executed, the OF bit is set to 1. The vectoring to the exception handler is considered part of the INTO instruction. Therefore the exception is considered to be taken as a trap, and the instruction pointer is left pointing to the instruction *following* the INTO.

Active modes: REAL, PROTECTED, VIRTUAL 8086. REAL-mode vectoring uses vector 4 of the REAL-mode interrupt vector table. PROTECTED-mode or VIRTUAL 8086-mode vectoring uses gate 4 in the PROTECTED-mode IDT.

Error code pushed in PROTECTED **mode:**   None.

Restartability: Since this exception is taken as a trap, the INTO instruction has already completed. The program can be resumed from the instruction following INTO.

EX 5   Interrupt if Bounds Violation   **EX 5**

Exception 5:   BOUND Instruction if Out-of-bounds Condition Is Detected

Description: This exception is generated if, when the BOUND instruction is executed, it detects an out-of-bounds condition. The vectoring to the exception handler is considered part of the BOUND instruction. Therefore the exception is considered to be taken as a trap, and the instruction pointer is left pointing to the instruction *following* the BOUND.

Active modes: REAL, PROTECTED, VIRTUAL 8086. REAL-mode vectoring uses vector 5 of the REAL-mode interrupt vector table. PROTECTED-mode or VIRTUAL 8086-mode vectoring uses gate 5 in the PROTECTED-mode IDT.

Error code pushed in PROTECTED mode: None.

Restartability: Since this exception is taken as a trap, the BOUND instruction has already completed. The program can be resumed from the instruction following BOUND.

EX 6   Invalid Instruction   **EX 6**

Exception 6:   Invalid Instruction

Description: This exception is generated if the processor is about to execute something other than a legal instruction. The cause could be an invalid opcode, [mod r/m] or [s-i-b] byte(s) (See Chapter 3 Instruction Format). The usual cause is an errant program gone awry and attempting to execute data. Attempted use of the LOCK prefix where it does not belong will also cause this exception (see allowable instruction forms below). In real mode, attempting the PROTECTED-mode instructions ARPL, LLDT, LTR, LAR, LSL, SLDT, STR, VERR, or VERW also cause this exception.

Active modes: REAL, PROTECTED, VIRTUAL 8086. REAL-mode vectoring uses vector 6 of the REAL-mode interrupt vector table. PROTECTED-mode or VIRTUAL 8086 mode vectoring uses gate 6 in the PROTECTED-mode IDT.

Error code pushed in PROTECTED mode: None.

Restartability: The processor state is preserved, so restart can be performed, assuming that restart of an illegal instruction makes any sense. A better strategy in dealing with this exception is to report the error and terminate the failing program.

Difference from 8086/8088:   This exception does not exist on the 8086/8088, which treat illegal instructions as NOPs (do nothing except increment the instruction pointer).

Difference from 8086/8088 and 80286:   The addition of paging capability to the 80386 made it necessary to restrict the use of the LOCK prefix to a small set of instructions where LOCKing can actually be guaranteed. An invalid opcode exception (exception 6) is generated otherwise. This restriction and exception applies to any mode of the 80386, regardless of whether paging is enabled or disabled.

The LOCK prefix legally can precede only certain instructions, particularly those that exchange register data with memory, and some of those that operate on a memory *destination* operand. Specifically, the LOCKable instruction forms are

```
XCHG    <mem EA>,genreg          ;Exchange memory with register
                                 ;80286 and 80386 autoLOCKs
                                 ;this instruction
XCHG    genreg,<mem EA>          ;Exchange register with memory
                                 ;80286 and 80386 autoLOCKs
                                 ;this instruction
ADD     <mem EA>,genreg          ;Add to memory operand
ADC     <mem EA>,genreg          ;Add using Carry flag
SUB     <mem EA>,genreg          ;Subtract from memory operand
SBB     <mem EA>,genreg          ;Subtract using Carry flag (borrow)
NEG     <mem EA>                 ;Negate memory operand
OR      <mem EA>,genreg          ;OR to memory operand
AND     <mem EA>,genreg          ;AND to memory operand
```

EX 6 Invalid Instruction **EX 6**

```
XOR       <mem EA>,genreg       ;XOR to memory operand
NOT       <mem EA>              ;NOT memory operand
BTC       <mem EA>              ;Complement memory bit operand
BTR       <mem EA>              ;Reset memory bit operand
BTS       <mem EA>              ;Set memory bit operand
```

Because of the paging support on the 80386, the 80386 must be more restrictive about the LOCK prefix than is the 8086 or 80286. In a paged environment such as the 80386 can provide, there is no way to assure, for example, the successful LOCKing of a repeated string instruction. For instance, the operating system may have to intervene to service a page fault, thus interrupting a supposedly LOCKed instruction. See page 44 for more information about the LOCK prefix.

EX 7   Numeric Coprocessor Not Available   **EX 7**

Exception 7: Numeric Coprocessor Not Available

Description: This exception is generated as a fault if the processor is about to execute a coprocessor instruction while the EM and MP flags indicate that the coprocessor is either not available or not available to the current task.

The EM and MP bits are controlled entirely by software. The EM bit should be set and the MP bit should be reset when the coprocessor is being emulated. The EM bit should be reset and the MP bit should be set when the coprocessor is actually in the system.

The TS bit is automatically set to 1 when the 80386 performs a task switch (see page 186). This causes the next coprocessor instruction of the incoming task to generate a coprocessor-not-available exception (exception 7). The coprocessor-not-available-exception handler presumably swaps the coprocessor state to that of the new task, clears the TS flag (possibly by using the CLTS instruction), and returns to the coprocessor instruction. Since the TS flag has been cleared, the numeric instruction now executes without raising an exception.

Flag settings in CR0			Generate Exception 7 upon WAIT Instruction?	Generate Exception 7 upon Coprocessor Instruction?
EM	MP	TS		
0	1	0	No	No
0	1	1	Yes, allows coprocessor context switch to be performed by exception-7 handler.	Yes, allows coprocessor context switch to be performed by exception-7 handler.
1	0	0	No, WAIT instruction does not need to be emulated when coprocessor is not present.	Yes, so coprocessor instruction can be emulated by exception-7 handler.
1	0	1	No, WAIT instruction does not need to be emulated when coprocessor is not present.	Yes, so coprocessor instruction can be emulated by exception-7 handler.

Active modes: REAL, PROTECTED, VIRTUAL 8086. REAL-mode vectoring uses vector 7 of the REAL-mode interrupt vector table. PROTECTED-mode or VIRTUAL 8086 mode vectoring uses gate 7 in the PROTECTED-mode IDT.

Error code pushed in PROTECTED **mode:**   None.

Restartability: All occurrences of this exception are restartable.

EX 7   Numeric Coprocessor Not Available   **EX 7**

Difference from 8086/8088:   This exception does not exist on the 8086/8088, which provide no exception for emulating the coprocessor. On the 8086/8088, coprocessor emulation can be accomplished, when necessary, by substituting or inserting into the object code an explicit INT *n* instruction for each coprocessor instruction.

EX 8   Double Fault   **EX 8**

Exception 8:   Double Fault

Description: This exception is generated if any exception is detected when the processor is attempting to transfer control to the handler for a prior exception 0, 10, 11, 12, or 13.

Active modes: PROTECTED. PROTECTED-mode vectoring uses gate 8 in the PROTECTED-mode IDT.

Error code pushed in PROTECTED **mode:**   Yes, but the error code is all zeros.

Restartability: The instruction causing the prior exception cannot be restarted, since detection of the second exception has prevented storing the state of the interrupted program and loading the entry-point information for the exception handler. Since, in the chain of exceptions, some of the original state information has been lost, restartability is no longer possible. This is the reason a special exception, exception 8, has been assigned to such a condition.

Difference from 8086/8088:   This exception does not exist on the 8086/8088.

Comments: To avoid this exception, ensure that the entry points of handlers for exceptions 0, 10, 11, 12, and 13 can be reached without causing further exception. To handle the exception 8 properly should it occur, ensure a proper TSS for the exception-8 handler by handling it in a separate task. To do this, place a task gate in position 8 of the IDT.

EX 9   Coprocessor Operand Segment Limit Violation   **EX 9**

Exception 9: Coprocessor Operand Segment Limit Violation

Description: This exception is generated if the processor detects an exception while it is involved with the transfer of an operand for the coprocessor. This exception can occur only under a condition of having a coprocessor operand wrap around a 4-gigabyte segment.

Active modes: PROTECTED. PROTECTED-mode vectoring uses gate 9 in the PROTECTED-mode IDT.

Error code pushed in PROTECTED mode: None.

Restartability: The numeric-coprocessor instruction causing this exception is not restartable, because it has already begun execution and changed the state of the coprocessor by the time this exception is detected by the 80386.

Difference from 8086/8088:   This exception does not exist on the 8086/8088.

Comments: This exception can be avoided by not allowing the coprocessor operand to wrap around the end of 4-gigabyte segments.

EX 10   Invalid Task State Segment   **EX 10**

Exception 10: Invalid Task State Segment

Description: This exception is generated during a task-switch operation if the processor detects that a task-state segment is too small to contain the fixed portion of the TSS or if the TSS contains inconsistent information. This exception is signaled as a fault in the context of the outgoing task if the TSS of the outgoing task is detected to be invalid or if the TSS of the incoming task is nonexistent. It is taken as a trap in the context of the incoming task if the incoming task's TSS is discovered to have a further problem.

Active modes: PROTECTED. PROTECTED-mode vectoring uses gate 10 in the PROTECTED-mode IDT.

Error code pushed in PROTECTED mode: An error code, as in Figure 16.2, is pushed. The selector index contained in the error code depends upon the condition detected, as listed below:

Exception 10 Error Code	Condition that Invalidated Either TSS Involved in Task Switch	Checked for Outgoing TSS?	Checked for Incoming TSS?
TSS Index + EXT Bit	The TSS descriptor is not valid (wrong type of descriptor, or indecipherable).	Yes	Yes
TSS Index + EXT Bit	A JMP, CALL, INT 3, INT n, INTO or BOUNDS instruction caused the task switch, but the incoming TSS is already marked busy (B = 1).	Yes	Yes
TSS Index + EXT Bit	An IRET instruction caused the task switch to an incoming task in which the current task is presumably nested, but the incoming task is marked *not busy* (B = 0).	Yes	Yes
TSS Index + EXT Bit	The limit in the 32-bit TSS descriptor is less than 103 (decimal) bytes required for the fixed portion of the TSS. (or less than 43 decimal for a 16-bit TSS descriptor).	Yes	Yes

EX 10   Invalid Task State Segment   EX 10

Exception 10 Error Code	Condition that Invalidated Either TSS Involved in Task Switch	Checked for Outgoing TSS?	Checked for Incoming TSS?
LDT Index + EXT Bit	Invalid LDT descriptor or LDT descriptor marked *not present*.	No	Yes
SS Index + EXT Bit	Stack segment selector is beyond descriptor table limit.	No	Yes
SS Index + EXT Bit	Stack segment selector does not refer to a writable data segment.	No	Yes
SS Index + EXT Bit	Stack segment DPL does not match new CPL (indicated by new code selector RPL).	No	Yes
SS Index + EXT Bit	Stack segment selector RPL ◊ new DPL.	No	Yes
CS Index + EXT Bit	Code segment selector is beyond descriptor-table limit.	No	Yes
CS Index + EXT Bit	Code segment selector does not refer to a code segment.	No	Yes
CS Index + EXT Bit	DPL of nonconforming code segment ◊ new CPL.	No	Yes
CS Index + EXT Bit	DPL of conforming code segment › new CPL.	No	Yes
DS, ES, FS, GS Index + EXT Bit	DS, ES, FS, or GS segment selector is beyond descriptor table limit.	No	Yes
DS, ES, FS, GS Index + EXT Bit	DS, ES, FS, or GS segment selector does not refer to a data segment.	No	Yes

Note: + connotes the Boolean OR operation used to form the error code, as in Figure 16.2.

Restartability: This exception is restartable unless caused by the fact that *part of* the fixed portion of the TSS is in a not-present page. Therefore, avoid having page boundaries fall within the fixed portion of the TSS.

Difference from 8086/8088:   This exception does not exist on the 8088/8086.

Comments: To ensure a proper TSS to handle the exception, the handler for exception 10 must be a task, invoked via placing a task gate in position 10 of the IDT. In any practical system, it is highly recommended to create only valid TSS descriptors, with valid TSS descriptor limit set large enough to hold at least the fixed portion of the TSS, and valid contents of the TSS itself.

EX 11   Segment Not Present   **EX 11**

Exception 11: **Segment Not Present**

Description: This exception is generated if the processor detects that the present
bit is 0 in any the descriptors for CS, DS, ES, FS, GS, or LDT, or in the trap gate,
interrupt gate, or task gate. The exception is taken as a fault upon an attempt to load
the selector of a not-present descriptor into a segment register. The exception is
taken as a fault upon an attempt to use the selector of a not-present gate in an
intersegment JMP, intersegment CALL, intersegment RET, intersegment RET *n*, INT
3, INT *n*, INTO, BOUND, IRET, MOV to DS/ES/FS/GS, or LDS/LES/LFS/LGS.

Special Considerations for Not Present Exception Detected During Task Switch: The Worst-Case Situation

If detected during a task switch, this exception is taken as a trap in the context of the
incoming task. During a task switch, the 80386 first establishes that the incoming
task's TSS exists and that its LDT (if any) exists, loads all the registers from the new
TSS, and then one by one reads the descriptors indicated by the selectors for each
segment register. If *any* needed descriptor is found to be not present, this exception
is immediately taken as a trap in the context of the new task. (Explanation: The task
switch occurred, but the first instruction of the new task has not yet been executed).
Because of this, the remaining descriptor caches may not be updated with the
needed descriptor contents. There are two ways to cope with this in the not-present-
exception (exception 11) handler:

1. Handle this exception with a separate task (a task gate in position 11 of the
    IDT). The task switch back to the interrupted task will cause the processor
    to reload the registers and descriptor caches for the interrupted task. The
    attempted task switch could, however, uncover a further exception, which
    will be vectored accordingly. When all exceptions generated by the task
    switch are handled, the switch back to the interrupted task will execute
    smoothly.
2. Handle this exception within the current task (a trap gate in position 11 of
    the IDT) and ensure that the handling routine itself makes all descriptor
    caches consistent with the selector values of those that were loaded during
    the task switch. The routine must therefore PUSH and then POP all seg-
    ment-register selectors. The POP operation will cause the 80386 to read the
    needed descriptor and update its corresponding descriptor cache on-chip.
    Be aware that each such POP instruction within the handler could possibly
    cause either another not-present exception or some other exception. There-

EX 11   Segment Not Present   **EX 11**

fore, the handler for this exception must be reentrant (all its temporary variables must be stored on the handler's stack).

Active modes: PROTECTED. PROTECTED-mode vectoring uses gate 11 in the PROTECTED mode IDT.

Error code pushed in PROTECTED mode: An error code, as in Figure 16.2, is pushed. The index field refers to the selector of a not-present descriptor or to the selector or IDT index of a not-present gate. The I bit is set if the error code refers to an IDT entry, resulting from, for instance, an INT *n* instruction referring to a not-present gate or a hardware interrupt referring to a not-present gate (the EXT bit would also be set in that case).

Restartability: All occurrences of this exception are restartable. If the exception 11 handler makes the segment or gate present (P = 1) and IRETurns, the interrupted program will resume execution.

Difference from 8086/8088:   This exception does not exist on an 8086/8088.

EX 12   Stack Fault   **EX 12**

Exception 12:   Stack Fault

Description: This exception is generated when the stack segment is not present or the limit of the stack segment is exceeded.

The exception is taken as a fault if detected because of a limit violation, with the instruction pointer pointing at the failing instruction.

The exception is taken as a fault upon an instruction attempting to load the selector of a not-present descriptor into the SS (stack segment) register. This can occur in an interlevel CALL, interlevel RET, interlevel RET *n*, interlevel INT *n*, interlevel IRET, LSS instruction, or a MOV or POP instruction to SS.

Special Considerations for Stack Exception Detected During Task Switch: The Worst-case Situation

If a stack is found to be not present, nonwritable, or of incorrect privilege level, during a task switch, this exception is taken as a trap in the context of the incoming task. During a task switch, the 80386 first establishes that the incoming task's TSS exists and that its LDT (if any) exists, loads all the registers from the new TSS, and then one by one reads the descriptors indicated for the selector in each segment register. If the SS descriptor is found to be not present, this exception is immediately taken as a trap in the context of the new task. (Explanation: The task switch occurred, but the first instruction of the new task is not yet executed.) Because of this, the remaining descriptor caches may not be updated with the needed descriptor contents. There are two ways to cope with this in the exception 12 handler:

1. Handle this exception with a separate task (a task gate in position 12 of the IDT). The task switch back to the interrupted task will cause the processor to reload the registers and descriptor caches for the interrupted task. The attempted task switch could, however, uncover a further exception, which will be vectored accordingly. When all exceptions generated by the task switch are handled, the switch back to the interrupted task will execute smoothly.
2. Handle this exception within the current task (a trap gate in position 12 of the IDT) and ensure that the handler routine for this exception makes all descriptor caches consistent with the selector values of these that were loaded during the task switch. The routine must therefore PUSH and then POP all segment register selectors. The POP operation will cause the 80386 to read the needed descriptor and update its corresponding descriptor cache on-chip. Be aware that each such POP instruction within the handler could possibly cause a not-present exception (exception 11) or some other

EX 12   Stack Fault   **EX 12**

exception. Further exception 12s could occur, however, so the exception-12 handler should be reentrant.

Active modes: REAL, PROTECTED, VIRTUAL 8086. REAL-mode vectoring uses vector 12 of the REAL-mode interrupt vector table. PROTECTED-mode or VIRTUAL 8086-mode vectoring uses gate 12 in the PROTECTED-mode IDT. This exception does not normally occur in real mode but can be forced to occur in that mode by creating a situation where a stack operand is partially beyond the 64K REAL-mode segment limit or by using the address-size prefix to create a 32-bit stack address beyond the 64K REAL-mode segment limit.

Error code pushed in PROTECTED mode: An error code, as in Figure 16.2, is pushed if the exception is caused by a stack segment being not present. If the exception is due to a stack segment limit violation, the error code is all 0.

Restartability: All occurrences of this exception are restartable. If the exception 12 handler makes the stack segment present (P = 1) or extends its limit as required and IRETurns, the interrupted program will resume execution.

Difference from 8086/8088: This exception does not exist on an 8086/8088. The fact that exception 12 can be forced to occur in REAL mode or VIRTUAL 8086 mode (by deliberate means of limit violation) is not a practical concern with commercial 8086 software.

EX 13   General Protection   **EX 13**

Exception 13: General Protection

Description: This exception is generated if the processor detects a protection violation not specifically covered under the other exceptions. The possible causes are attempting one of the following:

Items 1 through 6 push an error code, as in Figure 16.2.

1. Transferring control to a segment that is not executable, unless the CS selector comes from the incoming TSS during a task switch, in which case a TSS exception 10 occurs.
2. Loading the SS register with a read-only segment or loading SS with the descriptor of an executable segment, unless the SS selector comes from the incoming TSS during a task switch, in which case a TSS exception 10 occurs.
3. Loading the SS, DS, ES, FS, or GS registers with the descriptor of a system segment, unless the SS selector comes from the incoming TSS during a task switch, in which case a TSS exception 10 occurs.
4. Loading DS, ES, FS, or GS with the descriptor of an executable segment that is not also readable.
5. Transferring control to a segment or through a gate that violates privilege rules, or loading SS, DS, ES, FS or GS with a segment that violates privilege rules.
6. Loading a register CS, SS, DS, ES, FS or GS with a selector that references the LDT (a selector with TI = 1) when the LDTR has been loaded with a null selector (no LDT defined).

Items 7 through 15 push an error code of all zeros.

7. Loading the SS register with the null selector, unless the null SS selector comes from the incoming TSS during a task switch, in which case an invalid-TSS exception (exception 10) occurs.
8. Exceeding the segment limit when using CS, DS, ES, FS, or GS.
9. Exceeding the table limit when referencing a descriptor table: GDT , LDT, or IDT.
10. Writing into a read-only data segment or into a code segment (Code segments are never writable in PROTECTED mode).
11. Reading from an execute-only code segment.
12. Accessing memory via DS, ES, FS, or GS when the segment register contains a null selector.

13. Loading CR0 with PG = 1 and PE = 0 (i.e., attempting to enable paging REAL mode.
14. Vectoring an interrupt or exception via trap gate or interrupt gate from VIRTUAL 8086 mode to a privilege level other than 0. Level 0 is required to be the destination level so the IRET instruction at the end of the handler routine can set the VM bit to 1 as required for return to the VIRTUAL 8086 mode.
15. Exceeding the maximum allowed instruction length of 15 bytes including prefix bytes (this can occur only by deliberately using redundant prefixes before an instruction).

Special Considerations for General Protection Exception Detected During Task Switch: The Worst-Case Situation

If detected during a task switch, this exception is taken as a trap in the context of the incoming task. During a task switch, the 80386 first establishes that the incoming task's TSS exists and that its LDT (if any) exists, loads all the registers from the new TSS, and then one by one reads the descriptors indicated by the selectors for each segment register. If *any* needed descriptor is found to be *not present*, this exception is immediately taken as a trap in the context of the new task. (Explanation: The task switch occurred, but the first instruction of the new task is not yet executed.) Because of this, the remaining descriptor caches may not be updated with the needed descriptor contents. There are two ways to cope with this in the exception 13 handler:

1. Handle this exception with a separate task (a task gate in position 13 of the IDT). The task switch back to the interrupted task will cause the processor to reload the registers and descriptor caches for the interrupted task. The attempted task switch could, however, uncover a further exception, which will be vectored accordingly. When all exceptions generated by the task switch are handled, the switch back to the interrupted task will execute smoothly.
2. Handle this exception within the current task (a trap gate in position 13 of the IDT) and ensure that the handling routine itself makes all descriptor caches consistent with the selector values of those that were loaded during the task switch. The routine must therefore PUSH and then POP all segment register selectors. The POP operation will cause the 80386 to read the needed descriptor and update its corresponding descriptor cache on-chip. Be aware that each such POP instruction within the handler could possibly cause another general-protection exception or some other exception.

EX 13   General Protection   **EX 13**

Therefore the handler for this exception must be reentrant (all its temporary variables must be stored on the handler's stack).

Active modes: REAL, PROTECTED, VIRTUAL 8086. REAL-mode vectoring uses vector 13 of the REAL-mode interrupt vector table. PROTECTED-mode or VIRTUAL 8086-mode vectoring uses gate 13 in the PROTECTED-mode IDT. This exception does not normally occur in REAL mode but can be forced to occur in that mode by creating a situation where an operand is partially beyond the 64K REAL-mode segment limit or by using the address-size prefix to create a 32-bit address beyond the 64K REAL-mode segment limit.

Error code pushed in PROTECTED **mode:**   An error code, as in Figure 16.2, is pushed if the exception was caused by the loading of a selector (Items 1 through 6 above). An error code of all 0s is pushed if the exception is due to another reason (Items 7 through 15).

Restartability: All occurrences of this exception are restartable.

Difference from 8086/8088:   This exception does not exist on the 8086/8088. The fact that exception 13 can be forced to occur in REAL or VIRTUAL 8086 mode (by deliberate means of limit violation) is not a practical concern with commercial 8086 software.

Exception 14:   Page Fault

Description: This exception is generated if the executing program requires a page marked *not present* or if it attempts to use a page in a way restricted by its access rights. This exception is always taken as a fault.

Ample error information promotes efficient handler algorithms. An error code, shown in Figure 16.3, is pushed, and system register CR2 holds the linear address that caused the page fault.

Active modes: PROTECTED, VIRTUAL 8086. REAL-mode vectoring uses vector 14 of the REAL-mode interrupt vector table. PROTECTED-mode or VIRTUAL 8086-mode vectoring uses gate 14 in the PROTECTED-mode IDT.

Error code pushed in PROTECTED mode: The page-fault error code, as in Figure 16.3, is unique to this exception. It indicates whether the page fault was due to a page-fault error code or to an access-rights violation, gives the privilege level at which the page fault occurred, and tells whether the access causing the violation was a read or write.

Restartability: All occurrences of this fault are restartable. Since the exception is taken as a fault, the return address pushed onto the handler's stack points to the instruction that needs to be restarted. This is the instruction that caused the exception.

Difference from 8086/8088:   This exception does not exist on the 8086/8088.

Comments: When initializing the level-0 stack that the page fault handler needs, ensure that a page fault does not cause the processor to use an invalid stack pointer SS:ESP. If initializing the level-0 stack in a paging system when paging is enabled, do *not* use the two-instruction sequence:

```
MOV   SS,  AX
MOV   ESP, STACK_TOP
```

The reason to avoid this sequence is that, since the second instruction must be fetched from memory and accesses memory, it is possible to get a page fault after SS has been changed but before SP has received the corresponding change. A page fault at this point would cause the page-fault handler ((which is also at level 0) to use the inconsistent stack, possibly causing a system crash.

EX 14   Page Fault   **EX 14**

Instead, software that executes at the same privilege level as the page-fault handler should use the single new LSS instruction rather than the instruction pair above. In the normal case, in which the page-fault handler executes at level 0, the scope of the LSS *requirement* is limited to the level-0 code, which typically is the operating system. However, the new LSS instruction is recommended for loading SS:ESP at any privilege level. The two-instruction sequence above is outdated.

Exception 16:   Numeric Coprocessor Error

Description: This exception is generated if the 80386 ERROR# pin is active when the 80386 attempts to initiate another coprocessor instruction. As the processor prepares to begin the coprocessor instruction, the ERROR# input is polled, and, if it is found to be active, exception 16 is taken as a trap with respect to the coprocessor instruction causing the numeric error.

Active modes: REAL, PROTECTED, VIRTUAL 8086. REAL-mode vectoring uses vector 16 of the REAL-mode interrupt vector table. PROTECTED-mode or VIRTUAL 8086-mode vectoring uses gate 16 in the PROTECTED-mode IDT.

Error code pushed in PROTECTED mode: None.

Restartability: All occurrences of this exception are restartable, from the point of view of the 80386, but the coprocessor state has been changed by the coprocessor instruction causing the error and therefore is not restartable. A good handler strategy is to report the error and possibly terminate the failing program.

Difference from 8086/8088:   This exception does not exist on the 8086/8088, which relies on the interrupt hardware to signal any numeric errors. The PC architecture, for example, uses the NMI pin to signal coprocessor numeric errors. This approach can be maintained on the 80386 systems if desired, but the signal should be held inactive while the numeric coprocessor is BUSY.

Simultaneous Interrupts and Exceptions

Interrupts are recognized only at instruction boundaries. Exceptions also are taken only at instruction boundaries, either as a fault immediately before the offending instruction or as traps immediately after the offending instruction. There is a possibility that several interrupts and exceptions can be active at the same instruction boundary. For example, a hardware interrupt, an exception generated as a trap from the previous instruction, and an exception generated as a fault prior to the next instruction could all be active simultaneously.

Simultaneously active interrupts and exceptions pose an *arbitration* problem handled by logic on-chip. *Arbitration logic* assures that certain events are tended to before others, creating, in effect, a set of priorities for handling the possible events.

However, a more explicit description is conveyed by considering a *sequence of checks*, performed by the 80386 at each instruction boundary. This activity can be conceptualized as a sequence that subdivides the instruction boundary into a series of steps. At each step, various types of active interrupts and exceptions are recognized. This sequence of priorities, determined by on-chip hardware, handles all possible cases of simultaneous events in the order shown in Table 16.3.

Table 16.3 Detailed 80386 Sequence of Interrupt and Exception Checking at Each Instruction Boundary.

Step	Function
1.	Check for exception-1 traps (from single-step via trap flag or data breakpoints set in the debug registers) generated by the previous instruction. If active, take exception 1 as trap.
2.	Check for external NMI. If active, take interrupt 2.
3.	Check for external INTR. If active, read interrupt vector and take interrupt n, $0 \leq= n \leq= 255$.
4.	Check for exception-1 faults (from instruction-execution breakpoint set in the debug registers) possibly generated by the next instruction. If active, take exception 1 as fault.
5.	Check for segmentation faults possibly generated by fetching the next instruction. If active, take the exception (11 or 13) as a fault.
6.	Check for page faults possibly generated by fetching the next instruction. If active, take exception 14 as fault.
7.	Check for faults possibly generated by decoding the next instruction. This will be exception 6 if illegal opcode or if a PROTECTED-mode instruction not available in REAL mode; it will be exception 13 if the instruction is more than 15 bytes or if instruction requires greater privilege in PROTECTED mode (i.e., not at IOPL or PL 0, as required). If active, then take the exception as a fault.
8.	If WAIT opcode is the next instruction, check if TS = 1 and MP = 1 in CRO. If so, take exception 7 as a fault.
9.	If coprocessor opcode for numeric coprocessor is the next instruction, check if EM = 1 or TS = 1. If so, take exception 7 as fault.
10.	If WAIT opcode or opcode for numeric coprocessor is the next instruction, check ER-ROR# input from numeric coprocessor. If it is active, take exception 16 as a trap (from point of view of coprocessor instruction that generated the numeric error).
11.	Check in order for each memory reference required by the instruction: a. Check for segmentation faults that would prevent transferring the entire memory operand. If so, take the exception (11, 12, or 13) as a fault. b. Check for page faults that would prevent transferring the entire memory operand. If so, take exception 14 as a fault.

Note that this order supports the concept that the paging mechanism is underneath the segmentation mechanism. For a given memory reference, segmentation exceptions, if any, will be generated before any paging exceptions.

CHAPTER 17

DEBUGGING FEATURES

The principal debugging support on the 80386 is provided through dedicated debug registers. These programmable breakpoint registers are actually the same facilities utilized by sophisticated 80386 in-circuit emulators, such as Intel's ICE-368, which gives a hint of the great debugging power of these new registers.

The debug registers support **breakpoints** for code and data. In general, breakpoints are addresses set to trigger a debug exception when a program executes code or accesses data stored at a breakpoint address. **Instruction breakpoints** allow detection of instruction execution at any given linear address. The instruction breakpoints allow setting breakpoints even in ROM-based code. **Data breakpoints** are an important innovation, in that they can pinpoint exactly when any given data operand is being accessed or overwritten, for whatever unknown cause.

The previous processors in the 8086 family offered only a single-step exception, and breakpoint opcode, both of which are still available on the 80386.

Built-in Debugging Capabilities

Overall, a comprehensive set of debugging capabilities is built into the hardware of each 80386. Specifically, the 80386 debugging features offer four types of debug capabilities:

1. The debug registers 0–3, which define four independent breakpoint addresses that can be individually enabled and used for instruction breakpoints or data breakpoints.
2. The TF (Trap Flag) bit in the EFLAG register, which allows code to be executed one step at a time.
3. The breakpoint instruction (opcode CCh), a single-byte instruction that can be inserted into code (in writable memory) at any address, to generate an instruction breakpoint at the given address.
4. The T (Trap) bit in the 32-bit TSS, which allows trapping immediately upon invoking any 32-bit task marked with a set T bit in its TSS.

The debug capabilities act as traps to detect certain conditions of interest to the programmer. When such a condition occurs, the appropriate debug feature is triggered, generating a debug exception (exception 1) to invoke the debugger service routine. All debug capabilities generate exception 1 when triggered, except for item 3 above, the breakpoint opcode, which generates a breakpoint interrupt (interrupt 3).

All capabilities above are available in PROTECTED-mode operation; only capabilities 1, 2, and 3 are available in REAL-mode operation. The task-trapping feature is of course not applicable to REAL-mode operation.

The Debug Registers

The 80386 debug registers consist of six 32-bit registers, depicted in Figure 17.1. They consist of:

- Four breakpoint registers, each holding the linear address of a breakpoint usable as an instruction breakpoint or as a data breakpoint.
- One debug-control register, used to qualify and enable the four breakpoints given in the breakpoint registers.
- One debug-status register, which, when a debug exception occurs, indicates which of the debug features was triggered.

Using new instructions for the purpose, these registers are readable and writable in REAL mode and at privilege level 0 of PROTECTED mode.

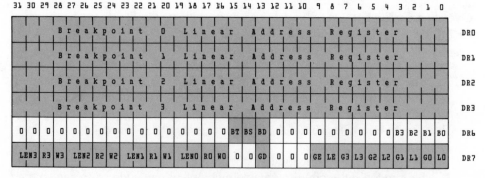

Figure 17.1   80386 Debug Registers.

DR0-DR3, the breakpoint registers, each contain the following field:

Breakpoint Linear Address is a 32-bit linear address that identifies the breakpoint zone.

Registers DR4 and DR5 are not implemented in the 80386. They may be implemented in future processors.

DR7, the debug-control register, contains several fields to further define the size of each breakpoint zone, to qualify the type of access that can trigger each breakpoint, and to enable each breakpoint. The DR6 fields are repeated in quadruplicate, once for each of the four breakpoints. The following description applies to the four identical fields in the DR6 register:

Table 17.1 Encoding of the LEN Field.

	Breakpoint Zone	
LEN Encoding	Size	Alignment
00	1 byte	At any linear address
01	2 bytes	WORD-aligned
10	*undefined, Do Not Use*	
11	4 bytes	DWORD-aligned

1. The LEN (Length) field indicates the size of the associated breakpoint zone, which may be 1, 2, or 4 bits. The LEN field is encoded as in Table 17.1.

    Each LEN field controls the size of the associated breakpoint field by controlling whether all low-order bits of the breakpoint register are used in detecting the breakpoint. Two-byte breakpoints ignore bit 0 of the linear address, resulting in a WORD-aligned breakpoint zone. Four-byte breakpoints ignore bits 0 and 1 of the linear address, resulting in a DWORD-aligned breakpoint zone.

2. RW (Read Write) defines the type of access that can trigger the breakpoint zone. The RW field is defined as in Table 17.2.

3. **G** and **L**, **Global Enable**, and **Local Enable**, are two enable bits for each of the breakpoints. If at least one of the enable bits is set to 1, the associated breakpoint is enabled. There is absolutely no difference in the function bits; the different names for each of the enables merely suggests the convention that, in a multitasking system, one of the enables could be the bit set by a global debugging routine and the other could be the bit set by a local debugging routine.

4. **GE** and **LE**, **Global Exact** and **Local Exact**, are two exact bits that affect *data* breakpointing. If at least one of these bits is set to 1, any data breakpoint will be reported exactly after completion of the instruction that caused the transfer. (Instruction breakpoints are always reported exactly, regardless of GE and LE bits.) If an exact data breakpoint match is not selected, then data breakpoints may not be reported until several instructions later—or may not even be reported at all. If you want to be certain of catching *all* data breakpoints, you must set at least one of these exact bits while debugging.

Exact reporting is provided by forcing the 80386 execution unit to wait for completion of any data-operand transfers before beginning execution of the next instruction. This will slow the 80386 program execution by a small amount.

Table 17.2   Encoding of the RW Field.

RW Encoding	Type of Access That Can Trigger the Breakpoint
00	Instruction execution only
01	Data writes only
10	*Undefined, Do Not Use*
11	Data reads or data writes only

DR6, the debug-status register, contains several fields revealing the reason a debug exception (exception 1) has occurred. Each field is a single-bit flag corresponding to one of the debug capabilities, and each can be automatically set by the 80386 as it vectors to the exception-1 routine. These bits are never reset automatically, however; the exception-1 routine bears the responsibility of resetting these indicator flags.

1. **B0, B1, B2, and B3, Breakpoints 0 1, 2, and 3,** if set to 1, indicate that the associated breakpoint was triggered.
2. **BD, Debug Registers in Use by ICE-386,** if set to 1, indicates that an attempt to read or write a debug register has been denied because the ICE-386 in-circuit emulator is currently using these facilities. Thus, during operation of ICE-386 for debugging, software debuggers cannot be used simultaneously.
3. **BS, Debug Exception Due to Single-step,** if set to 1, indicates that exception 1 was generated because the TF (single-step Trap Flag) was set in the EFLAG register. When the debugger is single-stepping through the target program, it would the BS bit being set would be expected.
4. **BT, Debug Exception Due to Task-switch Trap,** if set to 1, indicates that exception 1 was generated because a task switch activated a task whose 32-bit TSS's T (Trap) bit is set to 1.

If the instruction beginning at the breakpoint address is about to be executed, the instruction-breakpoint condition has occurred, and, if the breakpoint is enabled, an exception-1 *fault* will occur immediately before the instruction is executed.

Note that merely prefetching the instruction does not trigger the breakpoint: The instruction must actually be about to begin execution for the instruction breakpoint to occur.

Data Breakpointing with the Debug Registers

A data breakpoint can be set up by writing the linear address of the breakpoint into a debug register. For data breakpoints, the associated RW field must be 01 (data write only) or 11 (data write/read). The associated LEN field can be any of the defined values: 00, 10, or 11 (for 1-, 2-, or 4-byte breakpoint zones).

If a data access *entirely or partly* falls within a data-breakpoint zone, the data-breakpoint condition has occurred, and, if the breakpoint is enabled, an exception 1 *trap* will occur after the access occurs.

Restart Flag

A subtle feature that refines the operation of the 80386 debug capabilities is its RF (Restart Flag) bit in the EFLAG. The RF bit in EFLAG, when set to 1, can suppress an instruction breakpoint when the exception-1 handler returns to the very instruction that is still an instruction breakpoint.

The 80386 automatically sets RF in the EFLAG image on the stack when EFLAG is PUSHed as the 80386 enters into any *fault handler*. Therefore the IRET instruction at the end of the fault handler, as it POPs the EFLAG image from the stack, will set RF in the EFLAG register, and execution will resume at the breakpoint address without generating another breakpoint fault.

If, after a debug fault, RF is set to 1 and the debug handler retries the faulting instruction, it is possible that retrying the instruction will raise other faults. Since *any* fault handler sets the RF flag, the retry of the instruction after those faults will also be performed with RF equal to 1, so that the debug breakpoint for that one instruction will continue to be ignored. The processor automatically clears RF only after successful *completion* of the instruction.

Note that a programmer does not need to explicitly set or reset RF for correct operation. The processor automatically sets RF to 1, to suppress repeated debug exceptions when an instruction is retried. The processor automatically resets RF to 0 at successful completion of the instruction, so that an instruction breakpoint will not be suppressed on further instructions.

The 8086-Compatible Debugging Features

Single-Step Trap

If the TF bit (single-step trap flag) is set to 1, an exception-1 *trap* will occur after completion of the next instruction. In typical practice, a debugger sets the TF bit of the EFLAG image on the debugger's stack, then transfers control to the target program and loads the EFLAG image with a single instruction, the IRET instruction. The single-step trap occurs after executing one instruction of the target program.

Since exception 1 occurs as a trap, after the instruction has just completed execution, the CS:EIP pushed onto the debugger's stack points to the next unexecuted instruction of the program being debugged. An exception-1 handler can therefore efficiently single-step through the target program, merely by ending with an IRET instruction.

Breakpoint Instruction

A single-byte opcode breakpoint instruction is opcode CCh. The breakpoint opcode generates an exception-3 *trap* when executed. The breakpoint instruction is coded as a single-byte instruction, so it can be placed at any location without ever overwriting more than one instruction. The single-byte breakpoint instruction is a substitute for the two-byte general software interrupt instruction INT *n*, where *n* equals 3. However, the breakpoint instruction (opcode CCh) is never IOPL-sensitive, while INT *n* is IOPL-sensitive in PROTECTED mode and in VIRTUAL 8086 mode.

In typical use, the debugger can plant the single-byte breakpoint instruction at all desired instruction-execution breakpoints. Breakpoint instructions cannot be temporarily written into fixed memory, such as ROM devices. Also note that the breakpoint instruction cannot provide a data-breakpoint capability. The shortcomings are eliminated when using the 80386 debug registers to perform instruction breakpointing, as explained on page 228.

APPENDIX A

FLAG REGISTER AND
CONDITION CODES

The 32-bit Flag Register contains 8 status fields and 5 control fields. Undefined bits are read as zeros (except bit 1 which reads as one) and ignored when written. The lower 16 bits of EFLAG (Extended FLAG) can also be referenced as FLAG for 16-bit operations.

Table A.1   Flag Register.

31	30	···	19	18	17	16	15	14	13 12	11	10	9	8	7	6	5	4	3	2	1	0
0	0	· · ·	0	0	VM	RF	0	NT	IOPL	OF	DF	IF	TF	SF	ZF	0	AF	0	PF	1	CF

Status Bits		**Present in FLAG and EFLAG**	**Present only in EFLAG (i.e. new with 80386)**
SF	(Sign)	Yes	
PF	(Parity)	Yes	
OF	(Overflow)	Yes	
ZF	(Zero)	Yes	
CF	(Carry)	Yes	
AF	(Auxiliary Carry)	Yes	
IOPL	(I/O Privilege Level)	Yes	
NT	(Nested Task)	Yes	
Control Bits			
TF	(Trap Flag)	Yes	
IF	(Interrupt Enable)	Yes	
DF	(Direction Flag)	Yes	
RF	(Resume Flag)		Yes
VM	(Virtual 8086 Mode)		Yes

The flag fields of EFLAG are defined below, describing their behavior during instructions that affect these flags. There are, of course, several instructions that leave the flags completely unchanged from their previous state. Appendix B provides instruction details.

CF   Carry Flag, bit 0

CF is set if the operation resulted in a carry out of the high-order bit (addition) or a borrow into the high-order bit (subtraction). Otherwise CF is reset. For 8-, 16-, and 32-bit operations, CF is set according to carry or borrow at bits 7, 15, and 31 respectively.

PF   Parity Flag, bit 2

PF is set if the eight low-order bits of the operation's result contain an even number of 1s (even parity). PF is reset if the 8 low-order bits have an odd number of 1s (odd parity). PF is a function of only the 8 low-order bits, regardless of operand size.

AF   Auxiliary Carry Flag, bit 4

The Auxiliary Carry Flag is used to simplify the addition and subtraction of packed BCD quantities. AF is set if the operation resulted in a carry out of bit 3 (addition) or a borrow into bit 3 (subtraction). Otherwise AF is reset. AF is affected by a carry out of or a borrow into bit 3 only, regardless of overall operand length.

ZF   Zero Flag, bit 6

ZF is set if all bits of the result are zero. Otherwise it is reset.

SF   Sign Flag, bit 7

SF is set if the high-order bit of the result is set. It is reset otherwise. For 8-, 16-, and 32-bit operations, SF reflects the state of bit 7, 15, and 31 respectively.

TF   Trap Flag, bit 8

TF enables the single-step trap. When TF is set, the 80386 generates an exception 1 trap after the next instruction is executed. When TF is reset, exception 1 is generated only by the other debug features, provided by the Debug Registers.

IF   INTR Enable Flag, bit 9

The IF bit, when set, allows recognition of external interrupts signaled on the INTR pin. When IF is reset, external interrupts signaled on INTR are not recognized. IOPL indicates the maximum value of CPL at which the IF bit can be altered when new values are popped into the EFLAG (or FLAG) register. Task switches can always alter the IF bit as the new EFLAG image is loaded from the incoming task's TSS.

DF   Direction Flag, bit 10

DF defines whether the ESI and/or EDI index registers are decremented or incremented after each iteration of the string instructions. They are incremented if DF is reset (string is processed from left to right). Postdecrement occurs if DF is set (string is processed from right to left).

OF   Overflow Flag, bit 11

OF is set if the operation resulted in a signed overflow. Signed overflow occurs when the operation resulted in a carry/borrow into the sign bit of the result but did not result in a carry/borrow out of the sign bit, or vice versa. For 8-, 16-, and 32-bit operations, OF is set according to the sign bit at position 7, 15, and 31.

IOPL   IO Privilege Level, bits 12–13

This two-bit flag field applies to PROTECTED mode. IOPL indicates the numerical maximum of CPL at which I/O can be unconditionally performed. At any larger value of CPL, the I/O permission bitmap is automatically consulted by the 80386. This flag also indicates the maximum CPL value allowing alteration of the IF (INTR Enable Flag) flag bit when new values are popped into EFLAG. The POPF and IRET instruction can alter the IOPL flag only when CPL equals 0. Task switches can always alter the IOPL field as the new EFLAG image is loaded from the incoming task's TSS.

NT   Nested Task, bit 14

This flag applies to PROTECTED mode. This bit is set or reset automatically by the 80386 during task switches. NT is set by the 80386 to indicate that the execution of the current task is nested within a parent task. If set, it indicates that the current task's TSS holds a valid back-link selector of the TSS of the parent task. The value of NT is tested by the IRET instruction to determine whether it must perform an intertask return to the task indicated by the back link (NT = 1) or whether it must perform a normal IRETurn (NT = 0). A POPF or IRET instruction may affect the setting of NT according to the EFLAG image popped, at any CPL.

RF   Resume Flag, bit 16

RF is used in conjunction with the debug register breakpoints. It is checked at instruction boundaries before breakpoint processing.

When RF is set, it causes any debug fault (instruction execution breakpoint) to be ignored on the next instruction. RF is then automatically reset at the successful completion of every instruction (success is indicated by lack of any exceptions), except for the IRET instruction, the POPF instruction, and instructions causing a task switch (JMP, CALL, INT 3, INT *n*, INTO, BOUNDS, or IRET). These instructions set

RF according to the EFLAG loaded. For example, at the end of the instruction breakpoint fault-service routine (exception 1), the IRET instruction can pop an EFLAG image having the RF bit set and the resume program execution at the breakpoint address, without generating another breakpoint fault on the same instruction.

VM   Virtual 8086 Mode, bit 17

The VM bit provides VIRTUAL 8086 Mode within PROTECTED mode. If set while the 80386 is in PROTECTED mode, the 80386 will begin VIRTUAL 8086-mode operation, handling segment-register loads as in REAL mode but generating exception 13 faults on privileged opcodes. The VM bit can be set only in PROTECTED mode, by the IRET instruction if CPL equals 0, or by task switches at any privilege level. The VM flag is unaffected by the POPF. PUSHF always pushes a 0 in this bit even if executing in VIRTUAL 8086 mode. The EFLAG image pushed during interrupt processing or saved during task switches will, however, contain a 1 in this flag if the interrupted code was executing as a VIRTUAL 8086 task.

APPENDIX B

INSTRUCTION-SET DETAILS

This appendix analyzes one by one all instructions available for the 80386, explaining in detail their purpose, the manner in which they affect flags, and how they can be used in conjunction with the various addressing modes. The addressing modes are discussed in detail in Chapters 4 and 7.

Table B.1 summarizes the instruction categories and provides a quick overview of instruction availability in all operating modes. Generally speaking, most instructions are always available to the programmer, but special instructions that control system registers are restricted to privilege-level 0 in PROTECTED mode. In PROTECTED mode, I/O instructions are restricted to the level indicated by IOPL, unless the I/O permission bitmap allows I/O to the given I/O addresses at all privilege levels. In VIRTUAL 8086 mode, I/O instructions are restricted by the I/O permission bitmap.

Table B.1 also indicates each instruction's effect upon the 80386 code prefetcher. Most instructions allow the prefetcher to proceed unimpeded, unless the code-segment limit is reached or a not-present or unusable page is reached. However, the *unconditional* control transfer instructions (CALL, INT, JMP, RET, IRET) and the HLT instruction cause the prefetcher to stop, since code at subsequent addresses will not be immediately executed, and continued prefetching of those addresses would therefore waste bus bandwidth. The Jcc *conditional* jump instructions do not stop the prefetcher. Similar instructions, the LOOPcc instructions, do stop the prefetcher and so are preferred to produce maximum speed in executing iterative loops, where the test condition will most often be true (i.e., transfer will most often be taken).

Instruction prefixes are summarized in Table B.2.

Table B.1 Detailed 80386 Instruction List.

	Assembler Mnemonic	Instruction Description	Status (See Key)	REAL Mode	PROTECTED Mode	VIRTUAL 8086 Mode	Effect on Prefetcher	Details on Page
					80386 Availability (See Key Below)			
1.	AAA	ASCII Adjust after Addition	86	Yes	Yes	Yes	Continues	240
2.	AAD	ASCII Adjust before Division	86	Yes	Yes	Yes	Continues	242
3.	AAM	ASCII Adjust after Multiplication	86	Yes	Yes	Yes	Continues	244
4.	AAS	ASCII Adjust after Subtraction	86	Yes	Yes	Yes	Continues	246
5.	ADC	Integer Addition with Carry	86	Yes	Yes	Yes	Continues	248
6.	ADD	Integer Addition	86	Yes	Yes	Yes	Continues	250
7.	AND	Logical AND	86	Yes	Yes	Yes	Continues	252
8.	ARPL	Adjust PRL Field of Selector	PROT	No(a)	Yes	No(a)	Continues	254
9.	BOUND	Check Array Index against Bounds	186	Yes	Yes	Yes	Continues	256
10.	BSF	Bit String Scan Forward	386	Yes	Yes	Yes	Continues	258
11.	BSR	Bit String Scan Forward	386	Yes	Yes	Yes	Continues	260
12.	BT	Bit Test	386	Yes	Yes	Yes	Continues	262
13.	BTC	Bit Test, Then Complement Bit	386	Yes	Yes	Yes	Continues	264
14.	BTR	Bit Test, Then Reset Bit	386	Yes	Yes	Yes	Continues	266
15.	BTS	Bit Test, Then Set Bit	386	Yes	Yes	Yes	Continues	268
16.	CALL	Call Procedure (or Task in PROTECTED Mode)	86	Yes	Yes	Yes	Stops	270
17.	CBW/CWDE	Convert BYTE to WORD/WORD to DWORD to DWORD	86	Yes	Yes	Yes	Continues	275
18.	CLC	Clear Carry Flag	86	Yes	Yes	Yes	Continues	276
19.	CLD	Clear Direction Flag—Increment Index	86	Yes	Yes	Yes	Continues	277
20.	CLI	Clear Interrupt Flag—Disable Interrupts	86	Yes	IOPL	IOPL = 3	Continues	278
21.	CLTS	Clear Task-Switched Flag	PROT	Yes(a)	Yes	Yes(a)	Continues	280
22.	CMC	Complement Carry Flag	86	Yes	Yes	Yes	Continues	282
23.	CMP	Compare Operands	86	Yes	Yes	Yes	Continues	283
24.	CMPSB	Compare String Data (BYTE)	86	Yes	Yes	Yes	Continues	285
25.	CMPSW/CMPSD	Compare String Data (WORD or DWORD)	86	Yes	Yes	Yes	Continues	285
26.	CWD/CDQ	Convert WORD to DWORD/DWORD to QWORD	86	Yes	Yes	Yes	Continues	287
27.	DAA	Packed BCD Adjust after Addition	86	Yes	Yes	Yes	Continues	288
28.	DAS	Packed BCD Adjust after Subtraction	86	Yes	Yes	Yes	Continues	290
29.	DEC	Decrement by 1	86	Yes	Yes	Yes	Continues	292
30.	DIV	Unsigned Divide	86	Yes	Yes	Yes	Continues	294
31.	ENTER	Make Stack Frame for Procedure Entrance	186	Yes	Yes	Yes	Continues	296
32.	HLT	Halt Until Interrupt	86	Yes	Level0	No(b)	Stops	298
33.	IDIV	Integer (Signed) Divide	86	Yes	Yes	Yes	Continues	300
34.	IMUL	Integer (Signed) Multiply	86	Yes	Yes	Yes	Continues	302
35.	IN	Input Data from I/O Address	86	Yes	IOPL/BIT	BIT	Continues	304
36.	INC	Increment by 1	86	Yes	Yes	Yes	Continues	306
37.	INSB	Input String Data from I/O Address (BYTE)	186	Yes	IOPL/BIT	BIT	Continues	309
38.	INSW/INSD	Input String from I/O Address (WORD or DWORD)	186	Yes	IOPL/BIT	BIT	Continues	309
39.	INT 3	Interrupt 3 (Breakpoint)	86	Yes	Yes	Yes	Stops	310
40.	INTO	Interrupt 4 If Overflow	86	Yes	Yes	Yes	Stops	312
41.	INT n	Interrupt n	86	Yes	Yes	IOPL = 3	Stops	314
42.	IRET/IRETD	Return from Interrupt (or Task in PROTECTED Mode)	86	Yes	Yes	IOPL = 3	Stops	319
43.	Jcc	Jump on Condition True	86	Yes	Yes	Yes	Continues	325
44.	JCXZ/JECXZ	Jump on CX/ECX Zero	86	Yes	Yes	Yes	Continues	327
45.	JMP	Jump to Code (or Task in PROTECTED Mode)	86	Yes	Yes	Yes	Stops	329
46.	LAHF	Load AH Register from EFLAG	PROT	No(a)	Level0	No(a)	Continues	333
47.	LAR	Load Access Rights into Register	86	Yes	Yes	Yes	Continues	334
48.	LEA	Load Effective Address	86	Yes	Yes	Yes	Continues	336
49.	LEAVE	High Level Procedure Exit	186	Yes	Yes	Yes	Continues	338
50.	LGDT	Load Global Descriptor Table Register	PROT	Yes(a)	Level0	No(b)	Continues	339
51.	LIDT	Load Interrupt Descriptor Table Register	PROT	Yes(a)	Level0	No(b)	Continues	341
52.	LDS	Load Full Pointer to DS:genreg	86	Yes	Yes	Yes	Continues	343
53.	LES	Load Full Pointer to ES:genreg	86	Yes	Yes	Yes	Continues	343
54.	LFS	Load Full Pointer to FS:genreg	386	Yes	Yes	Yes	Continues	343
55.	LGS	Load Full Pointer to GS:genreg	386	Yes	Yes	Yes	Continues	343
56.	LSS	Load Full Pointer to SS:genreg	386	Yes	Yes	Yes	Continues	343
57.	LLDT	Load Local Descriptor Register	PROT	No(a)	Level0	No(a)	Continues	345

Table B.1   Detailed 80386 Instruction List (*Continued*).

Assembler Mnemonic	Instruction Description	Status (See Key)	REAL Mode	PROTECTED Mode	VIRTUAL 8086 Mode	Effect on Prefetcher	Details on Page
			80386 Availability (See Key Below)				
58. LMSW	Load Machine Status Word Register	PROT	Yes(a)	Level0	Yes(a)	Continues	347
59. LODSB	Load String Data (BYTE)	86	Yes	Yes	Yes	Continues	349
60. LODSW/LODSD	Load String Data (WORD or DWORD)	86	Yes	Yes	Yes	Continues	349
61. LOOP	Loop and Decrement ECX	86	Yes	Yes	Yes	Stops	351
62. LOOPE/LOPZ	Loop and Decrement ECX while Condition equal	86	Yes	Yes	Yes	Stops	353
63. LSL	Load Segment Limit into Register	PROT	No(a)	Yes	No(a)	Continues	357
64. LTR	Load Task Register	PROT	No(a)	Level0	No(a)	Continues	359
65. MOV	Move to/from General Registers	86	Yes	Yes	Yes	Continues	361
	Move to/from Segment Registers	86	Yes	Yes	Yes	Continues	363
	Move to/from System Registers	386	Yes	Level0	No(b)	Continues	364
66. MOVSB	Move String Data (BYTE)	86	Yes	Yes	Yes	Continues	366
67. MOVSW/MOVSD	Move String Data (WORD or DWORD)	86	Yes	Yes	Yes	Continues	366
68. MOVSX	Move Data Sign-Extended	86	Yes	Yes	Yes	Continues	368
69. MOVZX	Move Data Zero-Extended	86	Yes	Yes	Yes	Continues	370
70. MUL	Unsigned Multiply	86	Yes	Yes	Yes	Continues	372
71. NEG	Integer Negate	86	Yes	Yes	Yes	Continues	374
72. NOP	No Operation	86	Yes	Yes	Yes	Continues	376
73. NOT	Logical Complement	86	Yes	Yes	Yes	Continues	377
74. OR	Logical OR	86	Yes	Yes	Yes	Continues	379
75. OUT	Output to I/O Address	86	Yes	IOPL/BIT	BIT	Continues	381
76. OUTSB	Output String Data to I/O Address (BYTE)	186	Yes	IOPL/BIT	BIT	Continues	383
77. OUTSW/OUTSD	Output String to I/O Address (WORD or DWORD)	186	Yes	IOPL/BIT	BIT	Continues	383
78. POP	Pop from Stack to Register	86	Yes	Yes	Yes	Continues	385
79. POPA/POPAD	Pop from Stack to All General Registers	186	Yes	Yes	Yes	Continues	386
80. POPF/POPFD	Pop from Stack into FLAG/EFLAG	86	Yes	Yes	IOPL = 3	Continues	388
81. PUSH	Push onto Stack	86	Yes	Yes	Yes	Continues	390
82. PUSHA/PUSHAD	Push All General Registers onto Stack	186	Yes	Yes	Yes	Continues	393
83. PUSHF/PUSHFD	Push FLAG/EFLAG onto Stack	86	Yes	Yes	IOPL = 3	Continues	395
84. RCL/RCR	Rotate through Carry Flag Left/Right	86	Yes	Yes	Yes	Continues	397
85. RET	Return from Procedure	86	Yes	Yes	Yes	Stops	400
86. ROL/ROR	Rotate Left/Right	86	Yes	Yes	Yes	Continues	403
87. SAHF	Store AH Register into EFLAG	86	Yes	Yes	Yes	Continues	408
88. SAL/SAR	Arithmetic Shift Left/Right	86	Yes	Yes	Yes	Continues	409
89. SBB	Integer Subtraction with Borrow	86	Yes	Yes	Yes	Continues	411
90. SCASB	Scan String Data (BYTE)	86	Yes	Yes	Yes	Continues	413
91. SCASW/SCASD	Scan String Data (WORD or DWORD)	86	Yes	Yes	Yes	Continues	413
92. SETcc	Set Byte on Condition True	386	Yes	Yes	Yes	Continues	415
93. SGDT	Store Global Descriptor Table Register	PROT	Yes(a)	Yes	Yes(a)	Continues	417
94. SHL/SHR	Logical Shift Left/Right	86	Yes	Yes	Yes	Continues	419
95. SHLD/SHRD	Double Precision Shift Left/Right	386	Yes	Yes	Yes	Continues	421
96. SIDT	Store Interrupt Descriptor Table Register	PROT	Yes(a)	Yes	Yes(a)	Continues	424
97. SLDT	Store Local Descriptor Table Register	PROT	No(a)	Yes	No(a)	Continues	426
98. SMSW	Store Machine Status Word Register	PROT	Yes(a)	Yes	Yes(a)	Continues	428
99. STC	Set Carry Flag	86	Yes	Yes	Yes	Continues	430
100. STD	Set Direction Flag—Index Decrement	86	Yes	Yes	Yes	Continues	431
101. STI	Set Interrupt Flag—Enable Interrupts	86	Yes	IOPL	IOPL = 3	Continues	432
102. STOSB	Store String Data (BYTE)	86	Yes	Yes	Yes	Continues	434
103. STOSW/STOSD	Store String Data (WORD or DWORD)	86	Yes	Yes	Yes	Continues	434
104. STR	Store Task Register	PROT	No(a)	Yes	No(a)	Continues	436
105. SUB	Integer Subtraction	86	Yes	Yes	Yes	Continues	438
106. TEST	Logical Compare Operands	86	Yes	Yes	Yes	Continues	439
107. VERR	Verify a Segment for Reading	PROT	No(a)	Yes	No(a)	Continues	442
108. VERW	Verify a Segment for Writing	PROT	No(a)	Yes	No(a)	Continues	442
109. WAIT	Wait Until BUSY Pin Is Inactive	86	Yes	Yes	Yes	Continues	444
110. XCHG	Exchange Register/Memory with Register	86	Yes	Yes	Yes	Continues	446
111. XLATB	Table Look-up Translation	86	Yes	Yes	Yes	Continues	448
112. XOR	Logical Exclusive OR	86	Yes	Yes	Yes	Continues	450

Table B.2   Detailed Instruction Prefix List.

	Assembler Mnemonic	Instruction Description	Status (See Key)	80386 Availability (See Key Below) REAL Mode	PROTECTED Mode	VIRTUAL 8086 Mode	Effect on Prefetcher	Details on Page
a.	USE16/USE32	16/32-bit Address-Size Toggle	386	Yes	Yes	Yes	—	453
b.	USE16/USE32	16/32-bit Operand-Size Toggle	386	Yes	Yes	Yes	—	454
c.	CS:	Use Code Segment, Overriding Default Choice	86	Yes	Yes	Yes	—	455
d.	DS:	Use Data Segment, Overriding Default Choice	86	Yes	Yes	Yes	—	455
e.	ES:	Use Extra Data Segment ES, Overriding Default Choice	86	Yes	Yes	Yes	—	455
f.	FS:	Use Extra Data Segment FS, Overriding Default Choice	386	Yes	Yes	Yes	—	455
g.	GS:	Use Extra Data Segment GS, Overriding Default Choice	386	Yes	Yes	Yes	—	455
h.	SS:	Use Stack Segment, Overriding Default Choice	386	Yes	Yes	Yes	—	455
i.	REP	Repeat (for String Instructions INS, OUTS, and STOS)	86	Yes	Yes	Yes	—	457
j.	REPE	Repeat If Equal (for String Instructions CMPS and SCAS)	86	Yes	Yes	Yes	—	458
k.	REPNE	Repeat If Not Equal (for String Instructions CMPS and SCAS)	86	Yes	Yes	Yes	—	459
l.	LOCK	Assert Bus Lock Signal (for Instructions Listed on Page 000)	86	Yes	Yes	Yes	—	460

Status Key

86 Instruction originated with the 8086/8088 and is present on all processors in the 86 family: 8086/88, 80186/80188, 80286, and 80386.

186 Instruction was introduced on the 80186/80188 and is also present on the 80286 and 80386.

PROT Instruction was introduced to support PROTECTED mode, on the 80286 and 80386.

386 Instruction is a new feature of the 80386.

Availability Key

Yes Instruction or function is always available in this mode.

Yes(a) This instruction is available in REAL mode, to allow setting up for PROTECTED mode. It happens to also be available in VIRTUAL 8086 mode, although this instruction would typically not appear in 8086 code.

No(a) In REAL mode, this instruction is not recognized. Exception 6 is generated If instruction is attempted. The same is true for VIRTUAL 8086 mode.

IOPL/BIT In PROTECTED mode, instruction is available at levels at or above IOPL (i.e. CPL IOPL), unless the I/O permission bitmap permits I/O to the specific I/O addresses used in this instruction; exception 13 if attempted otherwise.

IOPL In PROTECTED mode, this instruction is available at levels at or above IOPL (i.e., if CPL IOPL); exception 13 if attempted otherwise.

Level_0 In PROTECTED mode, this instruction is available only at level 0 (i.e., if CPL = 0), the most-privileged level; exception 13 if attempted otherwise.

BIT   In VIRTUAL 8086 mode, this instruction is available if the I/O permission bitmap permits I/O to the specific I/O addresses used in this instruction; exception 13 if attempted otherwise.

IOPL = 3   In VIRTUAL 8086 mode, this instruction is available only if IOPL = 3, since VIRTUAL 8086 mode operates at privilege-level 3; exception 13 if attempted otherwise.

No(b)   In VIRTUAL 8086 mode, this instruction is not available, because it is a privilege-level 0 instruction (VIRTUAL 8086 mode operates at privilege-level 3); exception 13 if attempted.

AAA   ASCII Adjust after Addition   **AAA**

Format

AAA

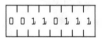

Function

```
IF ((AL AND 0Fh) > 9) OR (AF=1) THEN
BEGIN                    {begin adjustment}
  AL ⟵ (AL + 6) AND 0Fh;  {cause rollover in lower nibble OF AL}
  AH ⟵ AH + 1;           {add 1 to more significant digit      }
  AF ⟵ 1;
  CF ⟵ 1;
END;
ELSE
BEGIN                    {no adjustment needed}
  CF ⟵ 0;
  AF ⟵ 0;
END;
```

Description

This instruction can be used after addition of each digit of unpacked BCD values
(unpacked BCD: the lower nibble of each byte contains a single BCD digit). AAA is
useful immediately after performing addition of each unpacked digit, beginning of
course with the least significant digit. If the addition results in an unpacked value
larger than 9, AAA causes appropriate rollover of the BCD digit in register AL, and
increments the more significant unpacked BCD digit (in lower nibble of register
AH).

Example

```
    ADD    AL, BL    ;note that AL must be destination.
    AAA              ;adjust AL for unpacked BCD format.
```

The ADD and AAA instructions are often contained within a loop that adds the
unpacked BCD values digit-by-digit. To convert AL to an ASCII value, follow AAA
with OR AL,30h.

AAA   ASCII Adjust after Addition   **AAA**

Timing

`4 clock cycles; 0.2µsec @ 20MHz.`

Flags

CF and AF as described in *Function* above. OF, SF, ZF, and PF are undefined. Other flags are unchanged.

REAL-mode Exceptions:

None.

PROTECTED-mode Exceptions:

None.

VIRTUAL 8086-mode Exceptions:

None.

AAD   ASCII Adjust before Division   **AAD**

Format

```
AAD
```

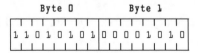

Byte 0   Byte 1

```
1 1 0 1 0 1 0 1   0 0 0 0 1 0 1 0
```

Function

```
AL ← (AH * 10) + AL;
AH ← 0;
```

Description

This instruction can be used before division of a two-digit unpacked BCD number (unpacked BCD: the lower nibble of each byte contains a single BCD digit). AAD causes register AX to become the binary equivalent of the original two unpacked BCD digits in AH and AL.

Example

```
AAD              ;adjust AX.
DIV    AX,BL     ;perform division yielding binary result.
```

Timing

19 clock cycles; 0.95µsec @ 20MHz.

Flags

SF, ZF, and PF affected according to result, as described in Appendix A. OF, AF, and CF are undefined. Other flags are unchanged.

AAD   ASCII Adjust before Division   **AAD**

REAL-**mode Exceptions:**

None.

PROTECTED-**mode Exceptions:**

None.

VIRTUAL 8086-**mode Exceptions:**

None.

AAM   ASCII Adjust after Multiplication   **AAM**

Format

```
AAM
```

```
        Byte 0         Byte 1
  ┌─┬─┬─┬─┬─┬─┬─┬─┬─┬─┬─┬─┬─┬─┬─┬─┐
  │1│1│0│1│0│1│0│0│0│0│0│0│1│0│1│0│
  └─┴─┴─┴─┴─┴─┴─┴─┴─┴─┴─┴─┴─┴─┴─┴─┘
```

Function

```
AH ⟵ AL / 10;
AL ⟵ AL MOD 10;
```

Description

This instruction can be used after multiplication of two single-digit unpacked BCD numbers (unpacked BCD: the lower nibble of each byte contains a single BCD digit). Since the result is less than 100, AAM unpacks the result by dividing AL by 10, leaving the quotient (most significant digit) in AH and the remainder (least significant digit) in AL.

Example

```
    MUL     AL,BL    ;multiply two unpacked BCD numbers.
    AAM              ;unpack result into AH and AL.
```

Timing

```
17 clock cycles; 0.85μsec @ 20MHz.
```

Flags

SF, ZF, and PF affected according to result, as described in Appendix A. OF, AF, and CF are undefined. Other flags are unchanged.

AAM   ASCII Adjust after Multiplication   **AAM**

REAL-mode Exceptions:

None.

PROTECTED-mode Exceptions:

None.

VIRTUAL 8086-mode Exceptions:

None.

AAS   ASCII Adjust after Subtraction   **AAS**

Format

AAS

Function

```
IF ((AL AND 0Fh) > 9) OR (AF=1) THEN
BEGIN                           (begin adjustment)
  AL ←── (AL - 6) AND 0Fh;    (cause rollunder in lower nibble of AL )
  AH ←── AH - 1;              (subtract 1 from more significant digit)
  AF ←── 1;
  CF ←── 1;
END;
ELSE
BEGIN                           (no adjustment needed)
  CF ←── 0;
  AF ←── 0;
END;
```

Description

This instruction can be used after subtraction of each digit of unpacked BCD values (unpacked BCD: the lower nibble of each byte contains a single BCD digit). AAS is useful immediately after performing subtraction of each unpacked digit, beginning of course with the least significant digit. If the subtraction results in an unpacked value larger than 9, AAS causes appropriate rollunder of the BCD digit in register AL, and decrements the more significant unpacked BCD digit (in lower nibble of register AH).

Example

```
    SUB     AL, BL    ;note that AL must be destination.
    AAS               ;adjust AL for unpacked BCD format.
```

The SUB and AAS instructions are often contained within a loop that subtracts the unpacked BCD values digit-by-digit. To convert AL to an ASCII value, follow AAS with OR AL,30h.

AAS   ASCII Adjust after Subtraction   **AAS**

Timing

```
4 clock cycles; 0.2µsec @ 20MHz.
```

Flags

CF and AF as described in *Function* above. OF, SF, ZF, and PF are undefined. Other flags are unchanged.

REAL-mode Exceptions:

None.

PROTECTED-mode Exceptions:

None.

VIRTUAL 8086-mode Exceptions:

None.

ADC   Integer Add with Carry   ADC

Format

```
ADC
```

	Byte 0	Byte 1	Subsequent Byte(s)
Register to Register	`0 0 0 1 0 0 d w`	`mod: reg : r/m`	
Register to Memory	`0 0 0 1 0 0 0 w`	`mod: reg : r/m`	
Memory to Register	`0 0 0 1 0 0 1 w`	`mod: reg : r/m`	
Immediate to Register/Memory	`1 0 0 0 0 0 s w`	`mod:0 1 0: r/m`	Immediate Data Byte(s)
Immediate to AL|AX|EAX Register (short encoding)	`0 0 0 1 0 1 0 w`	Immediate Data Byte(s)	

Function

```
DESTINATION  ←—  DESTINATION + SOURCE + CF;
    or
DESTINATION  ←—  DESTINATION + IMMEDIATE DATA + CF;
```

Description

Add both operands and the carry flag bit. One operand also serves as the destination for the resulting sum.

Example

```
    ADC    ECX, EDX
```

If CF = 1, ECX = 00000034h, and EDX = 00000052h, then as a result of the ADC instruction above, ECX is assigned 00000087h, and CF is assigned 0.

Timing

```
Register to Register:  2 clock cycles; 0.1µsec @ 20MHz.
Register to Memory:    7 clock cycles; 0.35µsec @ 20MHz.
Memory to Register:    6 clock cycles; 0.3µsec @ 20MHz.
Immediate to Register: 2 clock cycles; 0.1µsec @ 20MHz.
Immediate to Memory:   7 clock cycles; 0.35µsec @ 20MHz.
```

ADC   Integer Add with Carry   **ADC**

Flags

OF, CF, SF, ZF, AF, and PF affected as described in Appendix A. Other flags are unchanged.

REAL-mode Exceptions:

Same as for ADD instruction. See page 251.

PROTECTED-mode Exceptions:

Same as for ADD instruction. See page 251.

VIRTUAL 8086-mode Exceptions:

Same as for ADD instruction. See page 251.

ADD   Integer Add   **ADD**

Format

ADD

	Byte 0	Byte 1	Subsequent Byte(s)

Register to Register
| 0 0 0 0 0 0 d w | mod: reg : r/m |

Register to Memory
| 0 0 0 0 0 0 0 w | mod: reg : r/m |

Memory to Register
| 0 0 0 0 0 0 1 w | mod: reg : r/m |

Immediate to
Register/Memory
| 1 0 0 0 0 0 s w | mod:0 0 0: r/m | Immediate Data Byte(s)

Immediate to AL|AX|EAX
Register
(short encoding)
| 0 0 0 0 0 1 0 w | Immediate Data Byte(s)

Function

```
DESTINATION  ◄───  DESTINATION + SOURCE;
    or
DESTINATION  ◄───  DESTINATION + IMMEDIATE DATA;
```

Description

Add both operands. One operand also serves as the destination for the resulting sum.

Example

```
    ADD    ECX, EDX
```

If CF = 1, ECX = 00000034h, and EDX = 00000052h, then as a result of the ADD instruction above, ECX is assigned 00000086h, and CF is assigned 0.

Timing

```
Register to Register:  2 clock cycles; 0.1µsec @ 20MHz.
Register to Memory:    7 clock cycles; 0.35µsec @ 20MHz.
Memory to Register:    6 clock cycles; 0.3µsec @ 20MHz.
Immediate to Register: 2 clock cycles; 0.1µsec @ 20MHz.
Immediate to Memory:   7 clock cycles; 0.35µsec @ 20MHz.
```

ADD   Integer Add   **·ADD**

Flags

OF, CF, SF, ZF, AF, and PF affected as described in Appendix A. Other flags are unchanged.

REAL-mode Exceptions:

Interrupt 13 if any part of an operand in memory is at effective address greater than FFFFh in segments CS, DS, ES, FS, or GS. Interrupt 12 if any part of an operand in memory is at effective address greater than FFFFh in stack segment SS.

PROTECTED-mode Exceptions:

General Protection exception (exception 13) with error code of 0000h for operands in memory segments CS, DS, ES, FS, or GS if the destination is in a nonwritable segment, or if a source operand is in a nonreadable code segment, or if any part of the operand is at effective address beyond the segment limit. Stack exception (exception 12) with error code of 0000h for operands in stack segment if any part of the operand is at effective address beyond the segment limit. Stack exception with error code of segment selector if operand in memory is in segment SS marked not present. Not Present exception with error code of segment selector if operand in memory is in a segment DS, ES, FS, or GS marked not present. Not Present exception with error code of segment selector if operand in memory is in a segment DS, ES, FS, or GS marked not present. Page Fault exception (exception 14) with error code of fault code, and page-fault linear address in register CR2.

VIRTUAL 8086-mode Exceptions:

Same as REAL mode exceptions, but handled in PROTECTED mode at privilege-level 0. The format of the privilege-level-0 stack after an exception (with error code) or interrupt (no error code) is shown in Figure 12.2. Also Page Fault exception with error code of fault code, and page-fault linear address in register CR2.

AND   Logical AND   **AND**

Format

AND

	Byte 0	Byte 1	Subsequent Byte(s)

Register to Register `0 0 1 0 0 0 d w` `mod: reg : r/m`

Register to Memory `0 0 1 0 0 0 0 w` `mod: reg : r/m`

Memory to Register `0 0 1 0 0 0 1 w` `mod: reg : r/m`

Immediate to
Register/Memory `1 0 0 0 0 0 s w` `mod:1 0 0: r/m` Immediate Data Byte(s)

Immediate to AL|AX|EAX
Register
(short encoding) `0 0 1 0 0 1 0 w` Immediate Data Byte(s)

Function

```
DESTINATION  ←  DESTINATION ∧ SOURCE;
    or
DESTINATION  ←  DESTINATION ∧ IMMEDIATE DATA;
```

Description

Performs a bit-wise logical AND of both operands. One operand also serves as the destination for the result.

Example

```
    AND    EBX, EDI
```

If EBX = 00AD9034h, and EDI = 0B800052h, then as a result of the AND instruction above, EBX is assigned 00800010h.

Timing

```
Register to Register:   2 clock cycles; 0.1μsec @ 20MHz.
Register to Memory:     7 clock cycles; 0.35μsec @ 20MHz.
Memory to Register:     6 clock cycles; 0.3μsec @ 20MHz.
Immediate to Register:  2 clock cycles; 0.1μsec @ 20MHz.
Immediate to Memory:    7 clock cycles; 0.35μsec @ 20MHz.
```

AND   Logical AND   **AND**

Flags

OF = 0; CF = 0. SF, ZF, and PF affected as described in Appendix A. Other flags are unchanged.

REAL-mode Exceptions:

Same as for ADD instruction. See page 251.

PROTECTED-mode Exceptions:

Same as for ADD instruction. See page 251.

VIRTUAL 8086-mode Exceptions:

Same as for ADD instruction. See page 251.

ARPL   Adjust RPL Field of Selector   **ARPL**

Format

```
ARPL
```

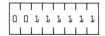

```
0 0 1 1 1 1 1 1
```

Function

```
IF RPL bits(1,0) of DEST < RPL bits(1,0) of SRC
THEN
  ZF ←── 1;
  RPL bits(1,0) of DEST ←── RPL bit(1,0) of SRC
ELSE
  ZF ←── 0
```

Description

ARPL is a PROTECTED mode instruction. ARPL typically appears only in operating system software. It is used to assure that a selector parameter to a subroutine does not request more privilege than the caller is allowed. The first operand is a 16-bit memory variable that is typically the selector parameter. The second operand of ARPL is normally a register that contains the CS selector value of the caller. By such a choice of operands, the operating system can assure that RPL of the selector is ≥ CPL of the caller.

Example

```
    MOV    EBP, ESP
    MOV    AX, WORD PTR [EBP]    ;move caller's CS from stack to
                                 ; AX.
    ARPL   SELECTOR_PARM, AX     ;adjust RPL of SELECTOR_PARM if
                                 ; needed.
```

If RPL of the caller's CS is 11b, and if RPL of the SELECTOR_PARM is 10b, then RPL of SELECTOR_PARM is adjusted to become 11b.

Timing

```
Register to Register:  20 clock cycles; 1μsec @ 20MHz.
Register to Memory:    21 clock cycles; 1.05μsec @ 20MHz.
```

ARPL   Adjust RPL Field of Selector   **ARPL**

Flags

ZF as described in *Function* above. Other flags are unchanged.

REAL-mode Exceptions:

Interrupt 6. ARPL, a PROTECTED mode instruction, is not recognized in REAL mode.

PROTECTED-mode Exceptions:

Same as for ADD instruction. See page 251.

VIRTUAL 8086-mode Exceptions:

Same as REAL mode exception, but handled in PROTECTED mode at privilege-level 0. The format of the privilege-level-0 stack after an exception is shown in Figure 12.2. Also Page Fault exception (exception 14) with error code of fault code, and page-fault linear address in register CR2.

BOUND   Check Array Index Against Bounds   **BOUND**

Format

```
BOUND
```

```
          Byte 0          Byte 1
      +-----------------+-----------------+
      | 0 1 1 0 0 0 1 0 | mod: reg : r/m  |
      +-----------------+-----------------+
```

vv w1,13,c2,p3]**Function**

```
IF ((INDEX < LOWER BOUND) OR ((INDEX + OPERAND SIZE) > UPPERBOUND)))
THEN
  INTERRUPT 5;
```

Description

BOUND allows easy *run-time* checking of and array index against defined upper and lower limits. The left operand is a register containing the index value, the effective address of the operand. The right operand is a memory structure of two values: the lower bound followed by the upper bound. If any byte of the operand, whose location is identified by the index value and operand size, lie outside the bounds defined, an interrupt 5 is generated. Otherwise, no action is taken.

Example

```
    BOUND   EDI, ARRAY_LIMITS
```

Timing

```
If interrupt is not generated:  10 clock cycles; 0.5µsec @ 20MHz.
If interrupt 5 is generated:    44 clock cycles; 2.2µsec @ 20MHz.
```

Flags

No flags affected. All flags are unchanged.

REAL-mode Exceptions:

Interrupt 5 if bounds test fails, as described in *Function* above and other interrupts as described for the ADD instruction on page 251.

BOUND   Check Array Index Against Bounds   **BOUND**

PROTECTED-**mode Exceptions:**

Interrupt 5 if the bounds test fails. Other exceptions same as for ADD instruction. See page 251.

VIRTUAL **8086-mode Exceptions:**

Interrupt 5 if bounds test fails. Other exceptions same as for ADD instruction. See page 251.

BSF   Bit Scan Forward   **BSF**

Format

```
BSF
```

	Byte 0	Byte 1	Byte 2
	0 0 0 0 1 1 1 1	1 0 1 1 1 1 0 0	mod: reg : r/m

Function

```
GENERAL REGISTER  ←  OFFSET OF RIGHTMOST SET BIT IN SOURCE;
```

Description

Performs a scan of the source operand from its least significant bit (scanning right to left). The ZF is cleared if no bits are set; otherwise, ZF is set, and the offset of the rightmost bit is loaded into the destination register. In a four-byte source operand, bit offsets range from 0 to 31.

Example

```
    BSF    EDX, STATUS_DWORD
```

If location STATUS_WORD = 00AD9034h, then as a result of the BSF instruction above, EDX is assigned 00000002h, and ZF = 1.

Timing

```
10 + 3n clock cycles; [0.5 + 3(0.15)]μsec @ 20MHz.
```

(n is number of bit positions needed to scan from right when finding rightmost set bit)

BSF Bit Scan Forward **BSF**

Flags

ZF as indicated in *Description* above. Other flags are unchanged.

REAL-mode Exceptions:

Same as for ADD instruction. See page 251.

PROTECTED-mode Exceptions:

Same as for ADD instruction. See page 251.

VIRTUAL 8086-mode Exceptions:

Same as for ADD instruction. See page 251.

BSR   Bit Scan Reverse   **BSR**

Format

```
BSR
```

```
             Byte 0          Byte 1          Byte 2
        ┌─────────────────┬─────────────────┬─────────────────┐
        │0 0 0 0 1 1 1 1│1 0 1 1 1 1 0 1│mod: reg : r/m │
        └─────────────────┴─────────────────┴─────────────────┘
```

Function

```
GENERAL REGISTER  ⟵  OFFSET OF LEFTMOST SET BIT IN SOURCE;
```

Description

Performs a scan of the source operand from its most significant bit (scanning left to right). The ZF is cleared if no bits are set; otherwise, ZF is set, and the offset of the leftmost bit is loaded into the destination register. In a four-byte source operand, bit offsets range from 0 to 31.

Example

```
    BSR    EDX, STATUS_DWORD
```

If location STATUS_WORD = 00AD9034h, then as a result of the BSR instruction above, EDX is assigned 00000017h (23 decimal), and ZF = 1.

Timing

```
10 + 3n clock cycles; [0.5 + 3(0.15)]μsec @ 20MHz.
```

(*n* is number of bit positions needed to scan from left when finding leftmost set bit)

BSR   Bit Scan Reverse   **BSR**

Flags

ZF as indicated in *Description* above. Other flags are unchanged.

REAL-mode Exceptions:

Same as for ADD instruction. See page 251.

PROTECTED-mode Exceptions:

Same as for ADD instruction. See page 251.

VIRTUAL 8086-mode Exceptions:

Same as for ADD instruction. See page 251.

BT Bit Test **BT**

Format

BT

	Byte 0	Byte 1	Byte 2	
Register/ Memory, Immediate	0 0 0 0 1 1 1 1	1 0 1 1 1 0 1 0	mod:1 0 0: r/m	8-Bit Immediate Data
Register/ Memory, Register	0 0 0 0 1 1 1 1	1 0 1 0 0 0 1 1	mod: reg : r/m	

Function

CF ⟵ (<bitnumber> OF SOURCE);

Description

Test bit b of the source operand. The CF is set or reset in accordance with bit b. The source operand effective address is indicated by the first operand, and the bit offset is indicated by the second operand (or the immediate operand).

Note that the index of the selected bit, b, can be given by the immediate count in the instruction, or by a general register. If by immediate count, the count is taken modulo 32 so the range of immediate bit offsets is 0 . . . 31. This allows any bit within a general register to be accessed. For memory bit strings, the immediate field gives only the bit offset within a WORD or DWORD.

The assembler supports immediate bit offsets larger than 31 by using the immediate bit offset field in combination with the displacement field of the source memory operand. The assembler treats the immediate bit offset as a signed 32-bit quantity, allowing a range of ±2 Gbit. The low-order 3 to 5 bits of the immediate bit offset are stored in the immediate bit offset field, and the high-order 29-27 bits are shifted and combined with the byte displacement in the addressing mode.

When accessing a source in memory, the 80386 may actually access four bytes starting from the memory address given by:

Effective address + (4 * (bitoffset DIV 32))

for a DWORD operand size, or two bytes starting from the memory address given by:

Effective address + (4 * (bitoffset DIV 16))

for a WORD operand size. The programmer must therefore be careful not to use the BT instruction to reference memory near memory holes such as memory-mapped I/O registers. Instead, use the MOV instruction to load or store these addresses, and use the register form of BT to manipulate the bit data.

BT   Bit Test   **BT**

Example

```
    BT   EAX, 5
```

If location STATUS_WORD = 00000020h, then as a result of the BT instruction above, EAX remains 00000020h, and CF = 1.

Timing

```
register operand, immediate bit offset: 3 clock cycles; 0.15μsec @ 20MHz.
memory operand, immediate bit offset:   6 clock cycles; 0.3μsec @ 20MHz.
register operand, register bit offset:  3 clock cycles; 0.15μsec @ 20MHz.
memory operand, register bit offset:    12 clock cycles; 0.6μsec @ 20MHz.
```

Flags

CF as indicated in *Description* above. Other flags are unchanged.

REAL-mode Exceptions:

Same as for ADD instruction. See page 251.

PROTECTED-mode Exceptions:

Same as for ADD instruction. See page 251.

VIRTUAL 8086-mode Exceptions:

Same as for ADD instruction. See page 251.

BTC   Bit Test, then Complement Bit   **BTC**

Format

```
BTC
```

	Byte 0	Byte 1	Byte 2	

Register/
Memory,
Immediate

```
| 0 0 0 0 1 1 1 1 | 1 0 1 1 1 0 1 0 | mod:1 1 1: r/m |
```
8-Bit Immediate
Data

Register/
Memory, Register

```
| 0 0 0 0 1 1 1 1 | 1 0 1 1 1 0 1 1 | mod: reg : r/m |
```

Function

```
CF      ←——  (<bitnumber> OF SOURCE);
<bitnumber> OF SOURCE  ←—— ∿ (<bitnumber> OF SOURCE);
```

Description

Test bit b of the source operand. The CF is set or reset in accordance with bit b. Bit b is then complemented. The source operand effective address is indicated by the first operand, and the bit offset is indicated by the second operand (or the immediate data).

Note that the index of the selected bit, b, can be given by the immediate count in the instruction, or by a general register. If by immediate count, the count is taken modulo 32 so the range of immediate bit offsets is 0 ... 31. This allows any bit within a general register to be accessed. For memory bit strings, the immediate field gives only the bit offset within a WORD or DWORD.

The assembler supports immediate bit offsets larger than 31 by using the immediate bit offset field in combination with the displacement field of the source memory operand. The assembler treats the immediate bit offset as a signed 32-bit quantity, allowing a range of ±2 Gbit. The low-order 3 to 5 bits of the immediate bit offset are stored in the immediate bit offset field, and the high-order 29-27 bits are shifted and combined with the byte displacement in the addressing mode.

When accessing a source in memory, the 80386 may actually access four bytes starting from the memory address given by:

Effective address + (4 * (bitoffset DIV 32))

for a DWORD operand size, or two bytes starting from the memory address given by:

Effective address + (4 * (bitoffset DIV 16))

for a WORD operand size. The programmer must therefore be careful not to use the BTC instruction to reference memory near memory holes such as memory-mapped

BTC   Bit Test, then Complement Bit   **BTC**

I/O registers. Instead, use the MOV instruction to load or store these addresses, and use the register form of BTC to manipulate the bit data.

Example

```
    BTC    EAX, 5
```

If location STATUS_WORD = 00000020h, then as a result of the BTC instruction above, EAX remains 00000000h, and CF = 1.

Timing

```
register operand, immediate bit offset: 6 clock cycles; 0.3µsec @ 20MHz.
memory operand, immediate bit offset:   8 clock cycles; 0.4µsec @ 20MHz.
register operand, register bit offset:  6 clock cycles; 0.3µsec @ 20MHz.
memory operand, register bit offset:   13 clock cycles; 0.65µsec @ 20MHz.
```

Flags

CF as indicated in *Description* above. Other flags are unchanged.

REAL-mode Exceptions:

Same as for ADD instruction. See page 251.

PROTECTED-mode Exceptions:

Same as for ADD instruction. See page 251.

VIRTUAL 8086-mode Exceptions:

Same as for ADD instruction. See page 251.

BTR   Bit Test, then Reset Bit   **BTR**

Format

BTR

	Byte 0	Byte 1	Byte 2	
Register/ Memory, Immediate	0 0 0 0 1 1 1 1	1 0 1 1 1 0 1 0	mod:1 1 0: r/m	8-Bit Immediate Data Byte(s)
Register/ Memory, Register	0 0 0 0 1 1 1 1	1 0 1 1 0 0 1 1	mod: reg : r/m	

Function

```
CF  ←——  (<bitnumber> OF SOURCE);
<bitnumber> OF SOURCE  ←——  0;
```

Description

Test bit b of the source operand. The CF is set or reset in accordance with bit b. Bit b is then reset. The source operand effective address is indicated by the first operand, and the bit offset is indicated by the second operand (or the immediate data).

Note that the index of the selected bit, b, can be given by the immediate count in the instruction, or by a general register. If by immediate count, the count is taken modulo 32 so the range of immediate bit offsets is 0 . . . 31. This allows any bit within a general register to be accessed. For memory bit strings, the immediate field gives only the bit offset within a WORD or DWORD.

The assembler supports immediate bit offsets larger than 31 by using the immediate bit offset field in combination with the displacement field of the source memory operand. The assembler treats the immediate bit offset as a signed 32-bit quantity, allowing a range of ±2 Gbit. The low-order 3 to 5 bits of the immediate bit offset are stored in the immediate bit offset field, and the high-order 29-27 bits are shifted and combined with the byte displacement in the addressing mode.

When accessing a source in memory, the 80386 may actually access four bytes starting from the memory address given by:

Effective address + (4 * (bitoffset DIV 32))

for a DWORD operand size, or two bytes starting from the memory address given by:

Effective address + (4 * (bitoffset DIV 16))

for a WORD operand size. The programmer must therefore be careful not to use the BTR instruction to reference memory near memory holes such as memory-mapped I/O registers. Instead, use the MOV instruction to load or store these addresses, and use the register form of BTR to manipulate the bit data.

BTR   Bit Test, then Reset Bit   **BTR**

Example

```
BTR   EAX, 5
```

If location STATUS_WORD = 00000060h, then as a result of the BTR instruction above, EAX remains 00000040h, and CF = 1.

Timing

```
register operand, immediate bit offset: 6 clock cycles; 0.3μsec @ 20MHz.
memory operand, immediate bit offset:   8 clock cycles; 0.4μsec @ 20MHz.
register operand, register bit offset:  6 clock cycles; 0.3μsec @ 20MHz.
memory operand, register bit offset:   13 clock cycles; 0.65μsec @ 20MHz.
```

Flags

CF as indicated in *Description* above. Other flags are unchanged.

REAL-mode Exceptions:

Same as for ADD instruction. See page 251.

PROTECTED-mode Exceptions:

Same as for ADD instruction. See page 251.

VIRTUAL 8086-mode Exceptions:

Same as for ADD instruction. See page 251.

BTS <div align="center">Bit Test, then Set Bit</div> **BTS**

Format

BTS

	Byte 0	Byte 1	Byte 2	
Register/ Memory, Immediate	0 0 0 0 1 1 1 1	1 0 1 1 1 0 1 0	mod:1 0 1: r/m	8-Bit Immediate Data
Register/ Memory, Register	0 0 0 0 1 1 1 1	1 0 1 0 1 0 1 1	mod: reg : r/m	

Function

```
CF  ←—  (<bitnumber> OF SOURCE);
<bitnumber> OF SOURCE  ←—  1;
```

Description

Test bit b of the source operand. The CF is set or reset in accordance with bit b. Bit b is then set. The source operand effective address is indicated by the first operand, and the bit offset is indicated by the second operand (or the immediate data).

Note that the index of the selected bit, b, can be given by the immediate count in the instruction, or by a general register. If by immediate count, the count is taken modulo 32 so the range of immediate bit offsets is 0 . . . 31. This allows any bit within a general register to be accessed. For memory bit strings, the immediate field gives only the bit offset within a WORD or DWORD.

The assembler supports immediate bit offsets larger than 31 by using the immediate bit offset field in combination with the displacement field of the source memory operand. The assembler treats the immediate bit offset as a signed 32-bit quantity, allowing a range of ±2 Gbit. The low-order 3 to 5 bits of the immediate bit offset are stored in the immediate bit offset field, and the high-order 29-27 bits are shifted and combined with the byte displacement in the addressing mode.

When accessing a source in memory, the 80386 may actually access four bytes starting from the memory address given by:

Effective address + (4 * (bitoffset DIV 32))

for a DWORD operand size, or two bytes starting from the memory address given by:

Effective address + (4 * (bitoffset DIV 16))

for a WORD operand size. The programmer must therefore be careful not to use the BTS instruction to reference memory near memory holes such as memory-mapped I/O registers. Instead, use the MOV instruction to load or store these addresses, and use the register form of BTS to manipulate the bit data.

BTS   Bit Test, then Set Bit   **BTS**

Example

```
    BTS    EAX, 4
```

If location STATUS_WORD = 00000060h, then as a result of the BTS instruction above, EAX remains 00000070h, and CF = 0.

Timing

```
register operand, immediate bit offset: 6 clock cycles; 0.3µsec @ 20MHz.
memory operand, immediate bit offset:   8 clock cycles; 0.4µsec @ 20MHz.
register operand, register bit offset:  6 clock cycles; 0.3µsec @ 20MHz.
memory operand, register bit offset:   13 clock cycles; 0.65µsec @ 20MHz.
```

Flags

CF as indicated in *Description* above. Other flags are unchanged.

REAL-mode Exceptions:

Same as for ADD instruction. See page 251.

PROTECTED-mode Exceptions:

Same as for ADD instruction. See page 251.

VIRTUAL 8086-mode Exceptions:

Same as for ADD instruction. See page 251.

CALL   Call Procedure (or Task PROTECTED Mode)   **CALL**

Format

```
CALL
```

| | Byte 0 | Byte 1 | Subsequent Byte(s) |

Within current
code segment
Direct, Full
Displacement

| 1 1 1 0 1 0 0 0 | Full Displacement |

Within current
code segment
Indirect to
Absolute Offset

| 1 1 1 1 1 1 1 1 | mod:0 1 0: r/m |

Direct
Intersegment

| 1 0 0 1 1 0 1 0 | Absolute Offset, Segment Selector |

Indirect
Intersegment

| 1 1 1 1 1 1 1 1 | mod:0 1 1: r/m |

Function

```
IF (ADDRESS SIZE = 32) THEN
BEGIN
  PUSH EIP;
  RELOAD EIP FROM OPERAND;        (CALL always changes EIP or IP)
END
ELSE
BEGIN
  PUSH IP;
  RELOAD IP FROM OPERAND;         (CALL always changes EIP or IP)
END
IF CALL IS INTERSEGMENT THEN
BEGIN
  PUSH CS;
  RELOAD CS FROM OPERAND;         (intersegment CALL changes CS)
END
```

Description

CALL within the current code segment pushes the instruction pointer onto the stack. The operand modifies the instruction pointer in order to begin execution of a subroutine. When a CALL is made within the current code segment, the code segment register is not affected.

When an intersegment CALL occurs in REAL mode or VIRTUAL 8086 mode, the instruction pointer and code segment register are both pushed on the stack, and both are then replaced by the operand values to begin execution of a subroutine.

CALL   Call Procedure (or Task PROTECTED Mode)   **CALL**

When an intersegment CALL occurs in PROTECTED mode, the activities performed by the 80386 can be quite complex according to whether the destination selector is that of:

1. a code segment at the current privilege level, (DPL = CPL)
2. a code segment at a more privileged level, (DPL ≤ CPL)
3. a call gate,
4. a task state segment, or
5. a task gate.

Example:

```
CALL   SUBR_A
```

PROTECTED-mode Details

PROTECTED MODE CALL TO NONCONFORMING (i.e., regular) CODE SEGMENT:
   RPL of destination selector must be numerically ≤ CPL ELSE General Protection exception (error code of code segment selector).
   Descriptor DPL must be numerically = CPL ELSE General Protection exception (error code of code segment selector).
   Selector must be within its descriptor table limits ELSE General Protection exception (error code of code segment selector).
   Segment must be present ELSE Not Present exception (error code of code segment selector).
   Stack must have enough room to hold return address ELSE Stack Fault (error code of 0000h).
   Instruction pointer must be within code segment ELSE General Protection exception (error code of 0000h).
   Load code segment descriptor into CS descriptor cache (not visible to programmer).
   Load CS register with code segment selector.
   Load EIP with zero-extend(new offset).
   If operand size = 16 THEN EIP := EIP AND 0000FFFFh.
   Set RPL field of CS register to CPL.

PROTECTED MODE CALL TO CONFORMING CODE SEGMENT:
   DPL must be numerically ≤ CPL ELSE General Protection exception (error code of code segment selector).
   Selector must be within its descriptor table limits ELSE General Protection exception (error code of code segment selector).
   Segment index must be present ELSE Not Present exception (error code of code segment selector).
   Stack must have enough room to hold return address ELSE Stack Fault (error code of 0000h).
   Instruction pointer must be within code segment ELSE General Protection exception (error code of 0000h).
   Load code segment descriptor into CS descriptor cache (not visible to programmer).

CALL   Call Procedure (or Task PROTECTED Mode)   **CALL**

Load CS register with code segment selector.
Load EIP with zero-extend(new offset).
If operand size = 16 THEN EIP := EIP AND 0000FFFFh.
Set RPL field of CS register to CPL.

PROTECTED MODE CALL TO CALL GATE:
  Call gate DPL must be numerically ≥ CPL ELSE General Protection exception (error
code of call gate selector)
  Call gate DPL must be numerically ≥ RPL ELSE General Protection exception (error
code of call gate selector)
  Call gate must be present ELSE Not Present exception (error code of call gate
selector).
  Examine code segment selector found in call gate:
   Code selector must not be null ELSE General Protection exception (error code of
0000h).
   Selector index must be within its descriptor table limits ELSE General Protec-
tion exception (error code of code segment selector).
   AR byte of selected descriptor must indicate code segment ELSE General Protec-
tion exception(error code of code segment selector).
   DPL of selected descriptor must be s CPL ELSE General Protection exception (error
code of code segment selector).
   IF nonconforming code segment AND DPL < CPL THEN go to MORE-PRIVILEGE
   ELSE go to SAME-PRIVILEGE.
  Set RPL field of CS register to CPL.

MORE-PRIVILEGE:
  Get new SS selector for new privilege level from TSS (Task-state Segment).
   Check selector and descriptor for new SS:
    Selector must not be null ELSE Invalid TSS exception (error code of 0000h).
    Selector must be within its descriptor table limits ELSE General Protection ex-
ception (error code of code segment selector).
    Selector RPL must numerically = DPL of code segment ELSE Invalid TSS exception
(error code of stack segment selector).
    Stack segment DPL must numerically = DPL of code segment ELSE Invalid TSS ex-
ception (error code of stack segment selector).
    Descriptor must indicate writable data segment ELSE Invalid TSS exception (er-
ror code of stack segment selector).
    Segment present ELSE Stack Fault (error code of stack segment selector).
   If operand size = 32
   THEN
    New stack must have room for autocopied parameters (if any) plus 16 bytes ELSE
General Protection exception (error code of 0000h).
    EIP must be within code segment limit ELSE General Protection exception (error
code of 0000h).
    Load new SS:eSP value from Task-state Segment (TSS).
    Load new CS:EIP value from call gate.
   ELSE
    New stack must have room for autocopied parameters (if any) plus 8 bytes ELSE
General Protection exception (error code of 0000h).
    IP must be within code segment limit ELSE General Protection exception (error
code of 0000h).
    Load new SS:eSP value from Task-state Segment (TSS).
    Load new CS:IP value from call gate.
   Load CS descriptor into CS descriptor cache.

CALL   Call Procedure (or Task PROTECTED Mode)   **CALL**

Load SS descriptor into SS descriptor cache.
Push long word pointer of old stack onto new stack.
Get word count from call gate, mask to five bits (value 0-31).
Push return address onto new stack.
Set CPL to stack segment DPL.
Set RPL field of CS register to CPL.

SAME-PRIVILEGE:
  IF operand size = 32
  THEN
    Stack must have room for 6-byte return address (padded to 8 bytes) ELSE Stack
Fault (error code of 0000h).
    EIP must be within code segment limit ELSE General Protection exception (error
code of 0000h).
    Load CS:EIP from call gate.
  ELSE
    Stack must have room for 4-byte return address ELSE Stack Fault (error code of
0000h).
    IP must be within code segment limit ELSE General Protection exception (error
code of 0000h).
    Load CS:IP from call gate.
  Set RPL field of CS register to CPL.

PROTECTED MODE CALL TO TASK GATE:
  Task gate DPL must be numerically ≥ CPL ELSE Invalid TSS exception (error code
of gate selector).
  Task gate DPL must be numerically ≥ RPL ELSE Invalid TSS exception (error code
of gate selector).
  Task gate must be present ELSE Not Present exception (error code of gate
selector).
  Examine selector to TSS given in task gate:
  Must specify Global Descriptor Table (GDT) in Table Indicator (TI) bit ELSE In-
valid TSS exception (error code of TSS selector).
  Index must be within GDT limits ELSE Invalid TSS exception (error code of TSS
selector).
  TSS descriptor access rights byte must specify nonbusy TSS ELSE Invalid TSS ex-
ception (error code of TSS selector).
  Task-state Segment must be present ELSE Not Present exception (error code of TSS
selector).
  SWITCH-TASKS (with nesting, set NT bit in EFLAG) to task given by TSS selector.
  EIP must be within code segment limit ELSE Invalid TSS exception (error code of
0000h).

PROTECTED MODE CALL TO TASK STATE SEGMENT:
  TSS DPL must be numerically ≥ CPL ELSE Invalid TSS exception (error code of TSS
selector).
  TSS DPL must be numerically ≥ RPL ELSE Invalid TSS exception (error code of TSS
selector).
  TSS descriptor access rights byte must specify nonbusy TSS ELSE Invalid TSS exception (error code of TSS selector).

CALL   Call Procedure (or Task PROTECTED Mode)   **CALL**

```
     Task gate must be present ELSE Not Present exception (error code of gate
selector).
     SWITCH-TASKS (with nesting, set NT bit in EFLAG) to task given by TSS selector.
     EIP must be within code segment limit ELSE Invalid TSS exception (error code of
0000h).
```

Flags

No flags are affected, unless a task switch occurs in PROTECTED mode.

REAL-mode Exceptions:

Interrupt 13 if any part of an operand in memory is at effective address greater than FFFFh in segments CS, DS, ES, FS, or GS. Interrupt 12 if any part of an operand in memory is at effective address greater than FFFFh in stack segment SS.

PROTECTED-mode Exceptions:

General Protection exception (exception 13) with error code of 0000h for operands in memory segments CS, DS, ES, FS, or GS if a source operand is in a nonreadable code segment, or if any part of the operand is at effective address beyond the segment limit. Stack exception with error code of 0000h for operands in stack segment if any part of the operand is at effective address beyond the segment limit. Stack exception with error code of segment selector if operand in memory is in segment SS marked not present. Not Present exception (exception 11) with error code of segment selector if operand in memory is in a segment DS, ES, FS, or GS marked not present. Not Present exception with error code of segment selector if operand in memory is in a segment DS, ES, FS, or GS marked not present. Page Fault exception (exception 14) with error code of fault code, and page-fault linear address in register CR2. Invalid Task State Segment exception with error code of selector for inconsistencies in the Task State Segment if performing a task switch.

VIRTUAL 8086-mode Exceptions:

Same as REAL mode exceptions, but handled in PROTECTED mode at privilege-level 0. The format of the privilege-level-0 stack after an exception (with error code) or interrupt (no error code) is shown in Figure 12.2. Also Page Fault exception with error code of fault code, and page-fault linear address in register CR2.

CBW/CWDE   Convert Byte to Word / Convert Word to Doubleword   **CBW/CWDE**

Format

```
CBW/CWDE
```

```
1 0 0 1 1 0 0 0
```

Function

```
IF (OPERAND SIZE IS WORD)        {instruction is CBW}
THEN  AX  ←—  SIGN-EXTEND(AL);
ELSE  {OPERAND SIZE IS DWORD     {instruction is CWDE}
  EAX  ←—  SIGN-EXTEND(AX);
```

Description

CBW converts the signed BYTE in AL to a signed WORD in AX. CWDE converts the signed WORD in AX to a signed DWORD in EAX. Note that CWDE is different than instruction CWD, which uses DX:AX rather than EAX as the destination.

Timing

3 clock cycles; 0.15µsec @ 20MHz.

Flags

None are affected.

REAL-mode Exceptions:

None.

PROTECTED-mode Exceptions:

None.

VIRTUAL 8086-mode Exceptions:

None.

CLC   Clear Carry Flag   CLC

Format

CLC

Function

CF ⟵ 0;

Description

CLC resets the carry flag.

Example

CLC

Timing

2 clock cycles; 0.1μsec @ 20MHz.

Flags

CF as described in *Function* above. All other flags are unchanged.

REAL-mode Exceptions:

None.

PROTECTED-mode Exceptions:

None.

VIRTUAL 8086-mode Exceptions:

None.

CLD Clear Direction Flag − Increment Index **CLD**

Format

CLD

Function

DF ⟵ 0;

Description

CLD resets the direction flag. After CLD is executed, the string instructions and the repeated string instructions will increment the index registers that they use.

Example

CLD

Timing

2 clock cycles; 0.1μsec @ 20MHz.

Flags

DF as described in *Function* above. All other flags are unchanged.

REAL-mode Exceptions:

None.

PROTECTED-mode Exceptions:

None.

VIRTUAL 8086-mode Exceptions:

None.

CLI   Clear Interrupt Flag — Disable Interrupts   **CLI**

Format

```
CLI
```

Function

```
IF  ←  0;
```

Description

CLI resets the interrupt flag if allowed. In REAL mode CLI is always allowed. In PRO-TECTED mode or VIRTUAL 8086 mode, CPL must be numerically less than or equal to IOPL in order for CLI to be allowed.

Example

```
    CLI
```

Timing

```
3 clock cycles; 0.15µsec @ 20MHz.
```

Flags

IF as described in *Function* above. All other flags are unchanged.

REAL-mode Exceptions:

None.

PROTECTED-mode Exceptions:

General Protection exception (exception 13) with error code of 0000h if CPL is numerically greater than IOPL.

VIRTUAL 8086-mode Exceptions:

General Protection exception (exception 13) with error code of 0000h if IOPL is numerically smaller than 3, since CPL during VIRTUAL 8086 mode is always 3.

CLI   Clear Interrupt Flag − Disable Interrupts   **CLI**

Trapping this instruction during VIRTUAL 8086 mode by having IOPL values of 2, 1, or 0 allows the PROTECTED mode supervisor to virtualize the state of IF observed by the VIRTUAL 8086 software.

CLTS   Clear Task-Switched Flag in CR0   **CLTS**

Format

```
CLTS
```

```
        Byte 0        Byte 1
      ┌─────────────┬─────────────┐
      │0 0 0 0 1 1 1 1│0 0 0 0 0 1 1 0│
      └─────────────┴─────────────┘
```

Function

```
TS  ←  0;
```

Description

CLTS resets the task switched flag if allowed. In REAL mode CLTS is always allowed since it may be desired when initializing for PROTECTED mode. In PROTECTED mode, CPL must be 0 order for CLTS to be allowed.

Example

```
    CLTS
```

Timing

```
5 clock cycles; 0.25μsec @ 20MHz.
```

Flags

TS in register CR0 as described in *Function* above. All other flags in CR0 and EFLAG are unchanged.

REAL-mode Exceptions:

None. This instruction is valid in REAL mode to allow initialization for PROTECTED mode.

PROTECTED-mode Exceptions:

General Protection exception (exception 13) with error code of 0000h if CPL is not 0 (the supervisor level).

CLTS   Clear Task-Switched Flag in CR0   **CLTS**

VIRTUAL **8086-mode Exceptions:**

None.

CMC   Complement Carry Flag in EFLAG   **CMC**

Format

CMC

```
┌─┬─┬─┬─┬─┬─┬─┬─┐
│1│1│1│1│0│1│0│1│
└─┴─┴─┴─┴─┴─┴─┴─┘
```

Function

CF ⟵ ∽ CF;

Description

CLC complements the carry flag.

Example

CMC

Timing

2 clock cycles; 0.1μsec @ 20MHz.

Flags

CF as described in *Function* above. All other flags are unchanged.

REAL-mode Exceptions:

None.

PROTECTED-mode Exceptions:

None.

VIRTUAL 8086-mode Exceptions:

None.

CMP   Compare Operands (Subtract function to EFLAG, no result)   CMP

Format

CMP

	Byte 0	Byte 1	Subsequent Byte(s)

Register with
Register

```
0 0 1 1 1 0 d w | mod: reg : r/m
```

Register with
Memory

```
0 0 1 1 1 0 0 w | mod: reg : r/m
```

Memory with
Register

```
0 0 1 1 1 0 1 w | mod: reg : r/m
```

Immediate with
Register/Memory

```
1 0 0 0 0 0 s w | mod:1 1 1: r/m | Immediate Data Byte(s)
```

Immediate with
AL|AX|EAX
Register (short
encoding)

```
0 0 1 1 1 1 0 w | Immediate Data Byte(s)
```

Function

```
DESTINATION - SOURCE;          {affects EFLAG only}
   or
DESTINATION - IMMEDIATE DATA;  {affects EFLAG only}
```

Description

Compare operands or operand with immediate data. For the comparison, the operands are subtracted, but no result is stored. Only the flags are affected.

Example

```
    CMP   ECX, EDX
```

Timing

```
Register with Register:  2 clock cycles; 0.1µsec @ 20MHz.
Register with Memory:    6 clock cycles; 0.3µsec @ 20MHz.
Memory with Register:    5 clock cycles; 0.25µsec @ 20MHz.
Immediate with Register: 2 clock cycles; 0.1µsec @ 20MHz.
Immediate with Memory:   6 clock cycles; 0.3µsec @ 20MHz.
```

CMP   Compare Operands (Subtract function to EFLAG, no result)   **CMP**

Flags

OF, CF, SF, ZF, AF, and PF affected as described in Appendix A. Other flags are unchanged.

REAL-mode Exceptions:

Same as for ADD instruction. See page 251.

PROTECTED-mode Exceptions:

Same as for ADD instruction. See page 251.

VIRTUAL 8086-mode Exceptions:

Same as for ADD instruction. See page 251.

CMPSB/CMPSW/CMPSD   Compare String Data   CMPSB/CMPSW/CMPSD

Format

```
CMPSB/CMPSW/CMPSD
```

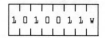

```
1 0 1 0 0 1 1 w
```

Function

```
SOURCE - DESTINATION;      {comparison affects EFLAG only}
IF (ADDRESS SIZE = 32) THEN
  ADJUST ESI and EDI;      {adjust indexes for source and destination}
ELSE    {ADDRESS SIZE = 16}
  ADJUST SI and DI;
```

Description

Compares operands of two similar memory strings. The strings are considered to be arrays of BYTES, WORDS, or DWORDS, depending on the operand size of the string instruction. After the comparison is made, the source index register and destination index registers are automatically advanced (incremented or decremented, according to DF) by an amount equaling the operand size.

If the address size of the instruction is DWORD, the operand of the source string is [ESI], while the operand of the destination string is ES:[EDI]. Otherwise, the operands are [SI] and [DI]. Load the correct index values before executing CMPS.

Note that the direction of subtraction is [ESI] − [EDI] or [SI] − [DI]. The left operand is the source, and the right operation is the destination. This is the reverse of the usual Intel convention used for the SUB, SBB, and CMP instructions, where the left operand is the destination, and the right operand is the source.

Example

```
        CMPSB       ;compares BYTE operands from BYTE strings

  or

   REPE    CMPSB    ;repeat instruction while comparison matches
                    ; and ECX register has not expired (See page 458).

  or

   REPNE   CMPSB    ;repeat instruction while comparison does not
                    ; match and ECX register has not expired
                    ; (See page 459).
```

Because the source and destination registers must be loaded to use this instruction, CMPSB/W/D is often placed in a loop and used for several iterations.

CMPSB/CMPSW/CMPSD   Compare String Data   **CMPSB/CMPSW/CMPSD**

Timing

```
nonrepeated:    10 clock cycles; 0.5μsec @ 20MHz.
repeated:   5 + 9n clock cycles; 0.25 + 0.45nμsec @ 20MHz.
```

(*n* is number of iterations performed)

Flags

OF, CF, SF, ZF, AF, and PF affected as described in Appendix A. Other flags are unchanged.

REAL-mode Exceptions:

Same as for ADD instruction. See page 251.

PROTECTED-mode Exceptions:

Same as for ADD instruction. See page 251.

VIRTUAL 8086-mode Exceptions:

Same as for ADD instruction. See page 251.

CWD/CDQ   Convert Wrd to Dblwrd / Convert Dblwrd to Quadwrd   **CWD/CDQ**

Format

```
CWD/CDQ
```

Function

```
IF (OPERAND SIZE IS WORD)        {instruction is CWD}
THEN  DX:AX  ⟵  SIGN-EXTEND(AX);
ELSE                   {operandsize is DWORD; instruction is CDQ}
  EDX:EAX  ⟵  SIGN-EXTEND(EAX);
```

Description

CWD converts the signed WORD in AX to a signed DWORD in DX:AX. CWDE converts the signed DWORD in EAX to a signed QUADWORD in EDX:EAX. Note that CWD is different than instruction CWDE, which uses EAX rather than DX:AX as the destination.

Timing

```
2 clock cycles; 0.1μsec @ 20MHz.
```

Flags

None are affected.

REAL-mode Exceptions:

None.

PROTECTED-mode Exceptions:

None.

VIRTUAL 8086-mode Exceptions:

None.

DAA   Decimal Adjust AL after Addition   **DAA**

Format

DAA

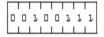

Function

```
IF ((AL AND 0Fh) > 9) OR (AF=1) THEN
BEGIN                    {begin adjustment}
  AL ⟵ (AL + 6);          {cause rollover in lower nibble of AL}
  AF ⟵ 1;
END;
ELSE
  AF ⟵ 0;                 {no adjustment of lower nibble needed}
  IF (AL > 9Fh) OR (CF=1) THEN
BEGIN                    {begin adjustment}
  AL ⟵ (AL + 60h);        {cause rollover in upper nibble of AL}
  CF ⟵ 1;
END;
ELSE
  CF ⟵ 0;                 {no adjustment of upper nibble needed}
```

Description

This instruction can be used after an addition that leaves two BCD digits in the AL register. If the subtraction results in either or both nibbles having a value larger than 9, DAA causes appropriate rollover of those nibbles in register AL, and sets the flags as required so addition can be performed on more significant bytes of multibyte operands.

Example

```
        ADC     AL, BL   ;note that AL must be destination.
        DAA              ;adjust AL for packed BCD (decimal) format.
```

The ADC and DAA instructions are often contained within a loop that adds the packed BCD values (decimal values) byte-by-byte, beginning with the least significant byte.

DAA   Decimal Adjust AL after Addition   **DAA**

Timing

`4 clock cycles; 0.2µsec @ 20MHz.`

Flags

CF and AF as described in *Function* above. OF, SF, ZF, and PF are undefined. Other flags are unchanged.

REAL-mode Exceptions:

None.

PROTECTED-mode Exceptions:

None.

VIRTUAL 8086-mode Exceptions:

None.

DAS   Decimal Adjust AL after Subtraction   **DAS**

Format

DAS

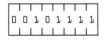

Function

```
IF ((AL AND 0Fh) > 9) OR (AF=1) THEN
BEGIN                       {begin adjustment}
  AL ← (AL - 6);            {cause rollunder in lower nibble of AL }
  AF ← 1;
END;
ELSE
  AF ← 0;                   {no adjustment of lower nibble needed}
IF (AL > 9Fh) OR (CF=1) THEN
BEGIN                       {begin adjustment}
  AL ← (AL - 60h);          {cause rollunder in upper nibble of AL }
  CF ← 1;
END;
ELSE
  CF ← 0;                   {no adjustment of upper nibble needed}
```

Description

This instruction can be used after a subtraction that leaves two BCD digits in the AL register. If the subtraction results in either or both nibbles having a value larger than 9, DAS causes appropriate rollunder of those nibbles in register AL, and sets the flags as required so subtraction can be performed on more significant bytes of multibyte operands.

Example

```
    SBB     AL, BL   ;note that AL must be destination.
    DAS              ;adjust AL for packed BCD (decimal) format.
```

The SBB and DAS instructions are often contained within a loop that subtracts the packed BCD values (decimal values) byte-by-byte, beginning with the least significant byte.

DAS Decimal Adjust AL after Subtraction **DAS**

Timing

`4 clock cycles; 0.2μsec @ 20MHz.`

Flags

CF and AF as described in *Function* above. OF, SF, ZF, and PF are undefined. Other flags are unchanged.

REAL-mode Exceptions:

None.

PROTECTED-mode Exceptions:

None.

VIRTUAL 8086-mode Exceptions:

None.

DEC   Decrement by 1   **DEC**

Format

DEC

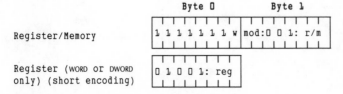

Function

DESTINATION ⟵ DESTINATION - 1;

Description

DEC subtracts 1 from the operand. DEC does not affect CF, however. To also affect CF, use the SUB instruction with an immediate value of 1.

Example

    DEC   EBX

If EBX = FFAD9034h, then as a result of the DEC instruction above, EBX is assigned FFAD9033h.

Timing

Decrement of Register: 2 clock cycles; 0.1µsec @ 20MHz.
Decrement of Memory: 6 clock cycles; 0.3µsec @ 20MHz.

Flags

OF, SF, ZF, AF, and PF affected as described in Appendix A. Other flags are unchanged.

DEC   Decrement by 1   **DEC**

REAL-mode Exceptions:

Same as for ADD instruction. See page 251.

PROTECTED-mode Exceptions:

Same as for ADD instruction. See page 251.

VIRTUAL 8086-mode Exceptions:

Same as for ADD instruction. See page 251.

DIV   Unsigned Divide   **DIV**

Format

```
DIV
```

	Byte 0 Byte 1
AL|AX|EAX by	1 1 1 1 0 1 1 w mod:1 1 0: r/m
Register/Memory	

Function

```
AL|AX|EAX ⟵ AX|DX:AX|EDX:EAX / SOURCE;   {unsigned division quotient}
AH|DX|EDX ⟵ REMAINDER;
```

Description

DIV performs unsigned division. The operand named is the divisor. Depending on the operand size, BYTE, WORD, or DWORD, the DIV instruction uses register(s) AX|DX:AX|EDX:EAX as the source dividend, and register AL|AX|EAX for the quotient. Register AH|DX|EDX holds the remainder.

Example

```
    DIV   ECX
```

If EDX = 000005D2h and EAX = 60F40000h and ECX = 00BC5200h, then as a result of the DIV instruction above, EAX = 00075A00h (quotient), and EDX = 00000000h (remainder). ECX is unchanged.

Timing

The number of clocks required to complete the instruction depends on the size of the dividend.

```
16-bit dividend:   19 clock cycles; 0.95µsec @ 20MHz.
32-bit dividend:   27 clock cycles; 1.35µsec @ 20MHz.
62-bit dividend:   43 clock cycles; 2.15µsec @ 20MHz.
```

Flags

OF, CF affected as described in Appendix A. SF, ZF, AF, and PF are undefined. Other flags are unchanged.

DIV Unsigned Divide **DIV**

REAL-mode Exceptions:

Interrupt 0 if the quotient is too large to fit in the register designated: AL I AX I EAX. Other exceptions same as for ADD instruction. See page 251.

PROTECTED-mode Exceptions:

Divide exception (exception 0) if the quotient is too large to fit in the register designated: AL I AX I EAX. For exception 0, no error code is pushed on the stack. Other exceptions same as for ADD instruction. See page 251.

VIRTUAL 8086-mode Exceptions:

Divide exception (exception 0) if the quotient is too large to fit in the register designated: AL I AX I EAX. For exception 0, no error code is pushed on the stack. Other exceptions same as for ADD instruction. See page 251.

ENTER   Make Stack Frame For Procedure Parameters   **ENTER**

Format

```
ENTER
```

```
1 1 0 0 1 0 0 0   16-Bit Displacement, 8-Bit Level
```

Function

```
LEVEL ⟵ LEVEL MOD 32
IF OPERAND SIZE = 16 THEN PUSH(BP) ELSE PUSH(EBP);
FRAME POINTER ⟵ ESP;
IF LEVEL > 0 THEN              (level is rightmost parameter)
BEGIN
  FOR I = 1 TO (LEVEL-1)
  DO     IF OPERAND SIZE = 16 THEN
    BEGIN
      BP  ⟵  BP - 2;
      PUSH(BP);
    END
    ELSE
    BEGIN
      EBP  ⟵  EBP - 4;
      PUSH(EBP);
    END
  END
  PUSH(FRAME POINTER);
END
IF (OPERAND SIZE = 16) THEN
  BP ⟵ FRAME POINTER;
ELSE
  EBP ⟵ FRAME POINTER;
IF ADDRESS SIZE = 16 THEN
  SP  ⟵  SP - FIRST OPERAND;
ELSE
  ESP  ⟵  ESP - FIRST OPERAND;
```

Description

ENTER creates the stack frame required by most block-structured high-level languages. The first operand specifies the number of bytes of dynamic storage allocated on the stack for the routine being entered. The second operand gives the lexical nesting level (0 to 31) of the routine within the high-level language source code. It determines the number of stack frame pointers copied into the new stack frame from the preceding frame. BP (or EBP, if the operand size attribute is 32 bits) is the current stack frame pointer.

ENTER Make Stack Frame For Procedure Parameters **ENTER**

If the operand size attribute is 16 bits, the processor uses BP as the frame pointer, and SP as the stack pointer. If the operand size attribute is 32 bits, the processor uses EBP for the frame pointer, and ESP for the stack pointer.

If the second operand is 0, ENTER pushes the frame pointer (BP or EBP) onto the stack. ENTER then subtracts the first operand from the stack pointer and sets the frame pointer to the current stack pointer value.

Example

```
ENTER  12,0
```

For example, a procedure with 12 bytes of local variables would have an ENTER 12, 0 instruction at its entry point and a LEAVE instruction before every RET. The 12 local bytes would be addressed as negative offsets from the frame pointer.

Timing

```
5 clock cycles; 0.25µsec @ 20MHz.
```

Flags

None are affected.

REAL-mode Exceptions:

None.

PROTECTED-mode Exceptions:

Exception 0 if the quotient is too large to fit in the register designated: AL I AX I EAX. For exception 0, no error code is pushed on the stack. Other exceptions same as for ADD instruction. See page 251.

VIRTUAL 8086-mode Exceptions:

General Protection exception (exception 13) with error code of 0000h. HLT is a privileged instruction that can be executed only at privilege 0. During VIRTUAL 8086 mode, the 80386 is operating at privilege-level 3.

HLT   Halt Until Interrupt   **HLT**

Format

```
HALT
```

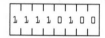

```
1 1 1 1 0 1 0 0
```

Function

```
The processor enters a halt state.
```

Description

No further instructions are fetched or executed until an interrupt is received, or until the processor is reset. Maskable interrupts (INTR pin) must be enabled to be recognized. Non-maskable interrupts (NMI pin) are always recognized.

Example

```
    HLT
```

The 80386 halts indefinitely until an interrupt is recognized. This instruction is typically used only when there is no other work the system can perform until the external interrupt occurs.

Timing

```
5 clock cycles; 0.25µsec @ 20MHz.
```

Flags

None are affected.

REAL-mode Exceptions:

None.

PROTECTED-mode Exceptions:

General Protection exception (exception 13) with error code of 0000h if the current privilege level is not 0.

HLT   Halt Until Interrupt   **HLT**

VIRTUAL **8086-mode Exceptions:**

General Protection exception (exception 13) with error code of 0000h. HLT is a privileged instruction that can be executed only at privilege 0. (During VIRTUAL 8086 mode, the 80386 is operating at privilege level 3).

IDIV   Integer (Signed) Divide   **IDIV**

Format

```
IDIV
```

```
        Byte 0          Byte 1
   ┌─┬─┬─┬─┬─┬─┬─┬─┐ ┌─┬─┬─┬─┬─┬─┬─┬─┐
   │1 1 1 1 0 1 1 w│ │mod:1 1 0: r/m │
   └─┴─┴─┴─┴─┴─┴─┴─┘ └─┴─┴─┴─┴─┴─┴─┴─┘
```

Function

```
AL|AX|EAX ←── AX|DX:AX|EDX:EAX / SOURCE;   (signed division quotient)

AH|DX|EDX ←── REMAINDER;
```

Description

IDIV performs signed division. The operand named is the divisor. Depending on the operand size, BYTE, WORD, or DWORD, the IDIV instruction uses register(s) AX I DX:AX I EDX:EAX as the source dividend, and register AL I AX I EAX for the quotient. Register AH I DX I EDX holds the remainder.

Example

```
    IDIV    ECX
```

If EDX = 000005D2h and EAX = 60F40000h and ECX = 00BC5200h, then as a result of the IDIV instruction above, EAX = 00075A00h (quotient), and EDX = 00000000h (remainder). ECX is unchanged.

Timing

The number of clocks required to complete the instruction depends on the size of the dividend.

```
16-bit dividend:   19 clock cycles; 0.95μsec @ 20MHz.
32-bit dividend:   27 clock cycles; 1.35μsec @ 20MHz.
62-bit dividend:   43 clock cycles; 2.15μsec @ 20MHz.
```

Flags

OF, CF affected as described in Appendix A. SF, ZF, AF, and PF are undefined. Other flags are unchanged.

IDIV Integer (Signed) Divide **IDIV**

REAL-mode Exceptions:

Interrupt 0 if the quotient is too large to fit in the register designated: AL I AX I EAX. Other exceptions same as for ADD instruction. See page 251.

PROTECTED-mode Exceptions:

Divide exception (exception 0) if the quotient is too large to fit in the register designated: AL I AX I EAX. For exception 0, no error code is pushed on the stack. Other exceptions same as for ADD instruction. See page 251.

VIRTUAL 8086-mode Exceptions:

Divide exception (exception 0) if the quotient is too large to fit in the register designated: AL I AX I EAX. For exception 0, no error code is pushed on the stack. Other exceptions same as for ADD instruction. See page 251.

IMUL   Integer (Signed) Multiply   **IMUL**

Format

IMUL

```
                 Byte 0           Byte1            Byte 2
Register with    ┌─┬─┬─┬─┬─┬─┬─┬─┬─┬─┬─┬─┬─┬─┬─┬─┬─────────────┐
Register/Memory  │0 0 0 0 1 1 1 1│1 0 1 0 1 1 1 1│mod: reg : r/m│
                 └─┴─┴─┴─┴─┴─┴─┴─┴─┴─┴─┴─┴─┴─┴─┴─┴─────────────┘

AL|AX|EAX with   ┌─┬─┬─┬─┬─┬─┬─┬──────────────────┐
Register/Memory  │1 1 1 1 0 1 1 w│mod:1 1 0: r/m│
(short encoding) └─┴─┴─┴─┴─┴─┴─┴──────────────────┘

Register/Memory  ┌─┬─┬─┬─┬─┬─┬─┬──────────────┬────────────────────┐
with Immediate   │0 1 1 0 1 0 s 1│mod: reg : r/m│Immediate Data Byte(s)│
to Register      └─┴─┴─┴─┴─┴─┴─┴──────────────┴────────────────────┘
```

Function

DESTINATION ⟵ DESTINATION × SOURCE;   {signed multiplication}

   or

DESTINATION ⟵ DESTINATION × IMMEDIATE DATA;   {signed multiplication}

Description

IMUL performs signed multiplication. Various forms of the instruction exist as shown in *Format* above.

Example

```
    IMUL    ECX, EDX
```

If ECX = 00000034h and EDX = FFFFFF52h, then as a result of the IMUL instruction above, ECX is assigned FFFFDCA8h.

Timing

IMUL uses an early-finish algorithm. The actual number of clocks required to complete the instruction depends on the position of the significant bit in the optimizing multiplier.

```
Register to Register:   9-41 clock cycles; 0.45-2.05µsec @ 20MHz.
Register to Memory:     12-44 clock cycles; 0.6-2.2µsec @ 20MHz.
Memory to Register:     12-44 clock cycles; 0.6-2.2µsec @ 20MHz.
Immediate to Register:  9-38 clock cycles; 0.45-1.9µsec @ 20MHz.
Immediate to Memory:    12-41 clock cycles; 0.6-2.05µsec @ 20MHz.
```

IMUL Integer (Signed) Multiply **IMUL**

Flags

OF, CF affected as described in Appendix A. SF, ZF, AF, and PF are undefined. Other flags are unchanged.

REAL-mode Exceptions:

Same as for ADD instruction. See page 251.

PROTECTED-mode Exceptions:

Same as for ADD instruction. See page 251.

VIRTUAL 8086-mode Exceptions:

Same as for ADD instruction. See page 251.

IN   Input from I/O Address   **IN**

Format

```
IN
```

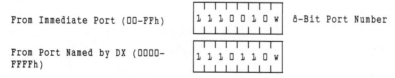

From Immediate Port (00-FFh)   `1 1 1 0 0 1 0 w`   8-Bit Port Number

From Port Named by DX (0000-FFFFh)   `1 1 1 0 1 1 0 w`

Function

```
[PORT DX]  ◄─── SOURCE;     (input data)
```

Description

Inputs an operand from the port named by the DX register or by the immediate data field. The operand is input to AL I AX I EAX, depending on the operand size of the string instruction: BYTE, WORD, or DWORD.

This instruction is always available in REAL mode. In PROTECTED mode, this instruction is always available when CPL ≤ IOPL. When CPL > IOPL in PROTECTED mode, the I/O permission bitmap determines if the instruction is permitted. All relevant bits of the I/O permission bitmap must be 0 for the I/O to proceed. In VIRTUAL 8086 mode, the I/O permission bitmap always determines if the IN instruction is permitted.

Example

```
    IN          ;inputs operand from port DX
```

Timing

REAL mode
Immediate port: 12 clock cycles; 0.6µsec @ 20MHz.
Variable port: 13 clock cycles; 0.65µsec @ 20MHz.

PROTECTED mode, CPL ≤ IOPL
Immediate port: 6 clock cycles; 0.3µsec @ 20MHz.
Variable port: 7 clock cycles; 0.35µsec @ 20MHz.

PROTECTED mode, CPL > IOPL
Immediate port: 26 clock cycles; 1.3µsec @ 20MHz.
Variable port: 27 clock cycles; 1.35µsec @ 20MHz.

VIRTUAL 8086 mode
Immediate port: 26 clock cycles; 1.3µsec @ 20MHz.
Variable port: 17 clock cycles; 1.35µsec @ 20MHz.

IN   Input from I/O Address   **IN**

Flags

None are affected.

REAL-mode Exceptions:

Same as for ADD instruction. See page 251.

PROTECTED-mode Exceptions:

If CPL > IOPL, the I/O permission bitmap must allow I/O to all byte ports involved. Other exceptions same as for ADD instruction. See page 251.

VIRTUAL 8086-mode Exceptions:

The I/O permission bitmap must allow I/O to all byte ports involved. Other exceptions same as for ADD instruction. See page 251.

INC   Increment by 1   **INC**

Format

```
INC
```

Register/Memory

1 1 1 1 1 1 w	mod:0 0 0: r/m

Register (WORD or DWORD only) (short encoding)

0 1 0 0 0: reg

Function

```
DESTINATION  ←  DESTINATION + 1;
```

Description

INC adds 1 to the operand. INC does not affect CF, however. To also affect CF, use the ADD instruction with an immediate value of 1.

Example

```
    INC    EBX
```

If EBX = FFAD9034h, then as a result of the INC instruction above, EBX is assigned FFAD9035h.

Timing

```
Increment of Register:  2 clock cycles; 0.1μsec a 20MHz.
Increment of Memory:    6 clock cycles; 0.3μsec a 20MHz.
```

Flags

OF, SF, ZF, AF, and PF affected as described in Appendix A. Other flags are unchanged.

INC Increment by 1 **INC**

REAL-**mode Exceptions:**

Same as for ADD instruction. See page 251.

PROTECTED-**mode Exceptions:**

Same as for ADD instruction. See page 251.

VIRTUAL **8086-mode Exceptions:**

Same as for ADD instruction. See page 251.

INSB/INSW/INSD   Input String Data from I/O Address   **INSB/INSW/INSD**

Format

```
INSB/INSW/INSD
```

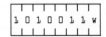

```
1 0 1 0 0 1 1 w
```

Function

```
[PORT DX]  ←—  [SOURCE]    {input data}
IF (ADDRESSSIZE = 32) THEN
  ADJUST EDI;                   {adjust index for source}
ELSE    {addresssize = 16}
  ADJUST DI;
```

Description

Inputs an operand from the port named by the DX register to a destination memory string. The source string is considered to be an array of BYTES, WORDS, or DWORDS, depending on the operand size of the string instruction. After the input is made, the destination index register is automatically advanced (incremented or decremented, according to DF) by an amount equaling the operand size.

If the address size of the instruction is DWORD, the operand of the destination string is ES:[EDI]. Otherwise, the operand is ES:[DI]. Load the correct index values before executing INS.

Example

```
        INSD    ;inputs DWORD operands from port DX


    or


    REP    INSD    ;repeated INS until ECX expires.
                   ; (See page 457 for details)
```

Because the source index register must be loaded to use this instruction, INSB/W/D is often placed in a loop and used for several iterations.

INSB/INSW/INSD   Input String Data from I/O Address   **INSB/INSW/INSD**

Timing

REAL mode
```
nonrepeated:      15 clock cycles; 0.75µsec @ 20MHz.
repeated:    13 +6n clock cycles; 0.65 + 0.3nµsec @ 20MHz.
```

PROTECTED mode, CPL ≤ IOPL
```
nonrepeated:       9 clock cycles; 0.45µsec @ 20MHz.
repeated:     7 +6n clock cycles; 0.35 + 0.3nµsec @ 20MHz.
```

PROTECTED mode, CPL > IOPL
```
nonrepeated:      29 clock cycles; 1.45µsec @ 20MHz.
repeated:    27 +6n clock cycles; 1.35 + 0.3nµsec @ 20MHz.
```

VIRTUAL 8086 mode
```
nonrepeated:      29 clock cycles; 1.45µsec @ 20MHz.
repeated:    27 +6n clock cycles; 1.35 + 0.3nµsec @ 20MHz.
```

(*n* is number of iterations performed)

Flags

None are affected.

REAL-mode Exceptions:

Same as for ADD instruction. See page 251.

PROTECTED-mode Exceptions:

If CPL > IOPL, the I/O permission bitmap must allow I/O to all byte ports involved. Other exceptions same as for ADD instruction. See page 251.

VIRTUAL 8086-mode Exceptions:

The I/O permission bitmap must allow I/O to all byte ports involved. Other exceptions same as for ADD instruction. See page 251.

INT 3   Interrupt 3 (Breakpoint)   **INT 3**

Format

INT 3

Function

INTERRUPT 3;

Description

INT 3 causes an interrupt 3. The next instruction executed is the entry point of the interrupt 3 routine. In PROTECTED mode, the general software interrupt instruction, INT n, is sensitive to IOPL. This specific software interrupt instruction, INT 3, is always available, however; it is not IOPL-sensitive. The single-byte INT 3 instruction is suitable for generating breakpoints when debugging software.

INT 3   Interrupt 3 (Breakpoint)   **INT 3**

Example

```
INT   3       ;interrupt 3; breakpoint interrupt
```

PROTECTED-mode Details:

Please turn to page 314 for details.

Timing

33 clock cycles; 1.65μsec @ 20MHz.

Flags

No flags affected. All flags are unchanged.

REAL-mode Exceptions:

None.

PROTECTED-mode Exceptions:

Page Fault exception (exception 14) with error code of fault code, and page-fault linear address in register CR2.

VIRTUAL 8086-mode Exceptions:

Page Fault exception (exception 14) with error code of fault code, and page-fault linear address in register CR2.

INTO   Interrupt 4 if Overflow   **INTO**

Format

```
INTO
```

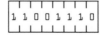

```
┌─┬─┬─┬─┬─┬─┬─┬─┐
│1│1│0│0│1│1│1│0│
└─┴─┴─┴─┴─┴─┴─┴─┘
```

Function

```
IF (OF = 1) THEN
  INTERRUPT 4;
```

Description

INTO allows run-time trapping of an overflow condition. If OF = 1 when INTO is executed, interrupt 4 is generated. Otherwise, no action is taken. INTO is not IOPL-sensitive so is always available; it can be included in application software to detect run-time overflow.

Example

```
    INTO     ;interrupt 4 if overflow flag is set
```

PROTECTED-mode Details:

Please turn to page 314 for details.

Timing

```
If interrupt is not generated:  3 clock cycles; 0.15μsec @ 20MHz.
If interrupt 4 is generated:   35 clock cycles; 0.5μsec @ 20MHz.
```

INTO   Interrupt 4 if Overflow   **INTO**

Flags

No flags affected. All flags are unchanged.

REAL-mode Exceptions:

Interrupt 4 if OF = 1.

PROTECTED-mode Exceptions:

Interrupt 4 if OF = 1. Page Fault exception (exception 14) with error code of fault code, and page-fault linear address in register CR2.

VIRTUAL 8086-mode Exceptions:

Interrupt 4 if OF = 1. Page Fault exception (exception 14) with error code of fault code, and page-fault linear address in register CR2.

INT n   Interrupt n   **INT n**

Format

```
INT n
```

```
          Byte 0        Byte 1
        ┌─┬─┬─┬─┬─┬─┬─┬─┬─┬─┬─┬─┬─┬─┬─┬─┐
        │0 1 1 0 0 0 1 0│       n       │
        └─┴─┴─┴─┴─┴─┴─┴─┴─┴─┴─┴─┴─┴─┴─┴─┘
```

Function

```
PUSH EFLAGS;
PUSH CS;
PUSH EIP;
RELOAD EIP FROM OPERAND;              (vector or gate n)
RELOAD CS FROM OPERAND;               (vector or gate n)
CLEAR INTERRUPT FLAG IN EFLAG REGISTER;
```

Description

When an INT *n* occurs in REAL mode or VIRTUAL 8086 mode, the flag register, instruction pointer and code segment register are all pushed on the stack. The interrupt flag in the flag register is cleared so further interrupts are not recognized. Both the instruction pointer and code segment register then replaced by the vector values in the interrupt vector to begin execution of a the service routine.

When an INT *n* occurs in PROTECTED mode, the activities performed by the 80386 can be quite complex according to whether the destination selector is that of:

1. a call gate to a code segment at the current privilege level (DPL = CPL),
2. a call gate to a code segment at a more privileged level (DPL ≤ CPL),
3. a task gate.

Example

```
    INT 34h   ;vector through vector or gate 34h (52 dec.)
```

PROTECTED-mode Details:

```
PROTECTED MODE:
   Interrupt vector must be within Interrupt Descriptor Table (IDT) limits ELSE Gen-
      eral Protection exception (error code of vector number * 8 + 2 + EXT).
   Gate Access Rights (AR) byte must indicate interrupt gate, trap gate, or task
      gate ELSE General Protection exception (error code of vector number * 8 + 2 +
      EXT).
   IF software interrupt (i.e., caused by INT 3, INTO, or INT n)
   THEN
```

INT n   Interrupt n   **INT n**

IF gate descriptor DPL must be ≥ CPL ELSE General Protection exception (error
  code of vector number * 8 + 2 + EXT).
Gate must be present ELSE Not Present exception (error code of vector number + 2
  + EXT).
IF trap gate OR interrupt gate
THEN go to TRAP-GATE-OR-INTERRUPT-GATE
ELSE go to TASK-GATE.

TRAP-GATE-OR-INTERRUPT-GATE:
  Examine CS selector and descriptor given in the gate descriptor.
  Selector must not be null ELSE General Protection exception (error code of EXT
    bit).
  Selector index must be within its descriptor table limit ELSE General Protection
    exception (error code of selector + EXT).
  Descriptor Access Rights (AR) byte must indicate code segment ELSE General Pro-
    tection exception (error code of code segment selector + EXT).
  Code segment must be present ELSE Not Present exception (error code of selector +
    EXT).
  IF segment is nonconforming and AND code segment DPL < CPL
  THEN go to INTERRUPT-TO-INNER-PRIVILEGE-LEVEL
  ELSE
  IF ((segment is conforming AND code segment DPL ≤ CPL) OR (segment DPL = CPL))
  THEN go to INTERRUPT-TO-SAME-PRIVILEGE-LEVEL
  ELSE General Protection exception (error code of code segment selector + EXT).

INTERRUPT-TO-INNER-PRIVILEGE-LEVEL:
  Check selector and descriptor for new stack in current TSS:
   Selector must not be null ELSE General Protection exception (error code of EXT
     bit).
   Selector index must be within its descriptor table limit ELSE General Protection
     exception (error code of selector + EXT).
   Selector RPL must = DPL of code segment ELSE Invalid TSS exception (error code
     of stack segment selector + EXT).
   Stack segment DPL must = DPL of code segment ELSE Invalid TSS exception (error
     code of stack segment selector + EXT).
   Descriptor Access Rights (AR) byte must writable segment ELSE Invalid TSS excep-
     tion (error code of stack segment selector + EXT).
   Stack segment must be present ELSE Stack Fault exception (error code of stack
     segment selector + EXT).
  IF 32-bit gate
   THEN new stack must have room for 20 bytes ELSE Stack Fault exception (error
     code of 0000h).
   ELSE new stack must have room for 10 bytes ELSE Stack Fault exception (error
     code of 0000h). {else 16-bit gate}
  Instruction pointer must be within CS limit ELSE General Protection exception
     (error code of 0000h).
  Load new SS and eSP values from TSS.
  IF 32-bit gate
   THEN load CS and EIP from gate
   ELSE load CS and IP from gate {16-bit gate}
  Load code segment descriptor into CS descriptor cache.
  Load stack segment descriptor into SS descriptor cache.
  IF 32-bit gate
   THEN

INT n   Interrupt n   INT n

```
      Push(long pointer to old stack).      {b bytes padded to 8 bytes}
      Push(EFLAG).
      Push(long pointer to return location). {b bytes padded to 8 bytes}
     ELSE  {16-bit gate}
      Push(long pointer to old stack).      {4 bytes}
      Push(EFLAG).
      Push(long pointer to return location). {4 bytes}
    Set CPL to new code segment DPL.
    Set RPL field of CS register to CPL.
    IF interrupt gate, then reset Interrupt Flag (IF) in EFLAG.  {disable interrupts}
    Reset Single-step Trap Flag (TF) in EFLAG.
    Reset Nested Task (NT) flag in EFLAG.

INTERRUPT FROM VIRTUAL 8086 MODE:
  TempEFLAGS := EFLAGS.
  Reset VIRTUAL 8086 Mode flag (VM) in EFLAG.  {interrupt causes exit from VIRTUAL
    8086 mode}
  Reset Single-step Trap Flag (TF) in EFLAG.
  IF service through interrupt gate THEN reset Interrupt Flag (IF) in EFLAG.
  Temp SS := SS.
  Temp ESP := ESP.
  SS := TSS.SS0.  {Change to level-0 stack segment as stored in Task State Segment}
  ESP := TSS.ESP. {Change to level-0 stack pointer as stored in Task State Segment}
  Push(GS).       {2 bytes padded to 4 bytes}
  Push(FS).       {2 bytes padded to 4 bytes}
  Push(DS).       {2 bytes padded to 4 bytes}
  Push(ES).       {2 bytes padded to 4 bytes}
  GS := 0.
  FS := 0.
  DS := 0.
  ES := 0.
  Push(TempSS).   {2 bytes padded to 4 bytes}
  Push(TempESP).
  Push(TempEFLAGS).
  Push(CS).       {2 bytes padded to 4 bytes}
  Push(EIP).
  Load CS:EIP from interrupt gate.
  {begin execution of interrupt routine in PROTECTED mode}

INTERRUPT-TO-SAME-PRIVILEGE-LEVEL:
  IF 32-bit gate
  THEN current stack limits must allow pushing 10 bytes ELSE Stack Fault exception
    (error code of 0000h).
  ELSE current stack limits must allow pushing 6 bytes ELSE Stack Fault exception
    (error code of 0000h).
  IF interrupt was caused by exception with error code
  THEN stack limit must allow push of two more bytes ELSE Stack Fault exception
    (error code of 0000h).
  Instruction pointer must be within code segment limit ELSE General Protection ex-
    ception (error code of 0000h).
  IF 32-bit gate
   THEN
    Push(EFLAG).
    Push(long pointer to return location). {b bytes padded to 8 bytes}
```

INT n <div align="center">Interrupt n</div> **INT n**

```
    Load CS:EIP from gate.
   ELSE  (16-bit gate)
    Push(EFLAG).
    Push(long pointer to return location). (4 bytes)
    Load CS:IP from gate.
  Load code segment descriptor into CS descriptor cache.
  Set RPL field of CS register to CPL.
  IF interrupt gate, then reset Interrupt Flag (IF) in EFLAG.  (disable interrupts)
  Reset Single-step Trap Flag (TF) in EFLAG.
  Reset Nested Task (NT) flag in EFLAG.

TASK-GATE:
  Examine selector to TSS given in task gate:
   Must specify Global Descriptor Table (GDT) in Table Indicator (TI) bit ELSE In-
     valid TSS exception (error code of TSS selector).
   Index must be within GDT limits ELSE Invalid TSS exception (error code of TSS
     selector).
   TSS descriptor access rights byte must specify nonbusy TSS ELSE Invalid TSS ex-
     ception (error code of TSS selector).
   Task-state Segment must be present ELSE Not Present exception (error code of TSS
     selector).
  SWITCH-TASKS (with nesting, set NT bit in EFLAG) to task given by TSS selector.
  IF interrupt was caused by fault with error code
  THEN
   Stack limits must allow push of two more bytes ELSE Stack Fault exception (error
     code of 0000h).
   Push error code onto stack.
  EIP must be within code segment limit ELSE Invalid TSS exception (error code of
    0000h).
```

Flags

No flags are affected, unless a task switch occurs in PROTECTED mode.

REAL-mode Exceptions:

Interrupt 13 if any part of an operand in memory is at effective address greater than FFFFh in segments CS, DS, ES, FS, or GS. Interrupt 12 if any part of an operand in memory is at effective address greater than FFFFh in stack segment SS.

PROTECTED-mode Exceptions:

General Protection exception (exception 13) with error code of 0000h for operands in memory segments CS, DS, ES, FS, or GS if a source operand is in a nonreadable code segment, or if any part of the operand is at effective address beyond the segment limit. Stack exception with error code of 0000h for operands in stack segment if any part of the operand is at effective address beyond the segment limit. Stack

INT n   Interrupt n   **INT n**

exception with error code of segment selector if operand in memory is in segment SS marked not present. Not Present exception (exception 11) with error code of segment selector if operand in memory is in a segment DS, ES, FS, or GS marked not present. Not Present exception with error code of segment selector if operand in memory is in a segment DS, ES, FS, or GS marked not present. Page Fault exception (exception 14) with error code of fault code, and page-fault linear address in register CR2. Invalid Task State Segment exception (exception 10) with error code of selector for inconsistencies in the Task-state Segment if performing a task switch.

VIRTUAL **8086-mode Exceptions:**

Same as REAL mode exceptions, but handled in PROTECTED mode at privilege-level 0. The format of the privilege-level-0 stack after an exception (with error code) or interrupt (no error code) is shown in Figure 12.2. Also Page Fault exception with error code of fault code, and page-fault linear address in register CR2.

IRET/IRETD   Return from Interrupt (or from Task in PROTECTED mode)   **IRET/IRETD**

Format

```
IRET
```

```
1 1 0 0 1 1 1 1
```

Function

```
IF (ADDRESS SIZE = 32) THEN
BEGIN
  POP EIP;                 {IRET pops EIP or IP}
  POP CS;                  {IRET also pops CS}
  POP EFLAGS;              {IRET also pops EFLAG or FLAG}
END
ELSE
BEGIN
  POP IP;                  {IRET pops EIP or IP}
  POP CS;                  {IRET also pops CS}
  POP FLAGS;               {IRET also pops EFLAG or FLAG}
END
```

Description

IRET typically appears at the end of interrupt service routines to return control to the interrupted program. IRET pops the instruction pointer and the code segment register from the stack, thus performing an intersegment return. It also pops the flag register, which contains the state of IF prior to the interrupt.

When IRET occurs in REAL mode or VIRTUAL 8086 mode, the instruction pointer and code segment register popped from the stack determine the address where processing of the main routine will resume.

When an IRET occurs in PROTECTED mode, the activities performed by the 80386 can be quite complex according to whether the destination selector is that of:

1. a code segment at the current privilege level, (DPL = CPL)
2. a code segment at a more privileged level, (DPL ≤ CPL), or
3. a task state segment.

The IRET instruction is also appropriate for the end of a nested task, where it causes a task switch back to the previous task (the nested task condition is indicated by NT = 1 in the EFLAG register).

IRET/IRETD   Return from Interrupt (or from Task in PROTECTED mode)   **IRET/IRETD**

Example

```
    IRET
```

PROTECTED-mode Details:

```
    IF VIRTUAL 8086 mode flag (VM) = 1 and IOPL <> 3
    THEN General Protection Exception (error code of 0000h)  (allow PROTECTED mode
      supervisor to emulate instruction)
    ELSE
     IF Nested Task flag (NT) = 1 THEN go to TASK-RETURN
     ELSE
      IF Virtual 8086 mode flag (VM) = 1 in flag image on stack
      THEN go to STACK-RETURN-TO-VIRTUAL-8086-MODE
      ELSE go to STACK-RETURN.

STACK-RETURN-TO-VIRTUAL-8086-MODE:  (Interrupted procedure was in VIRTUAL 8086
    mode)
  CPL must = 0 ELSE General Protection exception (error code of code segment
    selector).
  Top 36 bytes of level-0 stack must be within limits ELSE Stack Fault (error code
    of 0000h).
  Examine return CS selector and associated descriptor:
   Selector must not be null ELSE General Protection exception (error code of
    0000h).
   Selector index must be within table limits ELSE General Protection exception
    (error code of return selector).
   Access Rights (AR) byte must indicate code segment ELSE General Protection ex-
    ception (error code of return selector).
   Code segment DPL must = 3 ELSE General Protection exception (error code of re-
    turn selector).
   Code segment must be present ELSE Not Present exception (error code of return
    selector).
  Examine return SS selector and associated descriptor:
   Selector must not be null ELSE General Protection exception (error code of
    0000h).
   Selector index must be within table limits ELSE General Protection exception
    (error code of stack selector).
   Selector RPL must = RPL of return selector ELSE General Protection exception
    (error code of stack selector).
   Access Rights (AR) byte must indicate writable segment ELSE General Protection
    exception (error code of stack selector).
   Stack segment DPL must = 3 ELSE General Protection exception (error code of re-
    turn selector).
   Stack segment must be present ELSE Not Present exception (error code of return
    selector).
  Instruction pointer must be within code segment limit ELSE General Protection ex-
    ception (error code of 0000h).
  Load EFLAGS with SS:[eSP + 8]      (Sets Virtual 8086 mode flag (VM) in inter-
                                      rupted routine).

  EIP := Pop().
```

IRET/IRETD   Return from Interrupt (or from Task in PROTECTED mode)   **IRET/IRETD**

```
CS := Pop().          {CS and all other segment register values popped behave as
                       in 8086 due to VM = 1}
throwaway := Pop().   {Throwaway EFLAGS already loaded}
ES := Pop().          {Pop 4 bytes, throwaway upper 2 bytes}
DS := Pop().          {Pop 4 bytes, throwaway upper 2 bytes}
FS := Pop().          {Pop 4 bytes, throwaway upper 2 bytes}
GS := Pop().          {Pop 4 bytes, throwaway upper 2 bytes}
IF CS.RPL > CPL
THEN
 TempESP := Pop().
 TempSS := Pop().
 SS:ESP := TempSS:TempESP.
```

TASK-RETURN:
  Examine Back Link Selector in TSS addressed by the current Task Register (TR):
   Must specify global in global/local table indicator (TI) bit ELSE Invalid TSS
    exception (error code of TSS selector).
   Index must be within GDT limits ELSE Invalid TSS exception (error code of TSS
    selector).
   Access Rights (AR) byte must specify Task-state Segment ELSE Invalid TSS excep-
    tion (error code of TSS selector).
   New TSS must be busy ELSE Invalid TSS exception (error code of TSS selector).
   Task must be present ELSE Not Present exception (error code of TSS selector).
  SWITCH-TASKS without task nesting, to TSS specified by back link selector.
  Mark the task just exited as NOT BUSY.
  Instruction pointer must be within code segment limit ELSE General Protection ex-
   ception (error code of 0000h).

STACK-RETURN:
  IF operand size = 32
   THEN third word on stack must be within stack limits ELSE Stack Fault exception
    (error code of 0000h).
  ELSE second word on stack must be within stack limits ELSE Stack Fault exception
    (error code of 0000h).
  Return CS selector RPL must be ≥ CPL ELSE General Protection exception (error
   code of return selector).
  IF return selector RPL = CPL
   THEN go to RETURN-SAME-LEVEL
   ELSE go to RETURN-OUTER-LEVEL   {return to level of lesser privilege}

RETURN-SAME-LEVEL:
  IF operand size = 32
  THEN
   Top 12 bytes on stack must be within limits else Stack Fault exception (error
    code of 0000h).
   Return CS selector (at eSP + 4) must not be null ELSE General Protection excep-
    tion (error code of 0000h).
  ELSE
   Top 6 bytes on stack must be within limits else Stack Fault exception (error
    code of 0000h).
   Return CS selector (at eSP + 2) must not be null ELSE General Protection excep-
    tion (error code of 0000h).
  Selector index must be within its descriptor table limits ELSE General Protec-
   tion exception (error code of return selector).

IRET/IRETD   Return from Interrupt (or from Task in PROTECTED mode)   **IRET/IRETD**

Access Rights (AR) byte must indicate code segment, else General Protection ex-
ception (error code of return selector).
IF nonconforming code segment:
THEN code segment DPL must = CPL ELSE General Protection exception (error code
of return selector).
IF conforming code segment
THEN code segment DPL must be ≥ CPL ELSE General Protection exception (error
code of return selector).
Segment must be present ELSE Not Present exception (error code of return
selector).
Instruction pointer must be within code segment boundaries ELSE General Protec-
tion exception (error code of 0000).
IF operand size = 32
  THEN
  Pop CS:EIP from stack.
  Load CS descriptor cache with new code segment descriptor.
  Load EFLAGS with third DWORD from stack.
  Increment eSP by 12 to account for stack items popped.
  ELSE
  Load CS descriptor cache with new code segment descriptor.
  Load FLAGS with third word on stack.
  Increment SP by 6.

RETURN-OUTER-LEVEL:
  IF operand size = 32
  THEN top 20 bytes of stack must be within stack limits, ELSE Stack Fault excep-
  tion (error code of 0000h).
  ELSE top 10 bytes of stack must be within stack limits, ELSE Stack Fault excep-
  tion (error code of 0000h).
  Examine return CS selector and associated descriptor:
   Selector must not be null ELSE General Protection exception (error code of
   0000h).
   Selector index must be within its descriptor table limits ELSE General Protec-
   tion exception (error code of return selector).
   Access Rights (AR) byte must indicate code segment, else General Protection ex-
   ception (error code of return selector).
   IF nonconforming code segment
   THEN code segment DPL must = CS selector RPL ELSE General Protection exception
   (error code of return selector).
   IF conforming code segment
   THEN code segment DPL must be ≤ CPL ELSE General Protection exception (error
   code of return selector).
   Segment must be present ELSE Not Present exception (error code of return
   selector).
  Examine return SS selector and associated descriptor:
   Selector must not be null ELSE General Protection exception (error code of
   0000h).
   Selector index must be within table limits ELSE General Protection exception
   (error code of stack selector).
   Selector RPL must = RPL of return selector ELSE General Protection exception
   (error code of stack selector).
   Access Rights (AR) byte must indicate writable segment ELSE General Protection
   exception (error code of stack selector).

IRET/IRETD   Return from Interrupt (or from Task in PROTECTED mode)   **IRET/IRETD**

```
    Stack segment DPL must = RPL of the return CS selector ELSE General Protection
      exception (error code of return selector).
    Stack segment must be present ELSE Not Present exception (error code of return
      selector).
    Instruction pointer must be within code segment boundaries ELSE General Protec-
      tion exception (error code of 0000).
    IF operand size = 32
    THEN
      Load CS:EIP from stack.
      Load EFLAGS with values at SS:[eSP + 8].
    ELSE
      Load CS:IP from stack.
      Load EFLAGS with values at SS:[SP + 4].
    Load SS:eSP from stack.
    Set CPL to the RPL of the return CS selector.
    Load the CS descriptor cache with the CS descriptor.
    Load the SS descriptor cache with the SS descriptor.
    FOR each of ES, FS, GS, and DS
    DO
     If the current RPL value of the segment register is not valid for use at the
     outer level
     THEN zero the segment register and clear the associated valid flag bit.
     To be valid, the register setting must satisfy the following properties:
      selector index must be within descriptor table limits,
      Access Rights (AR) byte must indicate data segment or readable code segment,
      IF segment is data or nonconforming code, THEN DPL must be ≥ CPL or DPL must be
      ≥ RPL.
```

Flags

No flags are affected, unless a task switch occurs in PROTECTED mode.

REAL-mode Exceptions:

Interrupt 13 if any part of an operand in memory is at effective address greater than FFFFh in segments CS, DS, ES, FS, or GS. Interrupt 12 if any part of an operand in memory is at effective address greater than FFFFh in stack segment SS.

PROTECTED-mode Exceptions:

General Protection exception (exception 13) with error code of 0000h for operands in memory segments CS, DS, ES, FS, or GS if a source operand is in a nonreadable code segment, or if any part of the operand is at effective address beyond the segment limit. Stack exception (exception 12) with error code of 0000h for operands in stack segment if any part of the operand is at effective address beyond the segment limit. Stack exception with error code of segment selector if operand in memory is in segment SS marked not present. Not Present exception (exception 11) with error

IRET/IRETD   Return from Interrupt (or from Task in PROTECTED mode)   **IRET/IRETD**

code of segment selector if operand in memory is in a segment DS, ES, FS, or GS marked not present. Not Present exception with error code of segment selector if operand in memory is in a segment DS, ES, FS, or GS marked not present. Page Fault exception (exception 14) with error code of fault code, and page-fault linear address in register CR2. Invalid Task State Segment exception (exception 10) with error code of selector for inconsistencies in the Task State Segment if performing a task switch.

VIRTUAL 8086-mode Exceptions:

Same as REAL mode exceptions, but handled in PROTECTED mode at privilege-level 0. The format of the privilege-level-0 stack after an exception (with error code) or interrupt (no error code) is shown in Figure 12.2. Also Page Fault exception with error code of fault code, and page-fault linear address in register CR2.

Jcc Jump on Condition True **Jcc**

Format

```
Jcc
```

```
                                          Subsequent
                Byte 0          Byte 1     Byte(s)

8-bit        ┌─┬─┬─┬─┬─┬─┬─┬─┬─┬─┬─┬─┬─┬─┬─┬─┐
Displacement │0 1 1 1 c c c c│ 8-bit displ │
             └─┴─┴─┴─┴─┴─┴─┴─┴─┴─┴─┴─┴─┴─┴─┴─┘

Full         ┌─┬─┬─┬─┬─┬─┬─┬─┬─┬─┬─┬─┬─┬─┬─┬─┐ Full
Displacement │0 0 0 0 1 1 1 1│1 0 0 0 c c c c│ Displacement
             └─┴─┴─┴─┴─┴─┴─┴─┴─┴─┴─┴─┴─┴─┴─┴─┘
```

```
C C C C    CONDITION
0 0 0 0    Overflow
0 0 0 1    Not Overflow
0 0 1 0    Below / Not Above or Equal
0 0 1 1    Not Below / Above or Equal
0 1 0 0    Equal / Zero
0 1 0 1    Not Equal / Not Zero
0 1 1 0    Below or Equal / Not Above
0 1 1 1    Not Below or Equal / Above
1 0 0 0    Sign / Negative
1 0 0 1    Not Sign / Positive
1 0 1 0    Parity / Parity Even
1 0 1 1    Not Parity / Parity Odd
1 1 0 0    Less / Not Greater or Equal
1 1 0 1    Not Less / Greater or Equal
1 1 1 0    Less or Equal / Not Greater
1 1 1 1    Not Less or Equal / Greater
```

Function

```
IF (CONDITION = TRUE) THEN
   EIP ←── EIP + DISPLACEMENT;    {perform branch if condition true}
```

Description

Jcc provides conditional branching within the current code segment. If the condition is true, the displacement given as an operand is added to the instruction pointer in order to begin execution at a new offset. Note, the displacement operand is either an 8-bit signed quantity or a full offset signed quantity, full offset being 16-bits if the address size is 16 bits, or 32-bits if the address size is 32 bits. Thus, full displacements allow the branch destination to be anywhere in the current code segment.

Since these conditional jump instructions can branch only within a segment, the code segment register is not affected.

Jcc   Jump on Condition True   **Jcc**

Example

```
JNE     LABEL_D
```

Flags

No flags are affected.

REAL-mode Exceptions:

Interrupt 13 if any part of the destination instruction is at effective address greater than FFFFh in segment CS.

PROTECTED-mode Exceptions:

General Protection exception (exception 13) with error code of 0000h for the destination in memory segment CS if any part of the destination instruction is at effective address beyond the segment limit. Not Present exception (exception 11) with error code of segment selector if operand in memory is in segment CS marked not present. Page Fault exception (exception 14) with error code of fault code, and page-fault linear address in register CR2.

VIRTUAL 8086-mode Exceptions:

Same as REAL mode exceptions, but handled in PROTECTED mode at privilege-level 0. The format of the privilege-level-0 stack after an exception (with error code) or interrupt (no error code) is shown in Figure 12.2. Also Page Fault exception with error code of fault code, and page-fault linear address in register CR2.

JCXZ/JECXZ Jump if CX/ECX is Zero **JCXZ/JECXZ**

Format

```
JCXZ/JECXZ
```

	Byte 0	Byte 1
8-bit Displacement	1 1 1 0 0 0 1 1	8-bit displ

Function

```
IF (ECX = 0) THEN
    EIP ⟵ EIP + DISPLACEMENT;    (displacement is only 8 bits)
```

Description

JECXZ I JCXZ provides conditional branching within the current code segment on the basis of the ECX or CX register (depending on operand size). If the register is 0, the displacement given as an operand is added to the instruction pointer in order to begin execution at a new offset. Note, however, the displacement is only an 8-bit signed quantity, limiting the displacement range from −128 through +127.

Since this conditional jump instruction can branch only within a segment, the code segment register is not affected.

Example

```
    JECXZ    LABEL_E
```

Flags

No flags are affected.

REAL-mode Exceptions:

Interrupt 13 if any part of the destination instruction is at effective address greater than FFFFh in segment CS.

PROTECTED-mode Exceptions:

General Protection exception (exception 13) with error code of 0000h for the destination in memory segment CS if any part of the destination instruction is at effective address beyond the segment limit. Not Present (exception 11) exception with error code of segment selector if operand in memory is in segment CS marked not

JCXZ/JECXZ   Jump if CX/ECX is Zero   **JCXZ/JECXZ**

present. Page Fault exception (exception 14) with error code of fault code, and page-fault linear address in register CR2.

VIRTUAL 8086-mode Exceptions:

Same as REAL mode exceptions, but handled in PROTECTED mode at privilege-level 0. The format of the privilege-level-0 stack after an exception (with error code) or interrupt (no error code) is shown in Figure 12.2. Also Page Fault exception with error code of fault code, and page-fault linear address in register CR2.

JMP　　　　　　Jump to Code (or to Task in PROTECTED mode)　　　　**JMP**

Format

```
JMP
```

	Byte 0	Byte 1	Subsequent Byte(s)
Direct, Short Displacement	1 1 1 0 1 0 1 1	8-bit displ	
Direct, Full Displacement	1 1 1 0 1 0 0 1	Full Displacement	
Indirect to Absolute Offset	1 1 1 1 1 1 1 1	mod:1 0 0: r/m	
Direct Intersegment	1 1 1 0 1 0 1 0	Absolute Offset, Segment Selector	
Indirect Intersegment	1 1 1 1 1 1 1 1	mod:1 0 1: r/m	

Function

```
RELOAD EIP FROM OPERAND;
RELOAD CS FROM OPERAND;
```

Description

JMP within the current code segment modifies the instruction pointer in order to begin execution at a new offset. When a JMP is made within the current code segment, the code segment register is not affected.

When an intersegment JMP occurs in REAL mode or VIRTUAL 8086 mode, the instruction pointer and code segment register are both replaced by the operand values to begin execution at a subroutine.

When a JMP occurs in PROTECTED mode, the activities performed by the 80386 can be quite complex according to whether the destination selector is that of:

1. a code segment at the current privilege level (DPL = CPL),
2. a conforming code segment at a more privileged level (DPL ≤ CPL),
3. a call gate,
4. a task state segment, or
5. a task gate.

JMP   Jump to Code (or to Task in PROTECTED mode)   **JMP**

Example

```
JMP    LABEL_A
```

PROTECTED Mode Details:

PROTECTED MODE JMP TO NONCONFORMING (i.e., regular) CODE SEGMENT:
   RPL of destination selector must be numerically ≤ CPL ELSE General Protection
exception (error code of code segment selector).
   Descriptor DPL must be numerically = CPL ELSE General Protection exception (error
code of code segment selector).
   Selector must be within its descriptor table limits ELSE General Protection ex-
ception (error code of code segment selector).
   Segment must be present ELSE Not Present exception (error code of code segment
selector).
   Instruction pointer must be within code segment ELSE General Protection exception
(error code of 0000h).
   Load code segment descriptor into CS descriptor cache (not visible to
programmer).
   Load CS register with code segment selector.
   Load EIP with zero-extend(new offset).
   If operand size = 16 THEN EIP := EIP AND 0000FFFFh.
   Set RPL field of CS register to CPL.

PROTECTED MODE JMP TO CONFORMING CODE SEGMENT:
   Descriptor DPL must be numerically ≤ CPL ELSE General Protection exception (er-
ror code of code segment selector).
   Selector must be within its descriptor table limits ELSE General Protection ex-
ception (error code of code segment selector).
   Segment index must be present ELSE Not Present exception (error code of code seg-
ment selector).
   Instruction pointer must be within code segment ELSE General Protection exception
(error code of 0000h).
   Load code segment descriptor into CS descriptor cache (not visible to
programmer).
   Load CS register with code segment selector.
   Load EIP with zero-extend(new offset).
   If operand size = 16 THEN EIP := EIP AND 0000FFFFh.
   Set RPL field of CS register to CPL.

PROTECTED MODE JUMP TO CALL GATE:
   Call gate DPL must be numerically ≥ CPL ELSE General Protection exception (error
code of call gate selector)
   Call gate DPL must be numerically ≥ RPL ELSE General Protection exception (error
code of call gate selector)
   Call gate must be present ELSE Not Present exception (error code of call gate
selector).
   Examine code segment selector found in call gate:
   Code selector must not be null ELSE General Protection exception (error code of
0000h).
   Selector index must be within its descriptor table limits ELSE General Protection exception (error code of code segment selector).

JMP   Jump to Code (or to Task in PROTECTED mode)   **JMP**

AR byte of selected descriptor must indicate code segment ELSE General Protec-
tion exception(error code of code segment selector).
  IF nonconforming code segment
  THEN
    DPL of selected descriptor must be ≤ CPL ELSE General Protection exception (er-
ror code of code segment selector).
  ELSE
    DPL of selected descriptor must be ≤ CPL ELSE General Protection exception (er-
ror code of code segment selector).
  Set RPL field of CS register to CPL.
  Code segment must be present ELSE Not Present Exception (error code of code seg-
ment selector).
  Instruction pointer must be within limit of code segment ELSE General Protection
exception (error code of 0000h).
  IF operand size = 32
  THEN load CS:EIP from call gate
  ELSE load CS:IP from call gate.
  Load CS descriptor into CS descriptor cache.
  Set RPL field of CS register to CPL.

PROTECTED MODE JMP TO TASK GATE:
  Task gate DPL must be ≥ CPL ELSE Invalid TSS exception (error code of gate
selector).
  Task gate DPL must be ≥ RPL ELSE Invalid TSS exception (error code of gate
selector).
  Task gate must be present ELSE Not Present exception (error code of gate
selector).
  Examine selector to TSS given in task gate:
    Must specify Global Descriptor Table (GDT) in Table Indicator (TI) bit ELSE In-
valid TSS exception (error code of TSS selector).
    Index must be within GDT limits ELSE Invalid TSS exception (error code of TSS
selector).
    TSS descriptor access rights byte must specify nonbusy TSS ELSE Invalid TSS ex-
ception (error code of TSS selector).
    Task-state Segment must be present ELSE Not Present exception (error code of TSS
selector).
  SWITCH-TASKS (without nesting, reset NT bit in EFLAG) to task given by TSS
selector.
  EIP must be within code segment limit ELSE Invalid TSS exception (error code of
0000h).

PROTECTED MODE JMP TO TASK STATE SEGMENT:
  TSS DPL must be ≥ CPL ELSE Invalid TSS exception (error code of TSS selector).
  TSS DPL must be ≥ RPL ELSE Invalid TSS exception (error code of TSS selector).
  TSS descriptor access rights byte must specify nonbusy TSS ELSE Invalid TSS ex-
ception (error code of TSS selector).
  Task gate must be present ELSE Not Present exception (error code of gate
selector).
  SWITCH-TASKS (without nesting, reset NT bit in EFLAG) to task given by TSS
selector.
  EIP must be within code segment limit ELSE Invalid TSS exception (error code of
0000h).

JMP   Jump to Code (or to Task in PROTECTED mode)   **JMP**

Flags

No flags are affected, unless a task switch occurs in PROTECTED mode.

REAL-mode Exceptions:

Interrupt 13 if any part of an operand in memory is at effective address greater than FFFFh in segments CS, DS, ES, FS, or GS. Interrupt 12 if any part of an operand in memory is at effective address greater than FFFFh in stack segment SS.

PROTECTED-mode Exceptions:

General Protection exception (exception 13) with error code of 0000h for operands in memory segments CS, DS, ES, FS, or GS if a source operand is in a nonreadable code segment, or if any part of the operand is at effective address beyond the segment limit. Stack exception (exception 12) with error code of 0000h for operands in stack segment if any part of the operand is at effective address beyond the segment limit. Stack exception with error code of segment selector if operand in memory is in segment SS marked not present. Not Present exception with error code of segment selector if operand in memory is in a segment DS, ES, FS, or GS marked not present. Not Present exception (exception 11) with error code of segment selector if operand in memory is in a segment DS, ES, FS, or GS marked not present. Page Fault exception (exception 14) with error code of fault code, and page-fault linear address in register CR2. Invalid Task State Segment exception (exception 10) with error code of selector for inconsistencies in the Task State Segment if performing a task switch.

VIRTUAL 8086-mode Exceptions:

Same as REAL mode exceptions, but handled in PROTECTED mode at privilege-level 0. The format of the privilege-level-0 stack after an exception (with error code) or interrupt (no error code) is shown in Figure 12.2. Also Page Fault exception with error code of fault code, and page-fault linear address in register CR2.

LAHF   Load AH Register from EFLAG   **LAHF**

Format

`LAHF`

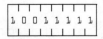

Function

`AH ←— low byte of EFLAG register;`

Description

LAHF loads the AH register with the low EFLAG byte. From MSB to LSB, AH takes on a value of SF, ZF, indeterminate, AF, indeterminate, PF, indeterminate, CF.

Timing

`2 clock cycles; 0.1µsec @ 20MHz.`

Flags

None are affected.

REAL-mode Exceptions:

None.

PROTECTED-mode Exceptions:

None.

VIRTUAL 8086-mode Exceptions:

None.

LAR   Load Access Rights   **LAR**

Format

```
LAR
```

Byte 0	Byte 1	Byte 2
0 0 0 1 1 1 1	0 0 0 0 0 0 1 0	mod: reg : r/m

Function

```
IF ACCESS IS VALID
  GENERAL REGISTER  ←── ACCESS RIGHTS OF GIVEN SELECTOR;
  ZF  ←── 1;
ELSE
  ZF  ←── 0;
```

Description

LAR is a PROTECTED mode instruction. LAR stores a masked form of the second DWORD of the descriptor of the source selector if the descriptor is visible at CPL (weakened by the selector's RPL). The second DWORD masking is accomplished by ANDing the DWORD with 00F0FF00h.

If the operand size of the instruction is WORD, only a WORD is loaded (the lower half of the DWORD normally masked). The masking value is FF00h.

If the descriptor type is accessible at CPL (weakened by the selector's RPL), ZF is set; otherwise ZF is reset.

All segment descriptors and gates are valid and accessible if CPL (weakened by the selector's RPL) ≤ DPL of the descriptor or gate.

Example

```
      LAR    ECX, DESCRIPTOR_PTR  ;load the r/m operand,
                                  ; interpreting the operand as
                                  ; the access rights of a
                                  ; descriptor or gate.
```

Timing

```
from register operand:  15 clock cycles; 0.75μsec @ 20MHz.
from memory operand:    16 clock cycles; 0.8μsec @ 20MHz.
```

LAR   Load Access Rights   **LAR**

Flags

ZF as described in *Function* above. Other flags are unchanged.

REAL-mode Exceptions:

Interrupt 6. LAR, a PROTECTED mode instruction, is not recognized in REAL mode.

PROTECTED-mode Exceptions:

Same as for ADD instruction. See page 251.

VIRTUAL 8086-mode Exceptions:

Same as REAL mode exception, but handled in PROTECTED mode at privilege-level 0. The format of the privilege-level-0 stack after an exception is shown in Figure 12.2. Also Page Fault exception (exception 14) with error code of fault code, and page-fault linear address in register CR2.

LEA   Load Access Rights   **LEA**

Format

```
LEA
```

```
          Byte 0           Byte 1
   ┌───────────────┬───────────────┐
   │1 0 0 0 1 1 0 1│mod: reg : r/m │
   └───────────────┴───────────────┘
```

Function

```
GENERAL REGISTER  ←—  EFFECTIVE ADDRESS;
```

Description

LEA calculates the effective address given a specified addressing mode. The effective address is computed as a DWORD if the address size used for the instruction is 32 bits. The effective address is computed as a WORD if the address size used for the instruction is 16 bits. The data size of the instruction determines if the effective address must be truncated to fit the destination register.

Example

```
    LEA    ECX, [EDX][4*ESI]DOLLAR
```

If EDX = 00000034h, and ESI = 00000052h, and DOLLAR = 00007289h, then as a result of the LEA instruction above, ECX is assigned 00007405h. 00007405h is the effective address calculated.

Timing

```
2 clock cycles; 0.1µsec @ 20MHz.
```

If the effective address involves two registers, such as in the *Example* above, LEA requires one extra clock cycle. In general, anytime an instruction specifies an effective address that involves two registers, the instruction will require an extra clock.

LEA   Load Access Rights   **LEA**

Flags

None are affected.

REAL-mode Exceptions:

Interrupt 6 if the second operand is a register.

PROTECTED-mode Exceptions:

Invalid Opcode exception (exception 6) if the second operand is a register. Exception 6 does not push an error code onto the stack.

VIRTUAL 8086-mode Exceptions:

Same as for PROTECTED mode.

LEAVE   High Level Procedure Exit   **LEAVE**

Format

```
LEAVE
```

Function

```
ESP  ←  EBP;        (affected by address size)
EBP  ←  POP();      (affected by operand size)
```

Description

LEAVE reverses the actions of the ENTER instruction. ESP and EBP are restored to their values prior to the ENTER instruction.

Example

```
LEAVE
RET
```

Timing

```
4 clock cycles; 0.2μsec @ 20MHz.
```

Flags

None are affected.

REAL-mode Exceptions:

Same as ADD instruction. See page 251.

PROTECTED-mode Exceptions:

Same as ADD instruction. See page 251.

VIRTUAL 8086-mode Exceptions:

Same as ADD instruction. See page 251.

LGDT   Load Global Descriptor Table Register   **LGDT**

Format

```
LGDT
```

```
        Byte 0          Byte 1          Byte 2
      ┌───────────────┬───────────────┬───────────────┐
      │0 0 0 0 1 1 1 1│0 0 0 0 0 0 0 1│mod:0 1 0: r/m │
      └───────────────┴───────────────┴───────────────┘
```

Function

```
IF (OPERAND SIZE = 32) THEN
   GDTR.LIMIT:GDTR.BASE  ←——  MEMORY 16:24;   (24 bits of base loaded)
ELSE
   GDTR.LIMIT:GDTR.BASE  ←——  MEMORY 16:32;   (32 bits of base loaded)
```

Description

LGDT loads a limit value and linear base address value into register GDTR, thus establishing the size and location of the GDT descriptor table in memory.

LGDT is an operating system instruction. It typically appears in REAL mode code when initializing a system to enter PROTECTED mode. LGDT also be executed in PROTECTED mode when CPL = 0. LGDT and LIDT are the only instructions in PROTECTED mode that load a linear address to a register.

Example

```
      LGDT    GDT_INFO    ;establish GDT size and limit
                          ; according to memory-based data
                          ; named GDT_INFO
```

LGDT   Load Global Descriptor Table Register   **LGDT**

Timing

11 clock cycles; 0.55μsec @ 20MHz.

Flags

None are affected.

REAL-mode Exceptions:

Same as ADD instruction. See page 251.

PROTECTED-mode Exceptions:

General Protection exception (exception 13) with error code of 0000h if CPL is not 0. Other exceptions same as ADD instruction. See page 251.

VIRTUAL 8086-mode Exceptions:

General Protection exception with error code of 0000h, since CPL is 3 (not equal to 0).

LIDT Load Interrupt Descriptor Table Register **LIDT**

Format

```
LIDT
```

	Byte 0		Byte 1		Byte 2
	0 0 0 0 1 1 1 1		0 0 0 0 0 0 0 1		mod:0 1 1: r/m

Function

```
IF (OPERAND SIZE = 32) THEN
   IDTR.LIMIT:IDTR.BASE  ←  MEMORY 16:24;   {24 bits of base loaded}
ELSE
   IDTR.LIMIT:IDTR.BASE  ←  MEMORY 16:32;   {32 bits of base loaded}
```

Description

LIDT loads a limit value and linear base address value into register IDTR, thus establishing the size and location of the IDT descriptor table in memory.

LIDT is an operating system instruction. It typically appears in REAL mode code when initializing a system to enter PROTECTED mode. LGDT also be executed in PROTECTEDmode when CPL = 0. LIDT and LGDT are the only instructions in PROTECTED mode that load a linear address to a register.

Example

```
LIDT   IDT_INFO  ;establish IDT size and limit
                 ; according to memory-based data
                 ; named IDT_INFO
```

LIDT   Load Interrupt Descriptor Table Register   **LIDT**

Timing

11 clock cycles; 0.55μsec @ 20MHz.

Flags

None are affected.

REAL-mode Exceptions:

Same as ADD instruction. See page 251.

PROTECTED-mode Exceptions:

General Protection exception (exception 13) with error code of 0000h if CPL is not 0. Other exceptions same as ADD instruction. See page 251.

VIRTUAL 8086-mode Exceptions:

General Protection exception with error code of 0000h, since CPL is 3 (not equal to 0).

LDS/LES/LFS/LGS/LSS   Load Full Pointer to Segment Register: General Register   **LDS/LES/LFS/LGS/LSS**

Format

LDS

```
        Byte 0          Byte 1          Byte 2
      ┌───────────────┬───────────────┐
      │1 1 0 0 0 1 0 1│mod: reg : r/m │
      └───────────────┴───────────────┘
```

LES

```
      ┌───────────────┬───────────────┐
      │1 1 0 0 0 1 0 0│mod: reg : r/m │
      └───────────────┴───────────────┘
```

LFS

```
      ┌───────────────┬───────────────┬───────────────┐
      │0 0 0 0 1 1 1 1│1 0 1 1 0 1 0 0│mod: reg : r/m │
      └───────────────┴───────────────┴───────────────┘
```

LGS

```
      ┌───────────────┬───────────────┬───────────────┐
      │0 0 0 0 1 1 1 1│1 0 1 1 0 1 0 1│mod: reg : r/m │
      └───────────────┴───────────────┴───────────────┘
```

LSS

```
      ┌───────────────┬───────────────┬───────────────┐
      │0 0 0 0 1 1 1 1│1 0 1 1 0 0 1 0│mod: reg : r/m │
      └───────────────┴───────────────┴───────────────┘
```

Function

```
IF (OPERAND SIZE = 32) THEN
BEGIN
   GENERAL REGISTER  ←─  [EFFECTIVE ADDRESS];      {32-bit eff. addr.}
   SEGMENT REGISTER  ←─  [EFFECTIVE ADDRESS + 4];  {16-bit selector}
END
ELSE
BEGIN
   GENERAL REGISTER  ←─  [EFFECTIVE ADDRESS];
   {16-bit eff. addr.}
   SEGMENT REGISTER  ←─  [EFFECTIVE ADDRESS + 2];
   {16-bit selector}
END
```

Description

These instructions load a full pointer from memory. A full pointer consists, of course, of a selector (to identify a particular segment) and an effective address (the offset within the segment). The selector is loaded into a segment register; the effective address into a general register.

When an assignment is made to a segment register in REAL mode or VIRTUAL 8086 mode, the selector value is shifted four places left to calculate the linear base ad-

LDS/LES/LFS/LGS/LSS   Load Full Pointer to Segment Register: General Register   **LDS/LES/LFS/LGS/LSS**

dress of the segment. When an assignment is made in PROTECTED mode, the segment's base and limit data is loaded from the descriptor table entry for the selector given.

Example

```
LDS   DATA_SEG     ;establish data segment
                   ; according to selector named
                   ; DATA_SEG
```

Timing

REAL mode or VIRTUAL 8086 mode: 7 clock cycles; 0.35μsec @ 20MHz.
PROTECTED mode: 22 clock cycles; 1.1μsec @ 20MHz.

Flags

None are affected.

REAL-mode Exceptions:

Same as ADD instruction. See page 251.

PROTECTED-mode Exceptions:

Same as ADD instruction. See page 251.

VIRTUAL 8086-mode Exceptions:

Same as ADD instruction. See page 251.

LLDT   Load Local Descriptor Table Register   **LLDT**

Format

```
LLDT
```

```
          Byte 0          Byte 1          Byte 2
     ┌─────────────────┬─────────────────┬─────────────────┐
     │ 0 0 0 0 1 1 1 1 │ 0 0 0 0 0 0 0 0 │mod:0 0 1: r/m   │
     └─────────────────┴─────────────────┴─────────────────┘
```

Function

```
LDTR  ←─  SELECTOR;        {16-bit selector}
```

Description

LLDT is a PROTECTED mode instruction. LLDT loads a selector into the LDTR (Local Descriptor Table Register). Doing so establishes the LDT. The LDT's base and limit data is loaded from the descriptor table entry for the selector given. The selector must refer to an LDT descriptor (descriptor type 2).

The selector can also be 0, however. If so, the LDT is considered to be invalid, and any descriptor references to the LDT cause a General Protection exception (except references by the LAR, LSL, VERR, or VERW instructions designed to allow testing selectors in a benign manner).

LLDT is a privileged instruction, executable only at privilege-level 0.

Example

```
    LLDT   INITIAL_LDT   ;establish local descriptor table
                         ; according to selector named
                         ; INITIAL_LDT
```

LLDT   Load Local Descriptor Table Register   **LLDT**

Timing

```
20 clock cycles; 1.0μsec @ 20MHz.
```

Flags

None are affected.

REAL-mode Exceptions:

Interrupt 6. LLDT is not a legal instruction in REAL mode.

PROTECTED-mode Exceptions:

General Protection exception (exception 13) with error code of 0000h if CPL is not 0. General-protection exception with error code of offending selector if selector operand does not refer to the GDT and a Local Descriptor Table Descriptor. Other exceptions same as ADD instruction. See page 251.

VIRTUAL 8086-mode Exceptions:

Invalid Opcode exception (exception 6). LLDT is not a legal instruction in VIRTUAL 8086 mode.

LMSW   Load Machine Status Word Register   **LMSW**

Format

```
LMSW
```

	Byte 0	Byte 1	Byte 2
	0 0 0 0 1 1 1 1	0 0 0 0 0 0 0 1	mod:1 1 0: r/m

Function

```
MSW  ←——  16-BIT OPERAND;      (MSW is low 16 bits of CR0)
```

Description

LMSW loads the lower half of CR0 from the source operand. The 80386 instruction MOV CR0,source instruction would more likely be used, however. (LMSW instruction provides 80286 opcode compatibility.)

LMSW is an operating system instruction. It typically appears in 80286 REAL mode code when initializing a system to enter PROTECTED mode. By setting the PE bit in CR0, this instruction can be used to switch into PROTECTED mode. If so, it must be followed by an intrasegment jump to flush the instruction prefetch queue of instructions decoded while in REAL mode. This instruction cannot reset the PE bit once set (strict 80286 compatibility). The 80386 MOV CR0,source instruction can, however, reset the PE bit.

Example

```
    LMSW   IDT_INFO   ;load the lower half of CR0
```

Timing

```
Operand from Register:  10 clock cycles; 0.5µsec @ 20MHz.
Operand from Memory:    13 clock cycles; 0.65µsec @ 20MHz.
```

LMSW   Load Machine Status Word Register   **LMSW**

Flags

None are affected.

REAL-mode Exceptions:

Same as ADD instruction. See page 251.

PROTECTED-mode Exceptions:

General Protection exception (exception 13) with error code of 0000h if CPL is not 0. Other exceptions same as ADD instruction. See page 251.

VIRTUAL 8086-mode Exceptions:

General Protection exception with error code of 0000h, since CPL is 3 (not equal to 0).

LODSB/LODSW/LODSD   Load String Data   **LODSB/LODSW/LODSD**

Format

```
LODSB/LODSW/LODSD
```

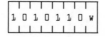

Function

```
IF (OPERANDSIZE = DWORD) THEN      {load operand to EAX/AX/AL}
  EAX  ←── [SOURCE_INDEX];
ELSE IF (OPERANDSIZE = WORD) THEN
  AX  ←── [SOURCE_INDEX];
ELSE      {operandsize = BYTE }
  AL  ←── [SOURCE_INDEX];
IF (ADDRESSSIZE = 32) THEN         {adjust index for source}
  ADJUST ESI;
ELSE      {addresssize = 16}
  ADJUST SI;
```

Description

LODS loads operands from a source memory string. The string is considered to be an array of BYTES, WORDS, or DWORDS, depending on the operand size of the string instruction. After the transfer is made, the source index register is automatically advanced (incremented or decremented, according to DF) by an amount equaling the operand size.

If the address size of the instruction is DWORD, the operand of the source string is [ESI]. Otherwise, the source operand is [SI]. Load the correct index value before executing LODS.

Example

```
    LODSW        ;loads WORD operand from string
```

Because the source index register must be loaded to use this instruction, LODSB/W/D is often placed in a loop and used for several iterations.

LODSB/LODSW/LODSD   Load String Data   **LODSB/LODSW/LODSD**

Timing

5 clock cycles; 0.25μsec @ 20MHz.

Flags

None are affected.

REAL-mode Exceptions:

Same as for ADD instruction. See page 251.

PROTECTED-mode Exceptions:

Same as for ADD instruction. See page 251.

VIRTUAL 8086-mode Exceptions:

Same as for ADD instruction. See page 251.

LOOP   Loop and Decrement ECX   **LOOP**

Format

```
LOOP
```

	Byte 0	Byte 1
8-bit Displacement	1 1 1 0 0 0 1 0	8-bit displ

Function

```
IF (ECX <> 0) THEN
  EIP  ⟵  EIP + DISPLACEMENT;    {displacement is only 8 bits}
```

Description

LOOP decrements the count register without changing any of the flags. The count register, ECX (if address size is 32 bits) or CX (if address size is 16 bits) is decremented as an unsigned iteration count and checked (but no flags are affected). If the count register is nonzero, a short jump is made using the 8-bit displacement operand given. The displacement is added to the instruction pointer in order to begin execution at a new offset. Note, however, the displacement is only an 8-bit signed quantity, limiting the displacement range from -128 through $+127$.

Since this loop instruction can branch only within a segment, the code segment register is not affected.

Example

```
        LOOP    LOOP_START    ;perform iteration the number of
                              ;  times specified in the count register.
```

Flags

No flags are affected.

REAL-mode Exceptions:

Interrupt 13 if any part of the destination instruction is at effective address greater than FFFFh in segment CS.

LOOP   Loop and Decrement ECX   **LOOP**

PROTECTED-mode Exceptions:

General Protection exception (exception 13) with error code of 0000h for the destination in memory segment CS if any part of the destination instruction is at effective
address beyond the segment limit. Not Present exception (exception 11) with error
code of segment selector if operand in memory is in segment CS marked not
present. Page Fault exception (exception 14) with error code of fault code, and
page-fault linear address in register CR2.

VIRTUAL 8086-mode Exceptions:

Same as REAL mode exceptions, but handled in PROTECTED mode at privilege-level 0.
The format of the privilege-level-0 stack after an exception (with error code) or interrupt (no error code) is shown in Figure 12.2. Also Page Fault exception with error
code of fault code, and page-fault linear address in register CR2.

LOOPE/LOOPZ   Loop and Decrement ECX while Condition Equal   **LOOPE/LOOPZ**

Format

```
LOOPE/LOOPZ
```

	Byte 0	Byte 1
8-bit Displacement	1 1 1 0 0 0 0 1	8-bit displ

Function

```
IF ((ECX <> 0) AND (ZF = 1)) THEN
   EIP  ←——  EIP + DISPLACEMENT;   {displacement is only 8 bits}
```

Description

LOOP decrements the count register without changing any of the flags. The count register, ECX (if address size is 32 bits) or CX (if address size is 16 bits) is decremented as an unsigned iteration count and checked (but no flags are affected). If the count register is nonzero and the zero-flag is set, a short jump is made using the 8-bit displacement operand given. The displacement is added to the instruction pointer in order to begin execution at a new offset. Note, however, the displacement is only an 8-bit signed quantity, limiting the displacement range from −128 through +127.

Since this loop instruction can branch only within a segment, the code segment register is not affected.

Example

```
     LOOPE    LOOP_START    ;perform iteration up to the number of
                            ; times specified by count register,
                            ; provided that ZF = 1 (i.e., equal
                            ; condition).
```

LOOPE/LOOPZ Loop and Decrement ECX while Condition Equal **LOOPE/LOOPZ**

Flags

No flags are affected.

REAL-mode Exceptions:

Same as LOOP instruction. See page 251.

PROTECTED-mode Exceptions:

Same as LOOP instruction. See page 251.

VIRTUAL 8086-mode Exceptions:

Same as LOOP instruction. See page 251.

LOOPNE/LOOPNZ Loop and Decrement ECX while Condition Not Equal **LOOPNE/LOOPNZ**

Format

```
LOOPNE/LOOPNZ
```

```
                              Byte 0         Byte 1
                          ┌─┬─┬─┬─┬─┬─┬─┬─┬─┬─────────────┐
8-bit Displacement        │1 1 1 0 0 0 0 0│  8-bit displ  │
                          └─┴─┴─┴─┴─┴─┴─┴─┴─┴─────────────┘
```

Function

```
IF ((ECX <> 0) AND (ZF = 1)) THEN
  EIP  ⟵  EIP + DISPLACEMENT;   {displacement is only 8 bits}
```

Description

LOOP decrements the count register without changing any of the flags. The count register, ECX (if address size is 32 bits) or CX (if address size is 16 bits) is decremented as an unsigned iteration count and checked (but no flags are affected). If the count register is nonzero and the zero-flag is set, a short jump is made using the 8-bit displacement operand given. The displacement is added to the instruction pointer in order to begin execution at a new offset. Note, however, the displacement is only an 8-bit signed quantity, limiting the displacement range from −128 through +127.

Since this loop instruction can branch only within a segment, the code segment register is not affected.

Example

```
        LOOPNE  LOOP_START  ;perform iteration up to the number of
                            ; times specified by count register,
                            ; provided that ZF = 0 (i.e., not equal
                            ; condition).
```

LOOPNE/LOOPNZ Loop and Decrement ECX while Condition Not Equal **LOOPNE/LOOPNZ**

Flags

No flags are affected.

REAL-mode Exceptions:

Same as LOOP instruction. See page 251.

PROTECTED-mode Exceptions:

Same as LOOP instruction. See page 251.

VIRTUAL 8086-mode Exceptions:

Same as LOOP instruction. See page 251.

LSL   Load Segment Limit into Register   **LSL**

Format

```
LSL
```

```
            Byte 0           Byte 1           Byte 2
      ┌─┬─┬─┬─┬─┬─┬─┬─┬─┬─┬─┬─┬─┬─┬─┬─┬─────────────┐
      │0 0 0 0 1 1 1 1│0 0 0 0 0 0 1 1│mod: reg : r/m│
      └─┴─┴─┴─┴─┴─┴─┴─┴─┴─┴─┴─┴─┴─┴─┴─┴─────────────┘
```

Function

```
IF ACCESS IS VALID
  GENERAL REGISTER  ←── SEGMENT LIMIT OF GIVEN SELECTOR;
  ZF  ←── 1;
ELSE
  ZF  ←── 0;
```

Description

LSL is a PROTECTED mode instruction. LSL loads an unscrambled segment limit from the descriptor if the descriptor is visible at CPL (weakened by the selector's RPL). LSL loads a byte segment limit. If the limit is page-granular in the descriptor, LSL will translate it to a byte limit before loading it in the destination register (shift page granular limit 12 bits left, then OR with 00000FFFh).

If the descriptor type is accessible at CPL (weakened by the selector's RPL), ZF is set; otherwise ZF is reset.

All segment descriptors are valid and accessible if CPL (weakened by the selector's RPL) ≤ DPL of the descriptor. Gates, however, are not valid types for this instruction since gates do not have a limit field.

Example

```
     LSL    ECX, DESCRIPTOR_PTR  ;load the r/m operand,
                                 ; interpreting the operand as
                                 ; the segment limit contained
                                 ; in a descriptor.
```

Timing

```
byte limit from register operand: 20 clock cycles; 1.0µsec @ 20MHz.
byte limit from memory operand:   21 clock cycles; 1.05µsec @ 20MHz.
page limit from register operand: 25 clock cycles; 1.25µsec @ 20MHz.
page limit from memory operand:   26 clock cycles; 1.3µsec @ 20MHz.
```

LSL Load Segment Limit into Register **LSL**

Flags

ZF as described in *Function* above. Other flags are unchanged.

REAL-mode Exceptions:

Interrupt 6. LSL, a PROTECTED mode instruction, is not recognized in REAL mode.

PROTECTED-mode Exceptions:

Same as for ADD instruction. See page 251.

VIRTUAL 8086-mode Exceptions:

Same as REAL mode exception, but handled in PROTECTED mode at privilege-level 0. The format of the privilege-level-0 stack after an exception is shown in Figure 12.2. Also Page Fault exception (exception 14) with error code of fault code, and page-fault linear address in register CR2.

LTR   Load Task Register   **LTR**

Format

```
LTR
```

```
        Byte 0          Byte 1          Byte 2
   ┌─┬─┬─┬─┬─┬─┬─┬─┬─┬─┬─┬─┬─┬─┬─┬─┬─────────────┐
   │0 0 0 0 1 1 1 1│0 0 0 0 0 0 0 0│mod:0 0 1: r/m│
   └─┴─┴─┴─┴─┴─┴─┴─┴─┴─┴─┴─┴─┴─┴─┴─┴─────────────┘
```

Function

```
TR  ←── SELECTOR;        {16-bit selector}
```

Description

LTR is a PROTECTED mode instruction. LTR loads a selector into the TR (Task Register). Doing so establishes the task's TSS (Task State Segment). It does not cause a task switch. The TSS's base and limit data is loaded from the descriptor table entry for the selector given. The selector must refer to a not-busy TSS descriptor (descriptor types 1 or 9) in the GDT.

LTR is a privileged instruction, executable only at privilege-level 0.

Example

```
    LTR   INITIAL_TSS   ;establish task segment
                        ; according to selector named
                        ; INITIAL_TSS
```

Timing

```
Selector in Register: 23 clock cycles; 1.15µsec @ 20MHz.
Selector in Memory:   27 clock cycles; 1.35µsec @ 20MHz.
```

LTR   Load Task Register   **LTR**

Flags

None are affected.

REAL-mode Exceptions:

Interrupt 6. LTR is not a legal instruction in REAL mode.

PROTECTED-mode Exceptions:

General Protection exception (exception 13) with error code of 0000h if CPL is not 0. General Protection exception with error code of offending selector if selector operand does not refer to the GDT and a Task State Segment Descriptor. Other exceptions same as ADD instruction. See page 251.

VIRTUAL 8086-mode Exceptions:

Invalid Opcode exception (exception 6). LTR is not a legal instruction in VIRTUAL 8086 mode.

MOV Move to/from General Registers **MOV**

Format

MOV

	Byte 0	Byte 1	Subsequent Byte(s)

Register to
Register/Memory ` 1 0 0 0 1 0 0 w | mod: reg : r/m `

AL|AX|EAX to
Memory (short ` 1 0 1 0 0 0 1 w | Full Displacement `
encoding)

Register/Memory ` 1 0 0 0 1 0 1 w | mod: reg : r/m `
to Register

Memory to
AL|AX|EAX (short ` 1 0 1 0 0 0 0 w | Full Displacement `
encoding)

Immediate to
Register/Memory ` 1 1 0 0 0 1 1 w | mod:0 0 0: r/m | Immediate Data Byte(s) `

Immediate to
Register (short ` 1 0 1 1:w: reg | Immediate Data Byte(s) `
encoding)

Function

```
DESTINATION  ←——  SOURCE;

    or

DESTINATION  ←——  IMMEDIATE DATA;
```

Description

Move the source operand (a register, memory location or immediate data) to the destination operand. The source operand remains unchanged, and the destination operand is overwritten with the source data.

Example

```
    MOV  ECX, EDX   ;EDX is the source; ECX is the destination
```

If ECX = 00000034h and EDX = 00000052h, then as a result of the MOV instruction above, ECX is assigned 00000052h. All flags are unchanged.

MOV   Move to/from General Registers   **MOV**

Timing

```
Register to Register:  2 clock cycles; 0.1μsec @ 20MHz.
Register to Memory:    2 clock cycles; 0.1μsec @ 20MHz.
Memory to Register:    4 clock cycles; 0.2μsec @ 20MHz.
Immediate to Register: 2 clock cycles; 0.1μsec @ 20MHz.
Immediate to Memory:   2 clock cycles; 0.2μsec @ 20MHz.
```

Flags

None are affected.

REAL-mode Exceptions:

Same as for ADD instruction. See page 251.

PROTECTED-mode Exceptions:

Same as for ADD instruction. See page 251.

VIRTUAL 8086-mode Exceptions:

Same as for ADD instruction. See page 251.

MOV   Move to/from Segment Registers   **MOV**

Format

MOV

	Byte 0	Byte 1

Register/Memory to
Segment Register

| 1 0 0 0 1 1 1 0 | mod:sreg : r/m |

Segment Register to
Register/Memory

| 1 0 0 0 1 1 0 0 | mod:sreg : r/m |

Function

```
SEGMENT REGISTER  ←  REGISTER/MEMORY   [load segment register]
REGISTER/MEMORY   ←  SEGMENT REGISTER  [store segment register]
```

Description

Store or load the 16-bit segment registers to or from the general registers or memory. 16-bit operand sizes are always used for these instruction, regardless of the operand size attribute. As with the other MOV instructions, the source operand remains unchanged, and the destination operand is overwritten with the source data.

Example

```
    MOV  DS, DATA_AREA   ;DS is the destination, and the
                         ;variable DATA_AREA is the
                         ;source containing a 16-bit
                         ;selector that is loaded into
                         ;the DS register
```

Timing

```
Loads
General Register to Segment Register:  18 clock cycles;  0.9μsec @ 20MHz.
Memory to Segment Register:            19 clock cycles;  0.95μsec @ 20MHz.

Stores
Segment Register to General Register:  2 clock cycles;  0.1μsec @ 20 MHz.
Segment Register to Memory:            2 clock cycles;  0.1μsec @ 20 MHz.
```

Flags

None are affected.

MOV   Move to/from System Registers   **MOV**

Format

MOV

	Byte 0	Byte 1	Byte 2
CR0/2/3 to General Register	0 0 0 0 1 1 1 1	0 0 1 0 0 0 1 0	1 1:r r r: reg
General Register to CR0/2/3	0 0 0 0 1 1 1 1	0 0 1 0 0 0 0 0	1 1:r r r: reg
DR0/1/2/3/6/7 to General Register	0 0 0 0 1 1 1 1	0 0 1 0 0 0 1 1	1 1:r r r: reg
General Register to DR0/1/2/3/6/7	0 0 0 0 1 1 1 1	0 0 1 0 0 0 0 1	1 1:r r r: reg
TR6/7 to General Register	0 0 0 0 1 1 1 1	0 0 1 0 0 1 1 0	1 1:r r r: reg
General Register to TR6/7	0 0 0 0 1 1 1 1	0 0 1 0 0 1 0 0	1 1:r r r: reg

r r r	CONTROL REGISTER	DEBUG REGISTER	TEST REGISTER
0 0 0	CR0	DR0	
0 0 1		DR1	
0 1 0	CR2	DR2	
0 1 1	CR3	DR3	
1 0 0			
1 0 1			
1 1 0		DR6	TR6
1 1 1		DR7	TR7

Function

SYSTEM REGISTER ⟵ GENERAL REGISTER; {load system register}

    or

GENERAL REGISTER ⟵ SYSTEM REGISTER; {store system register}

Description

Store or load the 32-bit system registers (the Control Registers, the Debug Registers and the Paging Test Registers) to or from the 32-bit general registers. 32-bit operand sizes are always used for these instructions, regardless of the operand size attribute. As with the other MOV instructions, the source operand remains unchanged, and the destination operand is overwritten with the source data.

MOV   Move to/from System Registers   **MOV**

Example

```
MOV  EAX, CR2   ;EAX is the destination, CR2 is the source.
                ; This example might appear in a routine
                ; that examines the page-fault address for an
                ; page-fault handling routine.
```

If ECX = 00000034h and EDX = 00000052h, then as a result of the MOV instruction above, ECX is assigned 00000052h. All flags are unchanged.

Timing

```
Loads
Register to CR0, CR2, CR3: 10 clock cycles; 0.5µsec @ 20MHz.
Register to DR0-DR3:       22 clock cycles; 1.1µsec @ 20MHz.
Register to DR6-DR7:       16 clock cycles; 1.8µsec @ 20MHz.
Register to TR6, TR7:      12 clock cycles; 0.6µsec @ 20MHz.

Stores
CR0, CR2, CR3 to Register:  6 clock cycles; 0.3µsec @ 20MHz.
DR0-DR3 to Register:       22 clock cycles; 1.1µsec @ 20MHz.
DR6-DR7 to Register:       14 clock cycles; 0.7µsec @ 20MHz.
TR6, TR7 to Register:      12 clock cycles; 0.6µsec @ 20MHz.
```

Flags

None are affected.

REAL-mode Exceptions:

None. It is valid to use these instructions in REAL mode.

PROTECTED-mode Exceptions:

General Protection exception (exception 13) with error code of 0000h if the current privilege level is not 0. In PROTECTED mode, these are privileged instructions, executable only at privilege-level 0.

VIRTUAL 8086-mode Exceptions:

General Protection exception with error code of 0000h if the instruction is attempted. This occurs because the CPL = 3 when in VIRTUAL 8086 mode.

MOVSB/MOVSW/MOVSD   Move String Data (WORD and DWORD)   **MOVSB/MOVSW/MOVSD**

Format

```
MOVSB/MOVSW/MOVSD
```

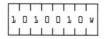

```
1 0 1 0 0 1 0 w
```

Function

```
[DESTINATION] ←── [SOURCE];     {operand transfer}
IF (ADDRESS SIZE = 32) THEN
   ADJUST ESI and EDI;     {adjust indexes for source and destination}
ELSE                       {address size = 16}
   ADJUST SI and DI;
```

Description

Moves operands from a source memory strings to a destination memory string. The strings are considered to be arrays of BYTES, WORDS, or DWORDS, depending on the operand size of the string instruction. After the transfer is made, the source index register and destination index registers are automatically advanced (incremented or decremented, according to DF) by an amount equaling the operand size.

If the address size of the instruction is DWORD, the operand of the source string is [ESI], while the operand of the destination string is ES:[EDI]. Otherwise, the operands are [SI] and [DI]. Load the correct index values before executing MOVS.

Example

```
        MOVSD       ;compares BYTE operands from BYTE strings

   or

   REP  MOVSD       ;repeated MOVS runs until ECX expires
                    ; (See page 457 for details)
```

Because the source and destination registers must be loaded to use this instruction, MOVSB/W/D is often placed in a loop and used for several iterations.

Timing

```
nonrepeated:  7 clock cycles; 0.5μsec @ 20MHz.
repeated:     7 +4n clock cycles; 0.5μsec @ 20MHz.
```

(*n* is number of repeated iterations performed)

MOVSB/MOVSW/MOVSD   Move String Data (WORD and DWORD)   **MOVSB/MOVSW/MOVSD**

Flags

None are affected.

REAL-mode Exceptions:

Same as for ADD instruction. See page 251.

PROTECTED-mode Exceptions:

Same as for ADD instruction. See page 251.

VIRTUAL 8086-mode Exceptions:

Same as for ADD instruction. See page 251.

MOVSX   Move Data Sign-Extended   **MOVSX**

Format

MOVSX

```
            Byte 0          Byte 1          Byte 2
        ┌─┬─┬─┬─┬─┬─┬─┬─┬─┬─┬─┬─┬─┬─┬─┬─┬─────────────┐
        │0 0 0 0 1 1 1 1│1 0 1 1 1 1 1 w│mod: reg : r/m│
        └─┴─┴─┴─┴─┴─┴─┴─┴─┴─┴─┴─┴─┴─┴─┴─┴─────────────┘
```

Function

DESTINATION ⟵ SIGN-EXTEND(SOURCE BYTE);

Description

Move the source operand (a byte in register or byte in memory) to the destination WORD or DWORD operand, sign-extending it in the process. The source operand remains unchanged, and the destination operand is overwritten with the sign-extended source data.

Example

```
    MOVSX  ECX, DL   ;ECX receives the sign-extended byte in DL
```

Timing

```
Register to Register:  3 clock cycles; 0.15μsec @ 20MHz.
Memory to Register:    6 clock cycles; 0.3μsec @ 20MHz.
```

MOVSX   Move Data Sign-Extended   **MOVSX**

Flags

None are affected.

REAL-mode Exceptions:

Same as for ADD instruction. See page 251.

PROTECTED-mode Exceptions:

Same as for ADD instruction. See page 251.

VIRTUAL 8086-mode Exceptions:

Same as for ADD instruction. See page 251.

MOVZX   Move Data Zero-Extended   **MOVZX**

Format

MOVZX

```
         Byte 0          Byte 1          Byte 2
     ┌─┬─┬─┬─┬─┬─┬─┬─┬─┬─┬─┬─┬─┬─┬─┬─┬─┬─┬─┬─┬─┬─┬─┬─┐
     │0 0 0 0 1 1 1 1│1 0 1 1 0 1 1 w│mod: reg : r/m│
     └─┴─┴─┴─┴─┴─┴─┴─┴─┴─┴─┴─┴─┴─┴─┴─┴─┴─┴─┴─┴─┴─┴─┴─┘
```

Function

DESTINATION ← XERO-EXTEND(SOURCE BYTE);

Description

Move the source operand (a byte in register or byte in memory) to the destination WORD or DWORD operand, zero-extending it in the process. The source operand remains unchanged, and the destination operand is overwritten with the zero-extended source data.

Example

```
    MOVSX  EBX, BL   ;EBX receives the zero-extended byte in BL
```

Timing

```
Register to Register: 3 clock cycles; 0.15µsec @ 20MHz.
Memory to Register:   6 clock cycles; 0.3µsec @ 20MHz.
```

MOVZX   Move Data Zero-Extended   **MOVZX**

Flags

None are affected.

REAL-mode Exceptions:

Same as for ADD instruction. See page 251.

PROTECTED-mode Exceptions:

Same as for ADD instruction. See page 251.

VIRTUAL 8086-mode Exceptions:

Same as for ADD instruction. See page 251.

MUL   Unsigned Multiply   **MUL**

Format

```
MUL
```

```
                        Byte 0          Byte 1
                      ┌─────────────┬─────────────┐
AL|AX|EAX with        │1 1 1 1 0 1 1 w│mod:1 1 0: r/m│
Register/Memory       └─────────────┴─────────────┘
```

Function

```
AL|AX|EAX  ◄───  DESTINATION × SOURCE;  (unsigned multiplication)
```

   or

```
AL|AX|EAX ◄─── DESTINATION × IMMEDIATE DATA;  (unsigned multiplication)
```

Description

MUL performs unsigned multiplication. MUL uses register AL I AX I EAX as the destination and one multiplier of the operation.

Example

```
    MUL   ECX, EDX
```

If ECX = 00000034h and EDX = 00000052h, then as a result of the MUL instruction above, ECX is assigned 000010A8h.

Timing

MUL uses an early-finish algorithm. The actual number of clocks required to complete the instruction depends on the position of the significant bit in the optimizing
multiplier.

```
Register to AL|AX|EAX:  9-41 clock cycles; 0.45-2.05µsec @ 20MHz.
Memory to AL|AX|EAX:   12-44 clock cycles; 0.6-2.2µsec @ 20MHz.
```

Flags

OF, CF affected as described in Appendix A. SF, ZF, AF, and PF are undefined.
Other flags are unchanged.

MUL   Unsigned Multiply   **MUL**

REAL-mode Exceptions:

Same as for ADD instruction. See page 251.

PROTECTED-mode Exceptions:

Same as for ADD instruction. See page 251.

VIRTUAL 8086-mode Exceptions:

Same as for ADD instruction. See page 251.

NEG Integer Negate **NEG**

Format

```
NEG
```

	Byte 0		Byte 1

```
┌─┬─┬─┬─┬─┬─┬─┬─┬─────────────┐
│1│1│1│1│0│1│1│w│mod:0 1 1: r/m│
└─┴─┴─┴─┴─┴─┴─┴─┴─────────────┘
```

Function

```
DESTINATION  ←  0 - DESTINATION;
```

Description

The operand is negated (2's complement). The operand also serves as the destination for the result

Example

```
    NEG    EAX
```

If EAX = 00000281h, then as a result of the NEG instruction above, EAX is assigned FFFFFD7Fh.

Timing

```
Register to Register:   2 clock cycles; 0.1µsec @ 20MHz.
Register to Memory:     7 clock cycles; 0.35µsec @ 20MHz.
Memory to Register:     6 clock cycles; 0.3µsec @ 20MHz.
Immediate to Register:  2 clock cycles; 0.1µsec @ 20MHz.
Immediate to Memory:    7 clock cycles; 0.35µsec @ 20MHz.
```

Flags

OF, CF, SF, ZF, AF, and PF affected as described in Appendix A. Other flags are unchanged.

NEG Integer Negate **NEG**

REAL-mode Exceptions:

Same as for ADD instruction. See page 251.

PROTECTED-mode Exceptions:

Same as for ADD instruction. See page 251.

VIRTUAL 8086-mode Exceptions:

Same as for ADD instruction. See page 251.

NOP	No Operation	**NOP**

Format

NOP

(alias for XCHG AX,AX)

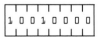

Function

EIP IS INCREMENTED TO THE NEXT INSTRUCTION.

Description

No substantial function is performed. The instruction pointer is merely incremented to the next instruction. NOP is an alias mnemonic for the XCHG AX,AX instruction.

Timing

3 clock cycles; 0.15μsec a 20MHz.

Flags

None are affected.

REAL-mode Exceptions:

None.

PROTECTED-mode Exceptions:

None.

VIRTUAL 8086-mode Exceptions:

None.

NOT   Logical Complement   **NOT**

Format

```
NOT
```

```
        Byte 0          Byte 1
      ┌─┬─┬─┬─┬─┬─┬─┬─┬─────────────┐
      │1 1 1 1 0 1 1 w│mod:0 1 0: r/m│
      └─┴─┴─┴─┴─┴─┴─┴─┴─────────────┘
```

Function

```
DESTINATION  ←  ∽ DESTINATION;
```

Description

Perform a bit-wise logical NOT of the operand. The operand also serves as the destination for the result.

Example

```
    NOT    ECX
```

If ECX = 90AD9034h, then as a result of the NOT instruction above, ECX is assigned 6F526FCDh.

Timing

```
Register to Register:   2 clock cycles; 0.1µsec @ 20MHz.
Register to Memory:     7 clock cycles; 0.35µsec @ 20MHz.
Memory to Register:     6 clock cycles; 0.3µsec @ 20MHz.
Immediate to Register:  2 clock cycles; 0.1µsec @ 20MHz.
Immediate to Memory:    7 clock cycles; 0.35µsec @ 20MHz.
```

Flags

OF = 0; CF =0. SF, ZF, and PF affected as described in Appendix ?. Other flags are unchanged.

NOT   Logical Complement   **NOT**

REAL-**mode Exceptions:**

Same as for ADD instruction. See page 251.

PROTECTED-**mode Exceptions:**

Same as for ADD instruction. See page 251.

VIRTUAL 8086-**mode Exceptions:**

Same as for ADD instruction. See page 251.

OR Logical OR **OR**

Format

OR

	Byte 0	Byte 1	Subsequent Byte(s)

Register to
Register

```
0 0 0 0 1 0 d w  mod: reg : r/m
```

Register to
Memory

```
0 0 0 0 1 0 0 w  mod: reg : r/m
```

Memory to
Register

```
0 0 0 0 1 0 1 w  mod: reg : r/m
```

Immediate to
Register/Memory

```
1 0 0 0 0 0 s w  mod:0 0 1: r/m  Immediate Data Byte(s)
```

Immediate to
AL|AX|EAX
Register (short
encoding)

```
0 0 0 0 1 1 0 w  Immediate Data Byte(s)
```

Function

DESTINATION ⟵ DESTINATION ∨ SOURCE;

   or

DESTINATION ⟵ DESTINATION ∨ IMMEDIATE DATA;

Description

Performs a bit-wise logical OR of both operands. One operand also serves as the destination for the result.

Example

```
OR    EBX, EDI
```

If EBX = 00AD9034h, and EDI = 0B800052h, then as a result of the OR instruction above, EBX is assigned 0BAD9076h.

OR   Logical OR   **OR**

Timing

```
Register to Register:   2 clock cycles; 0.1μsec ə 20MHz.
Register to Memory:     7 clock cycles; 0.35μsec ə 20MHz.
Memory to Register:     6 clock cycles; 0.3μsec ə 20MHz.
Immediate to Register:  2 clock cycles; 0.1μsec ə 20MHz.
Immediate to Memory:    7 clock cycles; 0.35μsec ə 20MHz.
```

Flags

OF = 0; CF = 0. SF, ZF, and PF affected as described in Appendix A. Other flags are unchanged.

REAL-mode Exceptions:

Same as for ADD instruction. See page 251.

PROTECTED-mode Exceptions:

Same as for ADD instruction. See page 251.

VIRTUAL 8086-mode Exceptions:

Same as for ADD instruction. See page 251.

OUT   Output to I/O Address   **OUT**

Format

```
OUT
```

To Immediate Port (00-FFh)   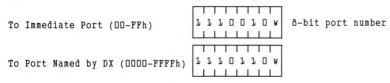 8-bit port number

To Port Named by DX (0000-FFFFh)

Function

```
[DESTINATION] ←— [PORT DX];   {output data}
```

Description

Outputs an operand from AL I AX I EAX, depending on the operand size of the string instruction: BYTE, WORD, or DWORD. The operand is output to the port named by the DX register or by the immediate data field.

This instruction is always available in REAL mode. In PROTECTED mode, this instruction is always available when CPL ≤ IOPL. When CPL >IOPL in PROTECTED mode, the I/O permission bitmap determines if the instruction is permitted. All relevant bits of the I/O permission bitmap must be 0 for the I/O to proceed. In VIRTUAL 8086 mode, the I/O permission bitmap always determines if the OUT instruction is permitted.

Example

```
        OUT        ;inputs operand from port DX
```

Timing

***REAL* mode**
Immediate port: 10 clock cycles; 0.5μsec @ 20MHz.
Variable port: 11 clock cycles; 0.55μsec @ 20MHz.

***PROTECTED* mode, CPL ≤ IOPL**
Immediate port: 4 clock cycles; 0.2μsec @ 20MHz.
Variable port: 5 clock cycles; 0.25μsec @ 20MHz.

***PROTECTED* mode, CPL > IOPL**
Immediate port: 24 clock cycles; 1.2μsec @ 20MHz.
Variable port: 25 clock cycles; 1.25μsec @ 20MHz.

***VIRTUAL 8086* mode**
Immediate port: 24 clock cycles; 1.2μsec @ 20MHz.
Variable port: 15 clock cycles; 1.25μsec @ 20MHz.

OUT   Output to I/O Address   **OUT**

Flags

None are affected.

REAL-mode Exceptions:

Same as for ADD instruction. See page 251.

PROTECTED-mode Exceptions:

If CPL > IOPL, the I/O permission bitmap must allow I/O to all byte ports involved. Other exceptions same as for ADD instruction. See page 251.

VIRTUAL 8086-mode Exceptions:

The I/O permission bitmap must allow I/O to all byte ports involved. Other exceptions same as for ADD instruction. See page 251.

OUTSB/OUTSW/OUTSD   Output String Data to I/O Address   **OUTSB/OUTSW/OUTSD**

Format

OUTSB/OUTSW/OUTSD

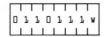

Function

```
[PORT DX] ←──  [SOURCE];        {output data}
IF (ADDRESS SIZE = 32) THEN
  ADJUST ESI;                   {adjust index for source}
ELSE    {address size = 16}
  ADJUST SI;
```

Description

Outputs an operand from a source memory string to the port named by the DX register. The source string is considered to be an array of BYTES, WORDS, or DWORDS, depending on the operand size of the string instruction. After the output is made, the source index register is automatically advanced (incremented or decremented, according to DF) by an amount equaling the operand size.

If the address size of the instruction is DWORD, the operand of the source string is [ESI]. Otherwise, the operand is [SI]. Load the correct index values before executing OUTS.

Example

```
        OUTSD           ;outputs DWORD operands to port DX

    or

    REP OUTSD           ;repeated OUTS until ECX expires.
                        ; (See page 457 for details)
```

Because the source index register must be loaded to use this instruction, OUTSB/W/D is often placed in a loop and used for several iterations.

OUTSB/OUTSW/OUTSD   Output String Data to I/O Address   **OUTSB/OUTSW/OUTSD**

Timing

REAL mode
nonrepeated: 14 clock cycles; 0.7μsec @ 20MHz.
repeated: 12 +5n clock cycles; 0.6 + 0.25nμsec @ 20MHz.

PROTECTED mode, CPL ≤ IOPL
nonrepeated: 8 clock cycles; 0.4μsec @ 20MHz.
repeated: 6 +5n clock cycles; 0.3 + 0.25nμsec @ 20MHz.

PROTECTED mode, CPL > IOPL
nonrepeated: 28 clock cycles; 1.4μsec @ 20MHz.
repeated: 26 +5n clock cycles; 1.3 + 0.25nμsec @ 20MHz.

VIRTUAL 8086 mode
nonrepeated: 28 clock cycles; 1.4μsec @ 20MHz.
repeated: 26 +5n clock cycles; 1.3 + 0.25nμsec @ 20MHz.

(*n* is number of iterations performed)

Flags

None are affected.

REAL-mode Exceptions:

Same as for ADD instruction. See page 251.

PROTECTED-mode Exceptions:

If CPL > IOPL, the I/O permission bitmap must allow I/O to all byte ports involved. Other exceptions same as for ADD instruction. See page 251.

VIRTUAL 8086-mode Exceptions:

The I/O permission bitmap must allow I/O to all byte ports involved. Other exceptions same as for ADD instruction. See page 251.

POP   Pop from Stack to Register   **POP**

Format

```
POP
```

	Byte 0	Byte 1
Register/Memory	1 0 0 0 1 1 1 1	mod:0 0 0: r/m
Register (short encoding)	0 1 0 1 1: reg	
Segment Register DS, ES, FS, GS, SS	0 0 0 0 1 1 1 1	1 0:sreg :0 0 1
Segment Register DS, ES, SS (short encoding)	0 0:sreg :1 1 1	

Function

```
IF (ADDRESS SIZE = 32) THEN
BEGIN
  POP (register);
  ESP ←— ESP + OPERAND SIZE;   {postincrement ESP by 2 or 4}
END
ELSE
BEGIN
  POP (register);
  SP ←— SP + OPERAND SIZE;     {postincrement SP by 2 or 4}
END
```

Description

The general register or segment register is loaded from the top of the stack. The ESP stack pointer register is then incremented by 2 if operand popped is a WORD, or by 4 if the operand popped is a DWORD.

Example

```
        POP EBP    ; pop 32-bit DWORD into EBP register.
```

Timing

```
To general register:    4 clock cycles;   0.2µsec @ 20MHz.
To segment register:   21 clock cycles;   1.05µsec @ 20MHz.
```

Flags

None are affected.

POPA/POPAD   Pop from Stack to All 16-bit/32-bit General Registers   **POPA/POPAD**

Format

```
POPA/POPAD
```

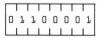

Function

```
IF (ADDRESS SIZE = 32) THEN
BEGIN
  POP(EDI);  or  POP (DI);   {EDI or DI, per on operand size}
  POP(ESI);  or  POP (SI);   {ESI or SI, per on operand size}
  POP(EBP);  or  POP (BP);   {EBP or BP, per operand size}
  POP(TEMP); or  POP (TEMP); {32 or 16-bit temp, per on size}
  POP(EBX);  or  POP (BX);   {EBX or BX, per operand size}
  POP(EDX);  or  POP (DX);   {EDX or DX, per operand size}
  POP(ECX);  or  POP (CX);   {ECX or CX, per operand size}
  POP(EAX);  or  POP (AX);   {EAX or AX, per operand size}
  ESP  ←   ESP + BLOCK SIZE; {increment ESP by BLOCK SIZE 16 or 32}
END
ELSE                         {address size = 16}
BEGIN
  POP(EDI);  or  POP (DI);   {EDI or DI, per on operand size}
  POP(ESI);  or  POP (SI);   {ESI or SI, per on operand size}
  POP(EBP);  or  POP (BP);   {EBP or BP, per operand size}
  POP(TEMP); or  POP (TEMP); {32 or 16-bit temp, per on size}
  POP(EBX);  or  POP (BX);   {EBX or BX, per operand size}
  POP(EDX);  or  POP (DX);   {EDX or DX, per operand size}
  POP(ECX);  or  POP (CX);   {ECX or CX, per operand size}
  POP(EAX);  or  POP (AX);   {EAX or AX, per operand size}
  ESP  ←   ESP + BLOCK SIZE; {increment ESP by BLOCK SIZE 16 or 32}
END
```

Description

The eight general registers (except ESP/SP) are popped from the stack. The ESP/SP stack pointer register is incremented by 16 if the operand size = WORD, or by 32 if the operand size = DWORD. The 80386 does not have a POPA instruction.

Example

```
POPA    ;pop all 16-bit general registers from stack.
POPAD   ;pop all 32-bit general registers from stack.
```

POPA/POPAD   Pop from Stack to All 16-bit/32-bit General Registers   **POPA/POPAD**

Timing

4 clock cycles; 0.2μsec @ 20MHz.

Flags

None are affected.

REAL-mode Exceptions:

Interrupt 12 if any part of the stack operand is at effective address greater than FFFFh in stack segment SS.

PROTECTED-mode Exceptions:

Stack exception (exception 12) with error code of 0000h for operands in memory segments SS if any part of an operand is at effective address beyond the segment limit. Stack exception with error code of segment selector if operand in memory is in segment SS marked not present. Page Fault exception (exception 14) with error code of fault code, and page-fault linear address in register CR2.

VIRTUAL 8086-mode Exceptions:

In VIRTUAL 8086 mode, this instructions causes a general protection exception) with error of 0000h if IOPL < 3, to permit emulation.

Stack exception with error code of 0000h for operands in stack segment if any part of the operand is at effective address beyond the segment limit. Exception is handled in PROTECTED mode at privilege-level 0. The format of the privilege-level-0 stack after an exception (with error code) or interrupt (no error code) is shown in Figure 12.2. Also Page Fault exception with error code of fault code, and page-fault linear address in register CR2.

POPF/POPFD   Pop from Stack to FLAG/EFLAG   **POPF/POPFD**

Format

```
POPF/POPFD
```

```
┌─┬─┬─┬─┬─┬─┬─┬─┐
│1│0│0│1│1│1│0│1│
└─┴─┴─┴─┴─┴─┴─┴─┘
```

Function

```
IF (ADDRESS SIZE = 32) THEN
BEGIN
  POP(EFLAG);  or  POP (FLAG);    {EFLAG or FLAG, per operand size}
  ESP  ←── ESP + OPERAND SIZE;    {postincrement ESP by 2 or 4}
END
ELSE
BEGIN
  POP(EFLAG);  or  POP (FLAG);    {EFLAG or FLAG, per operand size}
  SP  ←── SP + OPERAND SIZE;      {postincrement SP by 2 or 4}
END
```

Description

The EFLAG or FLAG register, depending on the operand size, is loaded from the top of the stack. The ESP stack pointer register is then incremented by 2 if the operand size = WORD (POPF instruction), or by 4 if the operand size = DWORD (POPFD instruction).

When EFLAG or FLAG is popped from the stack, the flag bits assume the new value popped, with the following exceptions. In PROTECTED mode, the IF (interrupt flag bit) remains unchanged CPL ≤ IOPL. In PROTECTED mode, the IOPL (IO privilege level indicator bits) remain unchanged unless CPL = 0.

Example

```
        POPF     ;pop FLAG register (16-bit) from stack.
        POPFD    ;pop EFLAG register (32-bit) from stack.
```

POPF/POPFD   Pop from Stack to FLAG/EFLAG   **POPF/POPFD**

Timing

4 clock cycles; 0.2μsec @ 20MHz.

Flags

None are affected.

REAL-mode Exceptions:

Interrupt 12 if any part of the stack operand is at effective address greater than FFFFh in stack segment SS.

PROTECTED-mode Exceptions:

Stack exception (exception 12) with error code of 0000h for operands in memory segments SS if any part of an operand is at effective address beyond the segment limit. Stack exception with error code of segment selector if operand in memory is in segment SS marked not present. Page Fault exception (exception 14) with error code of fault code, and page-fault linear address in register CR2.

VIRTUAL 8086-mode Exceptions:

In VIRTUAL 8086 mode, this instructions causes a General Protection exception (exception 13) with error of 0000h if IOPL < 3, to permit emulation.

Stack exception with error code of 0000h for operands in stack segment if any part of the operand is at effective address beyond the segment limit. Exception is handled in PROTECTED mode at privilege-level 0. The format of the privilege-level-0 stack after an exception (with error code) or interrupt (no error code) is shown in Figure 12.2. Also Page Fault exception with error code of fault code, and page-fault linear address in register CR2.

PUSH   Push onto Stack   **PUSH**

Format

PUSH

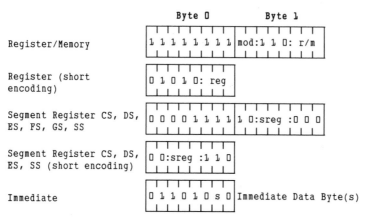

Function

```
IF (ADDRESS SIZE = 32) THEN
BEGIN
   ESP  ←  ESP ( OPERAND SIZE;     {predecrement ESP by 2 or 4}
   [ESP]  ←  OPERAND;              {push operand onto top of stack}
END
ELSE
BEGIN
   SP  ←  SP ( OPERAND SIZE;       {predecrement SP by 2 or 4}
   [SP]  ←  OPERAND;               {push operand onto top of stack}
END
```

Description

The ESP stack pointer register is decremented by 2 if the operand size = WORD, or by 4 if the operand size = DWORD. The operand (a general register, segment register, or immediate data) is then moved to the top of the stack, pointed to by ESP.

If the operand size is DWORD but the item push onto the stack is a segment register (which holds only 16 bits) the 80386 zero-extends the quantity from the segment register to 32 bits before pushing it onto the stack. Doing so keeps the stack aligned on DWORD boundaries.

The 80386 PUSH ESP and PUSH SP instructions push the value of ESP | SP as it existed before the instruction. This differs from the 8086, where PUSH SP pushes the new value (already decremented by 2).

PUSH Push onto Stack **PUSH**

Example

Typical examples assuming that address size = 32 and operand size = DWORD.

```
PUSH    EDI     ;push EDI register onto stack.
PUSH    DS      ;push 16 bits of 0 and 16-bit DS register
                ; onto stack.
```

Timing

```
Push Register Operand:  2 clock cycles; 0.1µsec @ 20MHz.
Push Memory Operand:    5 clock cycles; 0.25µsec @ 20MHz.
Push Immediate Operand: 2 clock cycles; 0.1µsec @ 20MHz.
```

Flags

None are affected.

REAL-mode Exceptions:

None. But insufficient stack space (SP = 1 when trying to push a WORD or SP = 1, 2, or 3 when trying to push a DWORD) can cause a shutdown because without stack space it is impossible to generate an interrupt (generating an interrupt requires pushing the CS, IP, and FLAGS onto the stack, but without stack space it is impossible to do).

PROTECTED-mode Exceptions:

General Protection exception (exception 13) with error code of 0000h for operands in memory segments CS, DS, ES, FS, or GS, if a source operand is in a nonreadable code segment, or if any part of an operand is at effective address beyond the segment limit. Stack exception (exception 12) with error code of 0000h for operands in memory segments SS if any part of an operand is at effective address beyond the segment limit. Stack exception with error code of segment selector if operand in memory is in segment SS marked not present. Not Present exception (exception 11) with error code of segment selector if operand in memory is in a segment DS, ES, FS, or GS marked not present. Page Fault exception (exception 14) with error code of fault code, and page-fault linear address in register CR2.

PUSH   Push onto Stack   **PUSH**

VIRTUAL **8086-mode Exceptions:**

Stack exception with error code of 0000h for operands in stack segment if any part of the operand is at effective address beyond the segment limit. Exception is handled in PROTECTED mode at privilege-level 0. The format of the privilege-level-0 stack after an exception (with error code) or interrupt (no error code) is shown in Figure 12.2. Also Page Fault exception with error code of fault code, and page-fault linear address in register CR2.

PUSHA/PUSHAD Push all 16-bit/32-bit General Registers **PUSHA/PUSHAD**

Format

```
PUSHA/PUSHAD
```

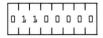

Function

```
IF (ADDRESS SIZE = 32) THEN
BEGIN
  TEMP   ←── ESP;
  ESP  ←──  ESP - BLOCK SIZE;    {decrement ESP by BLOCK SIZE 16 or 32}
  PUSH(EAX);  or  PUSH (AX);     {EAX or AX, per operand size}
  PUSH(ECX);  or  PUSH (CX);     {ECX or CX, per operand size}
  PUSH(EDX);  or  PUSH (DX);     {EDX or DX, per operand size}
  PUSH(EBX);  or  PUSH (BX);     {EBX or BX, per operand size}
  PUSH(TEMP); or  PUSH (TEMP);   {32 or 16-bit temp, per on size}
  PUSH(EBP);  or  PUSH (BP);     {EBP or BP, per operand size}
  PUSH(ESI);  or  PUSH (SI);     {ESI or SI, per on operand size}
  PUSH(EDI);  or  PUSH (DI);     {EDI or DI, per on operand size}

END
ELSE                            {address size = 16}
BEGIN
  TEMP   ←── SP;
  SP   ←──  SP - BLOCK SIZE;     {decrement SP by BLOCK SIZE 16 or 32}
  PUSH(EAX);  or  PUSH (AX);     {EAX or AX, per operand size}
  PUSH(ECX);  or  PUSH (CX);     {ECX or CX, per operand size}
  PUSH(EDX);  or  PUSH (DX);     {EDX or DX, per operand size}
  PUSH(EBX);  or  PUSH (BX);     {EBX or BX, per operand size}
  PUSH(TEMP); or  PUSH (TEMP);   {32 or 16-bit temp, per on size}
  PUSH(EBP);  or  PUSH (BP);     {EBP or BP, per operand size}
  PUSH(ESI);  or  PUSH (SI);     {ESI or SI, per on operand size}
  PUSH(EDI);  or  PUSH (DI);     {EDI or DI, per on operand size}
END
```

Description

The ESP I SP stack pointer register is decremented by 16 if the operand size = WORD, or by 32 if the operand size = DWORD. The eight general registers are then pushed on the stack.

This instruction pushes the value of ESP I SP as it existed before the instruction. This is consistent with the 80386 PUSH ESP I SP instruction. The 8086 does not have a PUSHA instruction.

PUSHA/PUSHAD Push all 16-bit/32-bit General Registers **PUSHA/PUSHAD**

Example

```
PUSHA    ;push all 16-bit general registers onto stack.
PUSHAD   ;push all 32-bit general registers onto stack.
```

Timing

18 clock cycles; 0.9μsec @ 20MHz.

Flags

None are affected.

REAL-mode Exceptions:

None. But insufficient stack space (SP = 1 when trying to push a WORD or SP = 1, 2, or 3 when trying to push a DWORD) can cause a shutdown because without stack space it is impossible to generate an interrupt (generating an interrupt requires pushing the CS, IP, and FLAGS onto the stack, but without stack space it is impossible to do).

PROTECTED-mode Exceptions:

Stack exception (exception 12) with error code of 0000h for operands in memory segments SS if any part of an operand is at effective address beyond the segment limit. Stack exception with error code of segment selector if operand in memory is in segment SS marked not present. Page Fault exception (exception 14) with error code of fault code, and page-fault linear address in register CR2.

VIRTUAL 8086-mode Exceptions:

Stack exception with error code of 0000h for operands in stack segment if any part of the operand is at effective address beyond the segment limit. Exception is handled in PROTECTED mode at privilege-level 0. The format of the privilege-level-0 stack after an exception (with error code) or interrupt (no error code) is shown in Figure 12.2. Also Page Fault exception with error code of fault code, and page-fault linear address in register CR2.

PUSHF/PUSHFD   Push FLAG/EFLAG onto Stack   **PUSHF/PUSHFD**

Format

```
PUSHF/PUSHFD
```

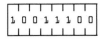

```
1 0 0 1 1 1 0 0
```

Function

```
IF (ADDRESS SIZE = 32) THEN
BEGIN
  ESP  ←── ESP ( OPERAND SIZE;    {predecrement ESP by 2 or 4}
  PUSH(EFLAG);  or  PUSH (FLAG);  {EFLAG or FLAG, per operand size}
END
ELSE
BEGIN
  SP  ←── SP ( OPERAND SIZE;      {predecrement SP by 2 or 4}
  PUSH(EFLAG);  or  PUSH (FLAG);  {EFLAG or FLAG, per operand size}
END
```

Description

The ESP stack pointer register is decremented by 2 if the operand size = WORD, or by 4 if the operand size = DWORD. The EFLAG or FLAG register, depending on the operand size, is then moved to the top of the stack.

Example

```
PUSHF      ;push FLAG register (16-bit) onto stack.
PUSHFD     ;push EFLAG register (32-bit) onto stack.
```

Timing

```
4 clock cycles; 0.2μsec @ 20MHz.
```

Flags

None are affected.

REAL-mode Exceptions:

None. But insufficient stack space (SP = 1 when trying to push a WORD or SP = 1, 2, or 3 when trying to push a DWORD) can cause a shutdown because without stack space it is impossible to generate an interrupt (generating an interrupt requires push-

PUSHF/PUSHFD Push FLAG/EFLAG onto Stack **PUSHF/PUSHFD**

ing the CS, IP, and FLAGS onto the stack, but without stack space it is impossible to do).

PROTECTED-mode Exceptions:

Stack exception (exception 12) with error code of 0000h for operands in memory segments SS if any part of an operand is at effective address beyond the segment limit. Stack exception with error code of segment selector if operand in memory is in segment SS marked not present. Page Fault exception (exception 14) with error code of fault code, and page-fault linear address in register CR2.

VIRTUAL 8086-mode Exceptions:

Stack exception with error code of 0000h for operands in stack segment if any part of the operand is at effective address beyond the segment limit. Exception is handled in PROTECTED mode at privilege-level 0. The format of the privilege-level-0 stack after an exception (with error code) or interrupt (no error code) is shown in Figure 12.2. Also Page Fault exception with error code of fault code, and page-fault linear address in register CR2.

RCL/RCR   Rotate Left/Right Through Carry   **RCL/RCR**

Format

RCL

	Byte 0	Byte 1
Register/Memory by 1	1 1 0 1 0 0 0 w	mod:0 1 0: r/m
Register/Memory by CL	1 1 0 1 0 0 1 w	mod:0 1 0: r/m
Register/Memory by Immediate Count	1 1 0 0 0 0 0 w	mod:0 1 0: r/m	8-Bit Immediate Count

RCR

	Byte 0	Byte 1
Register/Memory by 1	1 1 0 1 0 0 0 w	mod:0 1 1: r/m
Register/Memory by CL	1 1 0 1 0 0 1 w	mod:0 1 1: r/m
Register/Memory by Immediate Count	1 1 0 0 0 0 0 w	mod:0 1 1: r/m	8-Bit Immediate Count

Function

RCL

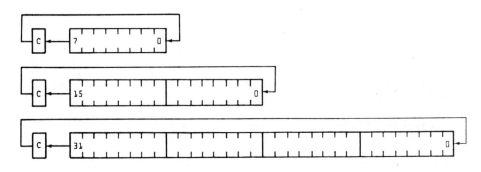

RCL/RCR   Rotate Left/Right Through Carry   **RCL/RCR**

RCR

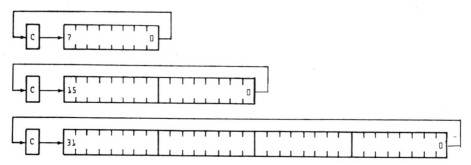

Description

The RCL and RCL instructions shift the bits of the register or memory quantity given by the first operand. The carry flag is part of the rotated quantity.

RCL shifts the bits upward (leftward), shifts the uppermost bit into CF and shifts CF into the lowest bit position. RCR shifts the bits downward (rightward), shifts the lowest bit into CF and shifts CF into the highest bit position.

The rotate is repeated the number of times indicated by the second operand, either an immediate quantity or the CL register. On the 80386 and 80286, the rotate count is masked to 5 bits (values 0 to 31) to reduce the maximum execution time of the instructions, and avoid potentially long interrupt latency. The 8086 and 8088 do not mask the rotate count.

Timing

Timing is independent of the number of bits rotated. The 80386 barrel shifter hardware performs multibit rotates as quickly as single-bit rotates.

```
Rotate of Register and CF:   9 clock cycles; 0.45μsec @ 20MHz.
Rotate of Memory and CF:    10 clock cycles; 0.5μsec @ 20MHz.
```

Flags

CF as described in *Function* above. OF is defined only for a rotate count of 1. For single-bit *right* rotates, OF is the result of XORing the two high-order bits after the rotate. For single-bit *left* rotates, OF is the result of XORing CF after the rotate with the high-order bit after the rotate. For multibit or zero-bit rotates, OF is undefined. Other flags are unchanged.

RCL/RCR   Rotate Left/Right Through Carry   **RCL/RCR**

REAL-mode Exceptions:

Same as for ADD instruction. See page 251.

PROTECTED-mode Exceptions:

Same as for ADD instruction. See page 251.

VIRTUAL 8086-mode Exceptions:

Same as for ADD instruction. See page 251.

RET   Return from Procedure   **RET**

Format

```
RET
```

Within Segment

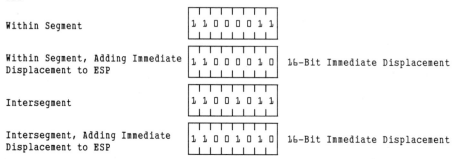

Within Segment, Adding Immediate
Displacement to ESP

Intersegment

Intersegment, Adding Immediate
Displacement to ESP

Within Segment	`1 1 0 0 0 0 1 1`	
Within Segment, Adding Immediate Displacement to ESP	`1 1 0 0 0 0 1 0`	16-Bit Immediate Displacement
Intersegment	`1 1 0 0 1 0 1 1`	
Intersegment, Adding Immediate Displacement to ESP	`1 1 0 0 1 0 1 0`	16-Bit Immediate Displacement

Function

```
IF (ADDRESS SIZE = 32) THEN
BEGIN
  POP EIP;                      {RET always pops EIP or IP}
END
ELSE
BEGIN
  POP IP;                       {RET always pops EIP or IP}
END
IF RET IS INTERSEGMENT THEN
BEGIN
  POP CS;                       {intersegment RET also pops CS}
END
IF RET HAS IMMEDIATE OPERAND THEN
BEGIN
  IF (OPERAND SIZE = 32) THEN
    ESP  ←— ESP + (2 * IMMEDIATE OPERAND);  {WORDs to be freed}
  ELSE
    SP  ←— SP + IMMEDIATE DATA;             {BYTEs to be freed}
END
```

Description

RET within the current code segment pops the instruction pointer from the stack, determining where processing of the main routine will resume. When a CALL is made within the current code segment, the code segment register is not affected.

When an intersegment CALL occurs in REAL mode or VIRTUAL 8086 mode, the instruction pointer and code segment register are both popped from the stack, determining the address where processing of the main routine will resume.

RET   Return from Procedure   **RET**

When an intersegment RET occurs in PROTECTED mode, the activities performed by the 80386 can be quite complex according to whether the destination selector is that of:

1. a code segment at the current privilege level, (DPL = CPL), or
2. a code segment at a more privileged level, (DPL ≤ CPL).

Any RET instruction can contain an optional numeric parameter that indicates the number of stack BYTES (operand size = 16) or WORDS (operand size = 32) to be released after the return address is popped. The space released typically has been used to store input parameters to the procedure when it was called. The RET instruction should be used at the end of a procedure, but not at the end of a task since RET cannot perform a task switch. The IRET instruction is appropriate for the end of a nested task, where it causes a task switch back to the previous task.

Example

```
     RET

TIMING
Within Segment:               10 + m clock cycles; 0.5μsec @ 20MHz.
Within Segment adding Immed: 10 + m clock cycles; 0.5μsec @ 20MHz.
Intersegment:                 18 + m clock cycles; 0.9μsec @ 20MHz.
Intersegment adding Immed:   18 + m clock cycles; 0.5μsec @ 20MHz.
```

m is the time required to fetch and begin execution of the destination instruction.

RET   Return from Procedure   **RET**

PROTECTED Mode Details:
IF operand size = 32
THEN third word on stack must be within stack limits ELSE Stack Fault exception
(error code of 0000h).
ELSE second word on stack must be within stack limits ELSE Stack Fault exception
(error code of 0000h).
Return selector RPL must be ≥ CPL ELSE General Protection exception (error code of
return selector).
IF return selector RPL = CPL
THEN go to SAME-LEVEL
ELSE go to OUTER-PRIVILEGE-LEVEL.

SAME-LEVEL:
Return selector must not be null ELSE General Protection exception (error code of
0000h).
Selector index must be within its descriptor table limits ELSE General Protection
exception (error code of return selector).
Descriptor Access Rights (AR) byte must indicate code segment ELSE General Protec-
tion (error code of return selector).
IF nonconforming code segment
THEN code segment DPL must = CPL ELSE General Protection Exception (error code of
   return selector). IF conforming code segment THEN code segment DPL must s CPL
ELSE
Code segment must be present ELSE Not Present exception (above).
Top word on stack must be within stack limits ELSE Stack Fault exception (error
code of 0000h).
IP must be within code segment limit ELSE Not Present exception (error code of
0000h).
IF operand size = 32
THEN
   Load CS:EIP from stack.
   Load CS descriptor cache with CS descriptor.
   Increment eSP by 8 plus two times the immediate offset (for parameters) if it
exists.
ELSE
   Load CS:IP from stack.
   Load CS descriptor cache with CS descriptor.
   Increment SP by 4 plus the immediate offset (for parameters) if it exists.

OUTER-PRIVILEGE-LEVEL:
   IF operand size = 32
   THEN Top(16 + immediate) bytes on stack must be within stack limits ELSE Stack
Fault exception (error code of 0000h).
   ELSE Top(8 + immediate) bytes on stack must be within stack limits ELSE Stack
Fault exception (error code of 0000h).
   Examine return CS selector and associated descriptor:
   Selector must not be null ELSE General Protection exception (error code of
0000h).
   Selector index must be within its descriptor table limits ELSE General Protec-
tion exception (error code of return selector).
   Access Rights (AR) byte must indicate code segment, else General Protection ex-
ception (error code of return selector).
   IF nonconforming code segment
   THEN code segment DPL must = CS selector RPL ELSE General Protection exception

RET   Return from Procedure   **RET**

(error code of return selector).
   IF conforming code segment
   THEN code segment DPL must be ≤ CPL ELSE General Protection exception (error
code of return selector).
   Segment must be present ELSE Not Present exception (error code of return
selector).
  Examine return SS selector and associated descriptor:
   Selector must not be null ELSE General Protection exception (error code of
0000h).
   Selector index must be within table limits ELSE General Protection exception
(error code of stack selector).
   Selector RPL must = RPL of return selector ELSE General Protection exception
(error code of stack selector).
   Access Rights (AR) byte must indicate writable segment ELSE General Protection
exception (error code of stack selector).
   Stack segment DPL must = RPL of the return CS selector ELSE General Protection
exception (error code of return selector).
   Stack segment must be present ELSE Not Present exception (error code of return
selector).
   Instruction pointer must be within code segment boundaries ELSE General Protec-
tion exception (error code of 0000).
   Set CPL to the RPL of the return CS selector.
  IF operand size = 32
  THEN
  Load CS:EIP from the stack.
  Set the RPL field of CS to CPL.
  Increment eSP by 8 plus the immediate offset if it exists.
  Load SS:eSP from stack.
  ELSE
  Load CS:IP from stack.
   Set the RPL field of CS to CPL.
  Increment eSP by 4 plus the immediate offset if it exists.
  Load SS:SP from stack.
  Load CS descriptor cache with the CS descriptor.
  Load SS descriptor cache with the SS descriptor.
  FOR each of ES, FS, GS, and DS
  DO
   If the current RPL value of the segment register is not valid for use at the
outer level
   THEN zero the segment register and clear the associated valid flag bit.
   To be valid, the register setting must satisfy the following properties:
   selector index must be within descriptor table limits,
   Access Rights (AR) byte must indicate data segment or readable code segment,
   IF segment is data or nonconforming code, THEN DPL must be ≥ CPL or DPL must be
≥ RPL.

RET   Return from Procedure   **RET**

Flags

No flags are affected, unless a task switch occurs in PROTECTED mode.

REAL-mode Exceptions:

Interrupt 13 if any part of an operand in memory is at effective address greater than FFFFh in segments CS, DS, ES, FS, or GS. Interrupt 12 if any part of an operand in memory is at effective address greater than FFFFh in stack segment SS.

PROTECTED-mode Exceptions:

General Protection exception (exception 13) with error code of 0000h for operands in memory segments CS, DS, ES, FS, or GS if a source operand is in a nonreadable code segment, or if any part of the operand is at effective address beyond the segment limit. Stack exception (exception 12) with error code of 0000h for operands in stack segment if any part of the operand is at effective address beyond the segment limit. Stack exception with error code of segment selector if operand in memory is in segment SS marked not present. Not Present exception (exception 11) with error code of segment selector if operand in memory is in a segment DS, ES, FS, or GS marked not present. Not Present exception with error code of segment selector if operand in memory is in a segment DS, ES, FS, or GS marked not present. Page Fault exception (exception 14) with error code of fault code, and page-fault linear address in register CR2.

VIRTUAL 8086-mode Exceptions:

Same as REAL mode exceptions, but handled in PROTECTED mode at privilege-level 0. The format of the privilege-level-0 stack after an exception (with error code) or interrupt (no error code) is shown in Figure 12.2. Also Page Fault exception with error code of fault code, and page-fault linear address in register CR2.

ROL/ROR　　　　　　　　Rotate Left/Right　　　　　　　　**ROL/ROR**

Format

ROL

	Byte 0	Byte 1	Subsequent Byte(s)

Register/Memory by 1　　　`1 1 0 1 0 0 0 w` `mod:0 0 0: r/m`

Register/Memory by CL　　　`1 1 0 1 0 0 1 w` `mod:0 0 0: r/m`

Register/Memory by
Immediate Count　　　`1 1 0 0 0 0 0 w` `mod:0 0 0: r/m`　　8-Bit Immediate Count

ROR

Register/Memory by 1　　　`1 1 0 1 0 0 0 w` `mod:0 0 1: r/m`

Register/Memory by CL　　　`1 1 0 1 0 0 1 w` `mod:0 0 1: r/m`

Register/Memory by
Immediate Count　　　`1 1 0 0 0 0 0 w` `mod:0 0 1: r/m`　　8-Bit Immediate Count

Function

ROL

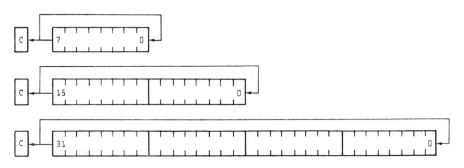

ROL/ROR Rotate Left/Right **ROL/ROR**

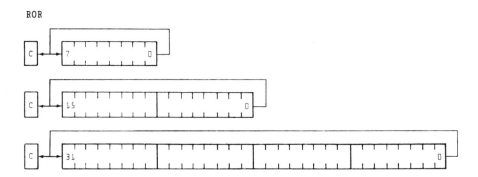

Description

The ROL and ROR instructions shift the bits of the register or memory quantity given by the first operand.

ROL shifts the bits upward (leftward) and shifts the uppermost bit into CF and into the lowest bit position. ROR shifts the bits downward (rightward) and shifts the lowest bit into CF and into the highest bit position.

The rotate is repeated the number of times indicated by the second operand, either an immediate quantity or the CL register. On the 80386 and 80286, the rotate count is masked to 5 bits (values 0 to 31) to reduce the maximum execution time of the instructions, and avoid potentially long interrupt latency. The 8086 and 8088 do not mask the rotate count.

Timing

Timing is independent of the number of bits rotated. The 80386 barrel shifter hardware performs multibit rotates as quickly as single-bit rotates.

```
Rotate of Register:  3 clock cycles; 0.15μsec @ 20MHz.
Rotate of Memory:    7 clock cycles; 0.35μsec @ 20MHz.
```

Flags

CF as described in *Function* above. OF is defined only for a rotate count of 1. For single-bit *right* rotates, OF is the result of XORing the two high-order bits after the rotate. For single-bit *left* rotates, OF is the result of XORing CF after the rotate with the high-order bit after the rotate. For multibit or zero-bit rotates, OF is undefined. Other flags are unchanged.

ROL/ROR   Rotate Left/Right   **ROL/ROR**

REAL-**mode Exceptions**:

Same as for ADD instruction. See page 251.

PROTECTED-**mode Exceptions**:

Same as for ADD instruction. See page 251.

VIRTUAL **8086-mode Exceptions**:

Same as for ADD instruction. See page 251.

SAHF   Store AH Register into EFLAG   **SAHF**

Format

SAHF

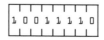

Function

low byte of EFLAG register ⟵ AH;

Description

SAHF stores the low EFLAG byte into the AH register. From MSB to LSB, the AH value is interpreted as: SF, ZF, don't care, AF, don't care, PF, don't care, CF.

Timing

2 clock cycles; 0.1μsec @ 20MHz.

Flags

None are affected.

REAL-mode Exceptions:

None.

PROTECTED-mode Exceptions:

None.

VIRTUAL 8086-mode Exceptions:

None.

SAL/SAR Arithmetic Shift Left/Right **SAL/SAR**

Format

SAL (same as SHL)

	Byte 0	Byte 1	Subsequent Byte(s)
Register/Memory by 1	1 1 0 1 0 0 0 w	mod:1 0 0: r/m	
Register/Memory by CL	1 1 0 1 0 0 1 w	mod:1 0 0: r/m	
Register/Memory by Immediate Count	1 1 0 0 0 0 0 w	mod:1 0 0: r/m	8-Bit Immediate Count

SAR

	Byte 0	Byte 1	Subsequent Byte(s)
Register/Memory by 1	1 1 0 1 0 0 0 w	mod:1 1 1: r/m	
Register/Memory by CL	1 1 0 1 0 0 1 w	mod:1 1 1: r/m	
Register/Memory by Immediate Count	1 1 0 0 0 0 0 w	mod:1 1 1: r/m	8-Bit Immediate Count

Function

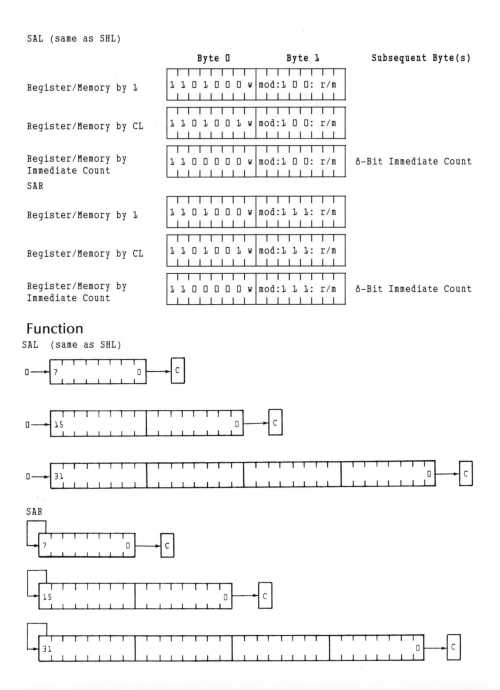

SAL/SAR   Arithmetic Shift Left/Right   **SAL/SAR**

Description

The SAL and SAR instructions shift the bits of the register or memory quantity given by the first operand.

SAL shifts the bits upward (leftward), shifts the uppermost bit into CF and shifts 0 into the lowest bit position. SAR shifts the bits downward (rightward), shifts the lowest bit into CF and duplicates the bit at the highest bit position.

The shift is repeated the number of times indicated by the second operand, either an immediate quantity or the CL register. On the 80386 and 80286, the shift count is masked to 5 bits (values 0 to 31) to reduce the maximum execution time of the instructions, and avoid potentially long interrupt latency. The 8086 and 8088 do not mask the shift count.

Timing

```
Arithmetic Shift of Register: 3 clock cycles; 0.15µsec @ 20MHz.
Arithmetic Shift of Memory:   7 clock cycles; 0.35µsec @ 20MHz.
```

Flags

CF as described in *Function* above. OF is defined only for a shift count of 1. For single-bit *right* shifts, OF is the result of XORing the two high-order bits after the shift. For single-bit *left* shifts, OF is the result of XORing CF after the shift with the high-order bit after the shift. For multibit or zero-bit shifts, OF is undefined. Other flags are unchanged.

REAL-mode Exceptions:

Same as for ADD instruction. See page 251.

PROTECTED-mode Exceptions:

Same as for ADD instruction. See page 251.

VIRTUAL 8086-mode Exceptions:

Same as for ADD instruction. See page 251.

SBB   Integer Subtraction with Borrow   **SBB**

Format

SBB

	Byte 0	Byte 1	Subsequent Byte(s)

Register from Register   `0 0 0 1 1 0 d w` `mod: reg : r/m`

Register from Memory   `0 0 0 1 1 0 0 w` `mod: reg : r/m`

Memory from Register   `0 0 0 1 1 0 1 w` `mod: reg : r/m`

Immediate from
Register/Memory   `1 0 0 0 0 0 s w` `mod:0 1 1: r/m`   Immediate Data Byte(s)

Immediate from AL|AX|EAX
Register (short
encoding)   `0 0 0 1 1 1 0 w` Immediate Data Byte(s)

Function

```
DESTINATION  ←  DESTINATION - SOURCE - CF;

    or

DESTINATION  ←  DESTINATION - IMMEDIATE DATA - CF;
```

Description

Subtract both operands and the carry flag bit. One operand also serves as the destination for the resulting difference.

Example

```
    SBB    ECX, EDX
```

If CF = 1, ECX = 00000034h, and EDX = 00000052h, then as a result of the SBB instruction above, ECX is assigned FFFFFFACh, and CF is assigned 1.

SBB   Integer Subtraction with Borrow   **SBB**

Timing

```
Register to Register:  2 clock cycles; 0.1µsec @ 20MHz.
Register to Memory:    7 clock cycles; 0.35µsec @ 20MHz.
Memory to Register:    6 clock cycles; 0.3µsec @ 20MHz.
Immediate to Register: 2 clock cycles; 0.1µsec @ 20MHz.
Immediate to Memory:   7 clock cycles; 0.35µsec @ 20MHz.
```

Flags

OF, CF, SF, ZF, AF, and PF affected as described in Appendix A. Other flags are unchanged.

REAL-mode Exceptions:

Same as for ADD instruction. See page 251.

PROTECTED-mode Exceptions:

Same as for ADD instruction. See page 251.

VIRTUAL 8086-mode Exceptions:

Same as for ADD instruction. See page 251.

SCASB/SCASW/SCASD   Scan String Data   **SCASB/SCASW/SCASD**

Format

```
SCASB/SCASW/SCASD
```

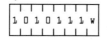

Function

```
AL|AX|EAX - [DESTINATION]    {perform subtraction for comparison}
IF (ADDRESS SIZE = 32) THEN
  ADJUST EDI;                {adjust index for destination}
ELSE    {address size = 16}
  ADJUST DI;
```

Description

Subtracts the memory operand in a destination memory string from the AL I AX I EAX register. The result is discarded. Only the flags are modified. The destination string is considered to be an array of BYTES, WORDS, or DWORDS, depending on the operand size of the string instruction. After the subtraction is made, the destination index register is automatically advanced (incremented or decremented, according to DF) by an amount equaling the operand size.

If the address size of the instruction is DWORD, the operand of the destination string is ES:[EDI]. Otherwise, the operand is ES:[DI].

Load the correct index values before executing MOVS.

Example

```
        SCASD          ;compares with EAX DWORD operand from DWORD string

  or

  REPE  SCASD          ;repeated DWORD scan runs while matching EAX and ECX
                       ; has not expired.
                       ; (See page 458 for details)

  or

  REPNE SCASD          ;repeated DWORD scan runs while not matching EAX and
                       ; ECX has not expired.
                       ; (See page 459 for details)
```

Because the destination index register must be loaded to use this instruction, SCASB/W/D is often placed in a loop and used for several iterations.

SCASB/SCASW/SCASD   Scan String Data   **SCASB/SCASW/SCASD**

Timing

```
nonrepeated:    7 clock cycles; 0.35µsec @ 20MHz.
repeated:       5 +8n clock cycles; 0.25 + 0.4nµsec @ 20MHz.
```

(*n* is number of iterations performed)

Flags

None are affected.

REAL-mode Exceptions:

Same as for ADD instruction. See page 251.

PROTECTED-mode Exceptions:

Same as for ADD instruction. See page 251.

VIRTUAL 8086-mode Exceptions:

Same as for ADD instruction. See page 251.

SETcc   Set Byte on Condition True   **SETcc**

Format

SETcc

```
        Byte 0          Byte 1          Byte 2
  ┌─────────────────┬─────────────────┬─────────────────┐
  │0 0 0 0 1 1 1 1  │1 0 0 1 c c c c  │mod:0 0 0: r/m   │
  └─────────────────┴─────────────────┴─────────────────┘
```

```
c c c c   CONDITION
0 0 0 0   Overflow
0 0 0 1   Not Overflow
0 0 1 0   Below / Not Above or Equal
0 0 1 1   Not Below / Above or Equal
0 1 0 0   Equal / Zero
0 1 0 1   Not Equal / Not Zero
0 1 1 0   Below or Equal / Not Above
0 1 1 1   Not Below or Equal / Above
1 0 0 0   Sign / Negative
1 0 0 1   Not Sign / Positive
1 0 1 0   Parity / Parity Even
1 0 1 1   Not Parity / Parity Odd
1 1 0 0   Less / Not Greater or Equal
1 1 0 1   Not Less / Greater or Equal
1 1 1 0   Less or Equal / Not Greater
1 1 1 1   Not Less or Equal / Greater
```

Function

```
IF (CONDITION = TRUE) THEN
   DESTINATION ⟵ 01h;   {indicate if condition true}
ELSE
   DESTINATION ⟵ 00h;   {indicate fi condition false}
```

Description

SETcc provides easy setting of Boolean variables. The variable is set according to whether a specific condition is true. If the condition is true, the byte Boolean variable is set to 01h. If the condition is false, the byte Boolean variable is set to 00h.

Example

```
    SETNO   TEST_PASSED  ;the variable TEST_PASSED is set to
                         ; 01h if there is no overflow.
```

Timing

```
Conditional Set Register:  4 clock cycles; 0.2μsec @ 20MHz.
Conditional Set Memory:    5 clock cycles; 0.25μsec @ 20MHz.
```

SETcc   Set Byte on Condition True   **SETcc**

Flags

None are affected.

REAL-mode Exceptions:

Same as for ADD instruction. See page 251.

PROTECTED-mode Exceptions:

Same as for ADD instruction. See page 251.

VIRTUAL 8086-mode Exceptions:

Same as for ADD instruction. See page 251.

SGDT   Store Global Descriptor Register   **SGDT**

Format

```
SGDT
```

```
           Byte 0         Byte 1         Byte 2
         ┌───────────────┬───────────────┬───────────────┐
         │0 0 0 0 1 1 1 1│0 0 0 0 0 0 0 1│mod:0 0 0: r/m │
         └───────────────┴───────────────┴───────────────┘
```

Function

```
IF (OPERAND SIZE = 32) THEN
   MEMORY 16:24  ⟵  GDTR.LIMIT:GDTR.BASE;    (24 bits of base stored)
ELSE
   MEMORY 16:32  ⟵  GDTR.LIMIT:GDTR.BASE;    (32 bits of base stored)
```

Description

SGDT stores a limit value and linear base address value from register GDTR.

SGDT is typically an operating system instruction. However, it can be executed at any privilege level (the 80286 considers only *loading* to be a privileged operation).

SGDT   Store Global Descriptor Register   **SGDT**

Example

```
SGDT    GDT_COPY    ;store GDTR value
```

Timing

9 clock cycles; 0.45μsec @ 20MHz.

Flags

None are affected.

REAL-mode Exceptions:

Same as ADD instruction. See page 251.

PROTECTED-mode Exceptions:

Same as ADD instruction. See page 251.

VIRTUAL 8086-mode Exceptions:

Same as ADD instruction. See page 251.

SHL/SHR   Logical Shift Left/Right   **SHL/SHR**

Format

SHL (same as SAR)

	Byte 0	Byte 1	Subsequent Byte(s)
Register/Memory by 1	1 1 0 1 0 0 0 w	mod:1 0 0: r/m	
Register/Memory by CL	1 1 0 1 0 0 1 w	mod:1 0 0: r/m	
Register/Memory by Immediate Count	1 1 0 0 0 0 0 w	mod:1 0 0: r/m	Immediate Count

SHR

	Byte 0	Byte 1	Subsequent Byte(s)
Register/Memory by 1	1 1 0 1 0 0 0 w	mod:1 0 1: r/m	
Register/Memory by CL	1 1 0 1 0 0 1 w	mod:1 0 1: r/m	
Register/Memory by Immediate Count	1 1 0 0 0 0 0 w	mod:1 0 1: r/m	Immediate Count

Function

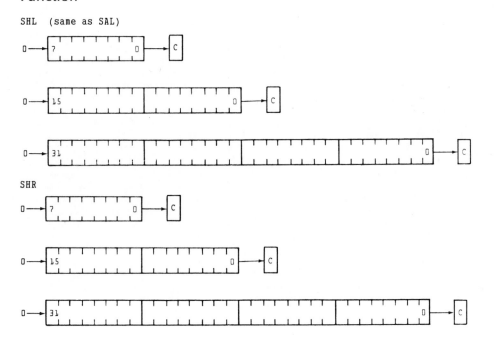

SHL (same as SAL)

SHR

SHL/SHR   Logical Shift Left/Right   **SHL/SHR**

Description

The SHL and SHR instructions shift the bits of the register or memory quantity given by the first operand.

SHL shifts the bits upward (leftward), shifts the uppermost bit into CF and shifts 0 into the lowest bit position. SHR shifts the bits downward (rightward), shifts the lowest bit into CF, and shifts 0 into the highest bit position.

The shift is repeated the number of times indicated by the second operand, either an immediate quantity or the CL register. On the 80386 and 80286, the shift count is masked to 5 bits (values 0 to 31) to reduce the maximum execution time of the instructions, and avoid potentially long interrupt latency. The 8086 and 8088 do not mask the shift count.

Timing

Timing is independent of the number of bits shifted. The 80386 barrel shifter hardware performs multibit shifts as quickly as single-bit shifts.

```
Arithmetic Shift of Register:  3 clock cycles; 0.15µsec @ 20MHz.
Arithmetic Shift of Memory:    7 clock cycles; 0.35µsec @ 20MHz.
```

Flags

CF as described in *Function* above. OF is defined only for a shift count of 1. For single-bit *right* shifts, OF is the result of XORing the two high-order bits after the shift. For single-bit *left* shifts, OF is the result of XORing CF after the shift with the high-order bit after the shift. For multibit or zero-bit shifts, OF is undefined. Other flags are unchanged.

REAL-mode Exceptions:

Same as for ADD instruction. See page 251.

PROTECTED-mode Exceptions:

Same as for ADD instruction. See page 251.

VIRTUAL 8086-mode Exceptions:

Same as for ADD instruction. See page 251.

SHLD/SHRD   Double Precision Shift Left/Right   **SHLD/SHRD**

Format

SHLD

	Byte 0	Byte 1	Byte 2	
Register/Memory by Immediate	0 0 0 0 1 1 1 1	1 0 1 0 0 1 0 0	mod: reg : r/m	8-Bit Immediate Count
Register/Memory by CL	0 0 0 0 1 1 1 1	1 0 1 0 0 1 0 1	mod: reg : r/m	

SHRD

Register/Memory by Immediate	0 0 0 0 1 1 1 1	1 0 1 0 1 1 0 0	mod: reg : r/m	8-Bit Immediate Count
Register/Memory by CL	0 0 0 0 1 1 1 1	1 0 1 0 1 1 0 1	mod: reg : r/m	

Function

SHLD

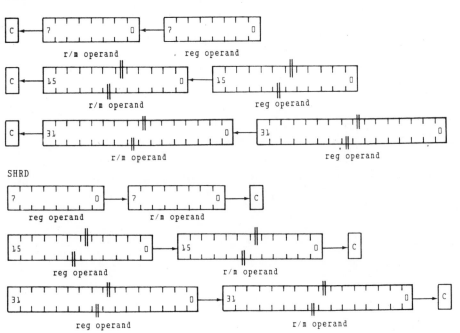

SHRD

SHLD/SHRD   Double Precision Shift Left/Right   **SHLD/SHRD**

Description

SHLD and SHRD are new instructions that perform shifts using two operands. When very long strings are being shifted, these instructions allow the shifting to occur on 32 bits per iteration, rather than just 16 bits per iteration. The first operand (the r/m operand) is shifted to the left or right as many bits as indicated in the immediate field or CL register. The register operand provides bits to be shifted in. The result is stored back to the r/m operand. The register remains unaltered.

The distinguishing and versatile feature of this instruction is allowing a register operand to provide the information shifted into the r/m operand, as illustrated in *Function* above. Because the bits to shift in are provided by specified registers, the operation is useful for multiprecision shifts (64 bits or more). SF, ZF, and PF flags are set according to the r/m result. CF is set to the value of the last bit shifted out.

Example

```
SHLD        ;store local descriptor table selector
```

Appendix H illustrates use of these instructions within bit string insert and bit string deletion algorithms.

Timing

Timing is independent of the number of bits shifted. The 80386 barrel shifter hardware performs a multibit double shift as quickly as a single-bit double shift.

```
Shift of Register:  3 clock cycles; 0.15µsec @ 20MHz.
Shift of Memory:    7 clock cycles; 0.35µsec @ 20MHz.
```

Flags

SF, ZF, and PF are set according to the r/m result. CF is set to the value of the last bit shifted out. AF and OF are undefined. Other flags are unchanged.

SHLD/SHRD   Double Precision Shift Left/Right   **SHLD/SHRD**

REAL-mode Exceptions:

Same as ADD instruction. See page 251.

PROTECTED-mode Exceptions:

Same as ADD instruction. See page 251.

VIRTUAL 8086-mode Exceptions:

Same as ADD instruction. See page 251.

SIDT   Store Interrupt Table Descriptor Register   **SIDT**

Format

```
SIDT
```

```
           Byte 0          Byte 1          Byte 2
       ┌─────────────┬─────────────┬─────────────────┐
       │0 0 0 0 1 1 1 1│0 0 0 0 0 0 0 1│mod:0 0 1: r/m │
       └─────────────┴─────────────┴─────────────────┘
```

Function

```
IF (OPERAND SIZE = 32) THEN
  MEMORY 16:24  ←──  IDTR.LIMIT:IDTR.BASE;    (24 bits of base stored)
ELSE
  MEMORY 16:32  ←──  IDTR.LIMIT:IDTR.BASE;    (32 bits of base stored)
```

Description

SIDT stores a limit value and linear base address value from register IDTR.

SIDT is typically an operating system instruction. However, it can be executed at any privilege level (the 80286 considers only *loading* to be a privileged operation).

SIDT   Store Interrupt Table Descriptor Register   **SIDT**

Example

```
        SIDT    IDT_COPY      ;store IDTR value
```

Timing

9 clock cycles; 0.45µsec @ 20MHz.

Flags

None are affected.

REAL-mode Exceptions:

Same as ADD instruction. See page 251.

PROTECTED-mode Exceptions:

Same as ADD instruction. See page 251.

VIRTUAL 8086-mode Exceptions:

Same as ADD instruction. See page 251.

SLDT   Store Local Descriptor Table Register   **SLDT**

Format

```
SLDT
```

```
          Byte 0          Byte 1          Byte 2
        ┌─────────────┬─────────────┬─────────────┐
        │0 0 0 0 1 1 1 1│0 0 0 0 0 0 0 0│mod:0 0 1: r/m│
        └─────────────┴─────────────┴─────────────┘
```

Function

```
OPERAND  ←   LDTR;        {16-bit selector}
```

Description

SLDT is a PROTECTED mode instruction. SLDT stores a selector from the LDTR (Local Descriptor Table Register).

SLDT is typically an operating system instruction. However, it can be executed at any privilege level (the 80286 considers only *loading* to be a privileged operation).

Example

```
        SLDT  LDT_COPY    ;store local descriptor table selector
```

Timing

```
Store to Register:  2 clock cycles; 0.1μsec @ 20MHz.
Store to Memory:    2 clock cycles; 0.1μsec @ 20MHz.
```

SLDT   Store Local Descriptor Table Register   **SLDT**

Flags

None are affected.

REAL-mode Exceptions:

Interrupt 6. SLDT is not a legal instruction in REAL mode.

PROTECTED-mode Exceptions:

Same as ADD instruction. See page 251.

VIRTUAL 8086-mode Exceptions:

Invalid Opcode exception (exception 6). SLDT is not a legal instruction in VIRTUAL 8086 mode.

SMSW   Store Machine Status Word Register   **SMSW**

Format

```
SMSW
```

```
            Byte 0          Byte 1          Byte 2
         ┌───────────────┬───────────────┬───────────────┐
         │0 0 0 0 1 1 1 1│0 0 0 0 0 0 0 1│mod:1 0 0: r/m │
         └───────────────┴───────────────┴───────────────┘
```

Function

```
16-BIT OPERAND  ←—  MSW;      (MSW is low 16 bits of CR0)
```

Description

SMSW stores the lower half of CR0 into the destination operand. The 80386 instruction MOV destination,CR0 instruction would more likely be used, however. (SMSW instruction provides 80286 opcode compatibility.)

SMSW is typically an operating system instruction. However, it can be executed at any privilege level (the 80286 considers only *loading* to be a privileged operation).

Example

```
        SMSW    IDT_INFO    ;store the lower half of CR0
```

Timing

```
Store to Register Operand:  2 clock cycles; 0.1µsec @ 20MHz.
Store to Memory Operand:    3 clock cycles; 0.15µsec @ 20MHz.
```

SMSW   Store Machine Status Word Register   **SMSW**

Flags

None are affected.

REAL-mode Exceptions:

Same as ADD instruction. See page 251.

PROTECTED-mode Exceptions:

Same as ADD instruction. See page 251.

VIRTUAL 8086-mode Exceptions:

Same as ADD instruction. See page 251.

STC   Set Carry Flag   **STC**

Format

STC

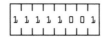

Function

CF ⟵ 1;

Description

STC sets the carry flag.

Example

STC

Timing

2 clock cycles; 0.1μsec @ 20MHz.

Flags

CF as described in *Function* above. All other flags are unchanged.

REAL-mode Exceptions:

None.

PROTECTED-mode Exceptions:

None.

VIRTUAL 8086-mode Exceptions:

None.

STD   Set Direction Flag — Decrement Index   **STD**

Format

STD

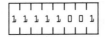

Function

DF ⟵ 1;

Description

STD sets the direction flag. After STD is executed, the string instructions and the repeated string instructions will decrement the index registers that they use.

Example

STD

Timing

2 clock cycles; 0.1μsec @ 20MHz.

Flags

DF as described in *Function* above. All other flags are unchanged.

REAL-mode Exceptions:

None.

PROTECTED-mode Exceptions:

None.

VIRTUAL 8086-mode Exceptions:

None.

STI   Set Interrupt Flag − Enable Interrupts   **STI**

Format

STI

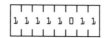

Function

IF ⟵ 1;

Description

STI sets the interrupt flag if allowed. In REAL mode STI is always allowed. In PRO-
TECTED mode or VIRTUAL 8086 mode, CPL must be numerically less than or equal to
IOPL in order for STI to be allowed.

If allowed as described above, STI enables interrupts after executing the *following*
instruction if the following allows IF to remain enabled. Specifically, if interrupts are
disabled and the instruction sequence STI, CLI is coded, external interrupts are not
recognized because CLI clears the interrupt flag during its execution.

Example

STI

Timing

3 clock cycles; 0.15μsec @ 20MHz.

Flags

IF as described in *Function* above. All other flags are unchanged.

REAL-mode Exceptions:

None.

PROTECTED-mode Exceptions:

General Protection exception (exception 13) with error code of 0000h if CPL is numerically greater than IOPL.

STI · Set Interrupt Flag — Enable Interrupts **STI**

VIRTUAL 8086-mode Exceptions:

General Protection exception with error code of 0000h if IOPL is numerically smaller than 3, since CPL during VIRTUAL 8086 mode is always 3.

Trapping this instruction during VIRTUAL 8086 mode by having IOPL values of 2, 1, or 0 allows the PROTECTED mode supervisor to virtualize the state of IF observed by the VIRTUAL 8086 software.

STOSB/STOSW/STOSD   Store String Data   **STOSB/STOSW/STOSD**

Format

```
STOSB/STOSW/STOSD
```

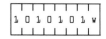

Function

```
IF (OPERAND SIZE = DWORD) THEN        (store operand from EAX/AX/AL)
  [DESTINATION-INDEX]  ←  EAX;
ELSE IF (OPERAND SIZE = WORD) THEN
  [DESTINATION-INDEX]  ←  AX;
ELSE     (operand size = BYTE )
  [DESTINATION-INDEX]  ←  AL;
IF (ADDRESS SIZE = 32) THEN           (adjust index for destination)
  ADJUST ESI;
ELSE    (address size = 16)
  ADJUST SI;
```

Description

STOS stores operands to a destination memory string. The string is considered to be an array of BYTES, WORDS, or DWORDS, depending on the operand size of the string instruction. After the transfer is made, the destination index register is automatically advanced (incremented or decremented, according to DF) by an amount equaling the operand size.

If the address size of the instruction is DWORD, the operand of the destination string is [ESI]. Otherwise, the source operand is [SI]. Load the correct index value before executing STOS.

Example

```
        STOSW          ;stores WORD operand to string

   or

   REP  STOSW          ;repeat store instruction until ECX expires
                       ; (See page 457.)
```

Because the source index register must be loaded to use this instruction, STOSB/W/D is often placed in a loop and used for several iterations.

STOSB/STOSW/STOSD   Store String Data   **STOSB/STOSW/STOSD**

Timing

`4 clock cycles; 0.2µsec @ 20MHz.`

Flags

None are affected.

REAL-mode Exceptions:

Same as for ADD instruction. See page 251.

PROTECTED-mode Exceptions:

Same as for ADD instruction. See page 251.

VIRTUAL 8086-mode Exceptions:

Same as for ADD instruction. See page 251.

STR   Store Task Register   **STR**

Format

```
STR
```

Byte 0	Byte 1	Byte 2
0 0 0 0 1 1 1 1	0 0 0 0 0 0 0 0	mod:0 0 1: r/m

Function

```
OPERAND  ←  TR;        (16-bit selector)
```

Description

STR is a PROTECTED mode instruction. STR stores a selector from the TR (Task Register).

STR is typically an operating system instruction. However, it can be executed at any privilege level (the 80286 considers only *loading* to be a privileged operation).

Example

```
    STR   TSS_COPY      ;stores the task segment selector
```

Timing

```
Store to Register:  2 clock cycles; 0.1µsec @ 20MHz.
Store to Memory:    2 clock cycles; 0.1µsec @ 20MHz.
```

STR   Store Task Register   **STR**

Flags

None are affected.

REAL-mode Exceptions:

Interrupt 6. STR is not a legal instruction in REAL mode.

PROTECTED-mode Exceptions:

Same as ADD instruction. See page 251.

VIRTUAL 8086-mode Exceptions:

Invalid Opcode exception (exception 6). STR is not a legal instruction in VIRTUAL 8086 mode.

SUB   Integer Subtraction   **SUB**

Format

SUB

	Byte 0	Byte 1	Subsequent Byte(s)
Register from Register	0 0 1 0 1 0 d w	mod: reg : r/m	
Register from Memory	0 0 1 0 1 0 0 w	mod: reg : r/m	
Memory from Register	0 0 1 0 1 0 1 w	mod: reg : r/m	
Immediate from Register/Memory	1 0 0 0 0 0 s w	mod:1 0 1: r/m	Immediate Data Byte(s)
Immediate from AL¦AX¦EAX Register (short encoding)	0 0 1 0 1 1 0 w	Immediate Data Byte(s)	

Function

```
DESTINATION  ←──  DESTINATION - SOURCE;

    or

DESTINATION  ←──  DESTINATION - IMMEDIATE DATA;
```

Description

Subtract the operands. One operand also serves as the destination for the resulting difference.

Example

```
    SUB   ECX, EDX
```

If CF = 1, ECX = 00000034h, and EDX = 00000052h, then as a result of the SUB instruction above, ECX is assigned FFFFFFADh, and CF is assigned 1.

SUB   Integer Subtraction   **SUB**

Timing

```
Register to Register:  2 clock cycles; 0.1μsec @ 20MHz.
Register to Memory:    7 clock cycles; 0.35μsec @ 20MHz.
Memory to Register:    6 clock cycles; 0.3μsec @ 20MHz.
Immediate to Register: 2 clock cycles; 0.1μsec @ 20MHz.
Immediate to Memory:   7 clock cycles; 0.35μsec @ 20MHz.
```

Flags

OF, CF, SF, ZF, AF, and PF affected as described in Appendix A. Other flags are unchanged.

REAL-mode Exceptions:

Same as for ADD instruction. See page 251.

PROTECTED-mode Exceptions:

Same as for ADD instruction. See page 251.

VIRTUAL 8086-mode Exceptions:

Same as for ADD instruction. See page 251.

TEST   Test Operand (AND function to EFLAG, no result)   **TEST**

Format

TEST

	Byte 0	Byte 1	Subsequent Byte(s)

Register/Memory and
Register

```
1 0 0 0 0 1 0 w | mod: reg : r/m
```

Immediate Data and
Register/Memory

```
1 1 1 1 0 1 1 w | mod:0 0 0: r/m    Immediate Data Byte(s)
```

Immediate Data and
AL|AX|EAX (short
encoding)

```
1 0 1 0 1 0 0 w | Immediate Data Byte(s)
```

Function

DESTINATION ∧ SOURCE;   (Affects EFLAG only)

    or

DESTINATION ∧ IMMEDIATE DATA; (Affects EFLAG only)

Description

Performs a bit-wise logical AND of both operands. The result is not actually stored. Only EFLAG is affected.

Example

        TEST   EBX, EDI

If EBX = 00AD9034h, and EDI = 0B800052h, then as a result of the TEST instruction above, the flags are modified as follows: SF = 0, ZF = 0, and PF = 0.

Timing

```
Register to Register:  2 clock cycles; 0.1μsec @ 20MHz.
Register to Memory:    7 clock cycles; 0.35μsec @ 20MHz.
Memory to Register:    6 clock cycles; 0.3μsec @ 20MHz.
Immediate to Register: 2 clock cycles; 0.1μsec @ 20MHz.
Immediate to Memory:   7 clock cycles; 0.35μsec @ 20MHz.
```

TEST   Test Operand (AND function to EFLAG, no result)   **TEST**

Flags

OF = 0; CF = 0. SF, ZF, and PF affected as described in Appendix A. Other flags are unchanged.

REAL-mode Exceptions:

Same as for ADD instruction. See page 251.

PROTECTED-mode Exceptions:

Same as for ADD instruction. See page 251.

VIRTUAL 8086-mode Exceptions:

Same as for ADD instruction. See page 251.

VERR/VERW   Verify a Segment for Reading/Writing   **VERR/VERW**

Format

VERR

Byte 0	Byte 1	Byte 2
0 0 0 0 1 1 1 1	0 0 0 0 0 0 0 0	mod:1 0 0: r/m

VERW

0 0 0 0 1 1 1 1	0 0 0 0 0 0 0 0	mod:1 0 1: r/m

Function

VERR:

```
IF SEGMENT WITH SELECTOR r/m IS ACCESSIBLE AND VALID FOR READING
   THEN ZF  ←— 1;
ELSE
   ZF  ←— 0;
```

VERW:

```
IF SEGMENT WITH SELECTOR r/m IS ACCESSIBLE AND VALID FOR WRITING
   THEN ZF  ←— 1;
ELSE
   ZF  ←— 0;
```

Description

VERR and VERW are PROTECTED mode instructions. Both instructions test the segment with selector given by the operand for accessibility from the current privilege level (weakened by the selector's RPL).

For the VERR instruction, if the descriptor type is accessible at CPL (weakened by the selector's RPL), and the segment is readable, ZF is set; otherwise ZF is reset.

For the VERW instruction, if the descriptor type is accessible at CPL (weakened by the selector's RPL), and the segment is writable, ZF is set; otherwise ZF is reset.

Only data segment descriptors are valid for these instructions. Special segments (GDT, LDT, TSS, and IDT) and gates are not valid types for this instruction since programs cannot read and write such objects directly (for the operating system to create or update these objects, it must create an alias data segment at the memory addresses where these objects exist).

VERR/VERW   Verify a Segment for Reading/Writing   **VERR/VERW**

Example

```
VERR    SEGMENT_X    ;check if segment whose selector
                     ; is variable SEGMENT_X is accessible
                     ; and readable.
```

Timing

```
verr selector in register:    10 clock cycles; 0.5µsec @ 20MHz.
verr selector in memory:      11 clock cycles; 0.55µsec @ 20MHz.
verw selector in register:    15 clock cycles; 0.75µsec @ 20MHz.
verw selector in memory:      16 clock cycles; 0.8µsec @ 20MHz.
```

Flags

ZF as described in *Function* above. Other flags are unchanged.

REAL-mode Exceptions:

Interrupt 6. LSL, a PROTECTED mode instruction, is not recognized in REAL mode.

PROTECTED-mode Exceptions:

Same as for ADD instruction. See page 251.

VIRTUAL 8086-mode Exceptions:

Same as REAL mode exception, but handled in PROTECTED mode at privilege-level 0. The format of the privilege-level-0 stack after an exception is shown in Figure 12.2. Also Page Fault exception (exception 14) with error code of fault code, and page-fault linear address in register CR2.

WAIT   Wait until BUSY Pin is Inactive   **WAIT**

Format

```
WAIT
```

Function

```
WHILE (BUSY PIN = HIGH) KEEP WAITING;
```

Description

This instruction tests the BUSY# pin (active low), which typically is connected to the 80387 or 80287 numeric coprocessor. Use of this instruction forces the 80386 to wait at the current point of its program until the coprocessor is finished processing its instruction.

This instruction is *not* needed when giving the coprocessor another instruction. It is needed only when the 80386 is going to read an operand the coprocessor is writing to memory. The 80386 WAIT instruction allows the 83086 program to be sure the 80387 has completely written all bytes of the operand to memory before the 80386 program proceeds to read the memory operand.

Example

```
        WAIT    ;provide data synchronization with
                ; the 80387 or 80287 numeric coprocessor.
```

Timing

```
6 clock cycles minimum; 0.3μsec minimum @ 20MHz.
```

The instruction is interruptable every cycle (every 6 clocks), so that interrupt latency is not affected. If this instruction is interrupted, the instruction pointer pushed onto stack points at the WAIT instruction so it will be resumed (to continue waiting) after the interrupt service.

WAIT   Wait until BUSY Pin is Inactive   **WAIT**

Flags

None are affected.

REAL-mode Exceptions:

Interrupt 16 if the ERROR# pin is asserted or becomes asserted, since that indicates the numeric coprocessor has detected an unmasked numeric error. Interrupt 7 if the TS bit in CR0 is set, indicating that the coprocessor context belongs to another task (TS is not likely to be set in REAL mode, since hardware task switches can't occur in REAL mode).

PROTECTED-mode Exceptions:

Interrupt 16 if the ERROR# pin is asserted or becomes asserted, since that indicates the numeric coprocessor has detected an unmasked numeric error. Interrupt 7 if the TS bit in CR0 is set, indicating that the coprocessor context belongs to another task (TS is not likely to be set in REAL mode, since hardware task switches can't occur in REAL mode).

VIRTUAL 8086-mode Exceptions:

Same as REAL mode exception, but handled in PROTECTED mode at privilege-level 0. The format of the privilege-level-0 stack after an exception is shown in Figure 12.2. Also Page Fault exception (exception 14) with error code of fault code, and page-fault linear address in register CR2.

XCHG   Exchange Register/Memory with Register   **XCHG**

Format

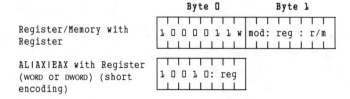

Function

```
TEMP      DESTINATION;
DESTINATION      SOURCE;
SOURCE      TEMP;
```

Description

Exchange operands with each other. One operand must be in a general register, and the other may be either in a general register or in memory. No flags are affected by this operation.

Example

```
    XCHG   ECX, EDX
```

If ECX = 39A5F034h, and EDX = B218CD52h, then as a result of the XCHG instruction above, ECX is assigned B218CD52h and EDX is assigned 39A5F034h.

Timing

```
Register with Register:  3 clock cycles; 0.15µsec @ 20MHz.
Register with Memory:    5 clock cycles; 0.25µsec @ 20MHz.
```

XCHG Exchange Register/Memory with Register **XCHG**

Flags

None are affected.

REAL-mode Exceptions:

Same as for ADD instruction. See page 251.

PROTECTED-mode Exceptions:

Same as for ADD instruction. See page 251.

VIRTUAL 8086-mode Exceptions:

Same as for ADD instruction. See page 251.

XLATB   Table Look-up Translation   **XLATB**

Format

```
XLATB
```

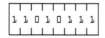

Function

```
IF (ADDRESS SIZE = 16) THEN
  AL  ⟵  (BX + ZEROEXTEND(AL));
ELSE
  AL  ⟵  (EBX + ZEROEXTEND(AL));
```

Description

Translate the byte in the AL register using the AL value to index into a translation table. Register EBX locates the base of the translation table, an array of 256 bytes, the translated values.

Example

```
XLAT
```

If AL = 34h, and the memory location [EBX + 34h] = CDh, then as a result of the XLAT instruction above, AL is assigned CDh.

XLATB   Table Look-up Translation   **XLATB**

Timing

5 clock cycles; 0.25μsec @ 20MHz.

Flags

None are affected.

REAL-mode Exceptions:

Same as for ADD instruction. See page 251.

PROTECTED-mode Exceptions:

Same as for ADD instruction. See page 251.

VIRTUAL 8086-mode Exceptions:

Same as for ADD instruction. See page 251.

XOR   Logical Exclusive OR   **XOR**

Format

XOR

	Byte 0	Byte 1	Subsequent Byte(s)

Register to Register   `0 0 1 1 0 0 d w` `mod: reg : r/m`

Register to Memory   `0 0 1 1 0 0 0 w` `mod: reg : r/m`

Memory to Register   `0 0 1 1 0 0 1 w` `mod: reg : r/m`

Immediate to
Register/Memory   `1 0 0 0 0 0 s w` `mod:1 1 0: r/m`   Immediate Data Byte(s)

Immediate to AL|AX|EAX
Register (short   `0 0 1 1 0 1 0 w` Immediate Data Byte(s)
encoding)

Function

```
DESTINATION ←— DESTINATION ⊕ SOURCE;

   or

DESTINATION ←— DESTINATION ⊕ IMMEDIATE DATA;
```

Description

Performs a bit-wise logical XOR of both operands. One operand also serves as the destination for the result.

Example

```
    XOR   EBX, EDI
```

If EBX = 00AD9034h, and EDI = 0B800052h, then as a result of the XOR instruction above, EBX is assigned 0B2D9066h.

Timing

```
Register to Register:  2 clock cycles; 0.1μsec @ 20MHz.
Register to Memory:    7 clock cycles; 0.35μsec @ 20MHz.
Memory to Register:    6 clock cycles; 0.3μsec @ 20MHz.
Immediate to Register: 2 clock cycles; 0.1μsec @ 20MHz.
Immediate to Memory:   7 clock cycles; 0.35μsec @ 20MHz.
```

XOR Logical Exclusive OR **XOR**

Flags

OF = 0; CF = 0. SF, ZF, and PF affected as described in Appendix A. Other flags are unchanged.

REAL-mode Exceptions:

Same as for ADD instruction. See page 251.

PROTECTED-mode Exceptions:

Same as for ADD instruction. See page 251.

VIRTUAL 8086-mode Exceptions:

Same as for ADD instruction. See page 251.

INSTRUCTION PREFIX DETAILS

Address Size   Prefix — 16/32 bit Address Size Toggle   **Address Size**

1b/32 bit Address Size Toggle 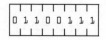 `0 1 1 0 0 1 1 1`

Description

·The presence of this prefix toggles the address size attribute from 16 bits to 32 bits, or vice versa. "Address size" indicates the size of the effective address, the offset from the base of the segment. If the address size is 32 bits, effective addresses are calculated as 32-bit values (0 to 4Gbyte). If the address size is 16 bits, effective addresses are calculated as 16-bit values (0 to 64Kbytes).

When this prefix is not present before an instruction, the address size is the default value for the code segment being executed.

For certain instructions, such as HLT or NOP, this prefix makes no effect.

Type of Code Segment Being Executed	Default Address Size
REAL-mode code segment	16 bits
VIRTUAL 8086-mode code segment	16 bits
PROTECTED mode-code segment whose code segment descriptor has D (default bit) = 0. (80286 compatible)	16 bits
PROTECTED mode-code segment whose code segment descriptor has D (default bit) = 1.	32 bits

Operand Size   Prefix — 16/32 bit Operand Size Toggle   **Operand Size**

16/32 bit Operand Size Toggle

Description

The presence of this prefix toggles the operand size attribute from 16 bits to 32 bits, or vice versa. "Operand size" indicates the size of the operand size if it is *not* byte. The operand size is therefore WORD or DWORD.

When this prefix is not present before an instruction, the operand size is the default value for the code segment being executed.

For certain instructions, such as HLT or NOP, this prefix makes no effect.

Type of Code Segment Being Executed	Default nonbyte Operand Size
REAL-mode code segment	WORD (16 bits)
VIRTUAL 8086-mode code segment	WORD (16 bits)
PROTECTED-mode code segment whose code segment descriptor has D (default bit) = 0. (80286 compatible)	WORD (16 bits)
PROTECTED-mode code segment whose code segment descriptor has D (default bit) = 1.	DWORD (32 bits)

DS/ES/FS/GS/SS   Prefix – Override Default Segment Choice   **DS/ES/FS/GS/SS**

CS:

```
0 0 1 0 1 1 1 0
```

DS:

```
0 0 1 1 1 1 1 0
```

ES:

```
0 0 1 0 0 1 1 0
```

FS:

```
0 1 1 0 0 1 0 0
```

GS:

```
0 1 1 0 0 1 0 1
```

SS:

```
0 0 1 1 0 1 1 0
```

Description

The presence of any one of these prefixes causes a memory operand of the instruction to be taken from the named segment (CS, DS, ES, FS, GS, and SS) instead of the default segment. The default segments used for particular types of memory reference are listed on the following page.

If, for some reason, multiple prefixes of this type precede a single instruction, then the last such prefix has effect. If these prefixes precede instructions that don't make memory references (such as GMC) or don't respond to segment override prefixes (such as PUSH), then the prefix simply has no effect.

DS/ES/FS/GS/SS   Prefix − Override Default Segment Choice   **DS/ES/FS/GS/SS**

TYPE OF OPERAND	DEFAULT SEGMENT USAGE	SEGMENT OVERRIDE PREFIXES POSSIBLE
Code Fetch	CS	None
Destination of PUSH, PUSHA, and PUSHF instructions	SS	None
Source of POP, POPA, and POPF instructions	SS	None
Other memory references, with effective address using base address of:		
[EAX]	DS	CS,SS,ES,FS,GS
[EBX]	DS	CS,SS,ES,FS,GS
[ECX]	DS	CS,SS,ES,FS,GS
[EDX]	DS	CS,SS,ES,FS,GS
[ESI]	DS	CS,SS,ES,FS,GS
[EDI]*	DS	CS,SS,ES,FS,GS
[EBP]	SS	CS,DS,ES,FS,GS
[ESP]	SS	CS,DS,ES,FS,GS

* Data references for the memory destination of the STOS, MOVS, CMPS, REP STOS, REP MOVS, and REP CMPS use EDI as the base register as ES as the segment, with no override possible.

REP   Prefix — Repeat   **REP**

REP

```
 1  1  1  1  0  0  1  0
```

Description

When this prefix precedes the STOS, LODS, MOVS, INS, or OUTS instructions, the instruction repeats until the count in register ECX expires. If this prefix precedes other instructions, it simply has no effect.

REPE   Prefix — Repeat if Equal   **REPE**

REPE

1	1	1	1	0	0	1	1

Description

When this prefix precedes the CMPS or SCAS instructions, the instruction repeats until ZF is not equal to 1, or until the count in register ECX expires. If this prefix precedes other instructions, it simply has no effect.

REPNE   Prefix — Repeat if Not Equal   **REPNE**

REPNE

```
| 1 | 1 | 1 | 1 | 0 | 0 | 1 | 0 |
```

Description

When this prefix precedes the CMPS or SCAS instructions, the instruction repeats until ZF is equal to 1, or until the count in register ECX expires. If this prefix precedes other instructions, it simply has no effect.

LOCK   Prefix — Assert Bus Lock Signal   **LOCK**

LOCK

Description

When this prefix precedes certain instructions, listed below, the 80386 will assert the bus LOCK# signal during all bus cycles used to transfer the instruction's memory operands. If this prefix precedes instructions other than those listed below, an Invalid Opcode exception (exception 6) is generated.

The LOCKable instruction forms are:

```
XCHG genreg, <mem EA>    ;Exchange register with memory.
XCHG <mem EA>, genreg    ;Exchange memory with register.
                         ;The 80286 and 80386 automatically
                         ;activate the LOCK# signal during the
                         ;memory read and memory write cycles
                         ;required for the XCHG instruction.
ADD <mem EA>, genreg     ;Add to memory operand.
ADC <mem EA>, genreg     ;Add using Carry flag.
SUB <mem EA>, genreg     ;Subtract from memory operand.
SBB <mem EA>, genreg     ;Subtract using Carry flag (borrow).
NEG <mem EA>             ;Negate memory operand.
OR  <mem EA>, genreg     ;OR to memory operand.
AND <mem EA>, genreg     ;AND to memory operand.
XOR <mem EA>, genreg     ;XOR to memory operand.
NOT <mem EA>             ;NOT memory operand.
BTC <mem EA>             ;Complement memory bit.
BTR <mem EA>             ;Reset memory bit operand.
BTS <mem EA>             ;Set memory bit operand.
```

APPENDIX C

80386 PAGING-MECHANISM PERFORMANCE

When 80386 paging is enabled, the processor automatically references the memory-resident paging tables, to obtain the required address translation data not stored in the on-chip TLB. The processor steps taken to access the paging tables are interesting. First, the 80386 accesses the page directory. Secondly, the 80386 accesses one of the page tables. These provide all the needed information about the page protection attributes and physical address. Based on this information, the 80386 determines whether the memory access is permissible, and, if so, it performs the desired access.

For example, in the typical reference to the paging tables, accessing the page directory and the page table adds five clock cycles to the time needed to complete the desired memory access. This is shown in Case II in Figure C.1 and Figure C.2.

Other cases arise when the page-directory entry, the page-table entry, or both are not already marked *accessed* or *dirty* but, as a result of the latest 80386 access, must be so marked. These cases create some additional delay in the desired memory access. Fortunately, such cases occur infrequently, since a given table entry needs marking only once during the entire time its associated page remains present in memory.

When the processor must modify the *accessed* or *dirty* bit, it does so by performing a LOCKed read and LOCKed write. The first read of each table is actually an unlocked read, on the presumption that most of the time, the *accessed* or *dirty* bits are already set from a previous table access.

Clock Cycle	Case I — On-chip Translation (No Page Table Reading)	Case II — Paging Table Read (no Table Update Required)	Case III — Paging Table Read (page-Directory Update Required)	Case IV — Paging Table Read (page-Table Update Required)	Case V — Paging Table Read (page-Directory and Page-Table Required)
1	Intended Cycle	Page Directory Read	Page Directory Read	Page Directory Read	Page Directory Read
2					
3					
4		Page Table Read	LOCKed Page Directory Read	Page Table Read	LOCKed Page Directory Read
5					
6		Intended Cycle			
7				LOCKed Page Table Read	
8			LOCKed Page Directory Write		LOCKed Page Directory Write
9					
10					
11			Page Table Read	LOCKed Page Table Write	Page Table Read
12					
13			Intended Cycle	Intended Cycle	
14					LOCKed Page Table Read
15					
16					
17					
18					LOCKed Page Table Write
19					
20					Intended Cycle
21					

Figure C.1 80386 Bus Cycles When Accessing Page Tables (0 Wait-state Memory).

Clock Cycle	Case I	Case II	Case III	Case IV	Case V
	On-Chip Translation (No Page Table Reading)	Paging Table Read (No Table Update Required)	Paging Table Read (Page-Directory Update Required)	Paging Table Read (Page-Table Update Required)	Paging Table Read (Page-Directory and Page-Table Update Required)
1					
2	Intended Cycle	Page Directory Read	Page Directory Read	Page Directory Read	Page Directory Read
3					
4					
5					
6		Page Table Read	LOCKed Page Directory Read	Page Table Read	LOCKed Page Directory Read
7					
8					
9		Intended Cycle			
10				LOCKed Page Table Read	
11			LOCKed Page Directory Write		LOCKed Page Directory Write
12					
13					
14					
15			Page Table Read	LOCKed Page Table Write	Page Table Read
16					
17					
18			Intended Cycle	Intended Cycle	
19					LOCKed Page Table Read
20					
21					
22					
23					
24					LOCKed Page Table Write
25					
26					
27					Intended Cycle
28					

Figure C.2   80386 Bus Cycles When Accessing Page Tables (1 Wait-state Memory).

APPENDIX D

INITIALIZATION CODE FOR 32-BIT
PROTECTED-MODE SYSTEM
WITH ONE PRIVILEGE LEVEL

The 80386 begins operation in the 8086-compatible REAL mode and requires a small program to enter PROTECTED mode. This appendix provides an example for the simplest of 32-bit PROTECTED-mode systems, one having a single privilege level.[1]

This initialization code of Figure D.1 provides a single, 4-gigabyte address space, typical of 32-bit systems. As it stands, the system does not take advantage of segmentation or paging. However, since the supervisor and user-code segment descriptors have the default bit D set equal to 1, 32-bit operand size and 32-bit address size are the default; 32-bit data operations and addressing are available.

In this single-level system, all code executes at a CPL of 0, the highest level (supervisor level), for availability of all sensitive operations, such as input/output, enabling/disabling interrupts, and executing certain instructions, such as HALT.

The necessary data structures include an image of the GDT, as shown in Figure D.2, with the null descriptor and two segment descriptors mentioned, one for code and one for data. For convenience, the selector values for the GDT descriptors are listed:

GDT Entry	Selector Value	Item
0	0000h	null descriptor
1	0008h	supervisor code segment
2	0010h	supervisor data segment

The final necessary data structure is the image of the IDT, as shown in Figure D.2. Each entry of the IDT is a gate, not a selector, and is referred to by its position number in the IDT. For example, an INT n instruction will vector through gate n in the IDT.

---

[1]Chapter 11 and Appendix E show initialization code for a 32-bit 2-level PROTECTED system.

```
ASSUME      CS:INITIAL, DS:TABLEDATA

INITIAL     SEGMENT  PUBLIC AT 0F000h
            ORG      FFF0h
            ASSUME   CS: INITIAL, DS: NOTHING, ES: NOTHING
;
; Begin from a reset condition.  Interrupts are disabled
; after reset.
;

RES_ADR:  JMP      BODY              ;Intrasegment jump to body
                                     ; of initialization routine.

          ORG      0D000h

BODY:     LGDT     GDT_PTR           ;Load GDT register
                                     ; to locate GDT in
                                     ; linear address space.
                                     ; Here, GDT is based at linear
                                     ; address FFFFC000h, and holds 3
                                     ; entries (24 bytes), limit=0017h.
          LIDT     IDT_PTR           ; Load IDT register
                                     ; to locate IDT in
                                     ; linear address space.
                                     ; Here, IDT is based at linear
                                     ; address FFFFC018h, and holds 256
                                     ; entries (2048 entries) the maximum
                                     ; size for the IDT, limit=07FFh.

          MOV EAX, CR0               ;Prepare to alter CR0.
          OR  EAX, 00000001h         ;Set bit 0 (PE) in CR0 image.
          MOV CR0, EAX               ;Enable PROTECTED mode.
;
;   Already in PROTECTED mode !
;
; Now establish the large, 4 gigabyte data segments.
;
          MOV AX,  0010h             ;0010h is selector for
                                     ; supervisor data segment.
          MOV SS,  AX                ;Load segment selector in SS.
          MOV DS,  AX                ;Load segment selector in DS.
          MOV ES,  AX                ;Load segment selector in ES.
          MOV FS,  AX                ;Load segment selector in FS.
          MOV GS,  AX                ;Load segment selector in GS.

;
;  Now establish the large, 4 gigabyte code segment.
;
          JMP DEST_OFFSET, DEST_SEL  ;Intersegment jump to load CS.
DEST:     MOV ESP, 00400000h         ;Initialize ESP, typically to
                                     ; the top of physical memory.
                                     ; In this case, assuming 4 Mbyte
                                     ; physical memory, ESP is set to
                                     ; 0040000h (4,194,304 decimal).
                                     ; The stack grows downward.
```

Figure D.1   32-bit PROTECTED-mode Supervisor Initialization Code (*Continued*).

```
;
;  80386 32-bit supervisor/user initialization is complete
;

YOUR_SUPERVISOR:    ...              ;your supervisor code begins here.
                    ...
                    ...


;
;  When the interrupt service routines are established, interrupts can
;  be enabled. (Use STI instruction, for example.)
;

INITIAL    ENDS
```

Figure D.1   (*Continued***).**

```
INITIAL    SEGMENT  PUBLIC AT 0F000h
;
;  Pointers defining the base address and size of the GDT and the IDT.
;  These are used as operands of the LGDT and LIDT instructions,
;  respectively.
;

            ORG      0BFF0h

GDT_PTR:    DW       0017h               ;limit for 3 descriptor slots
            DW       C000h               ;base at FFFFC000h (bits 15:0)
            DW       FFFFh               ;base at FFFFC000H (bits 31:16)

IDT_PTR:    DW       07FFh               ;limit for up to 256 gates
            DW       C018h               ;base at FFFFC018h (bits 15:0)
            DW       FFFFh               ;base at FFFFC018h (bits 31:16)

            ORG      0C000h

GDT:                                     ;Beginning of the GDT table.
GDT_0:                                   ;Descriptor 0: Null descriptor.
                                         ;Not used.
            DD       00000000h           ;The null descriptor always in GDT
            DD       00000000h           ; slot 0, requires 8 bytes of 00h.

GDT_1:                                   ;Descriptor 1: 32-bit Supervi-
                                         ; sor Code Segment (starts at 0
                                         ; and extends for 4 gigabytes)
            DW       FFFFh               ; limit 15..0 (limit is
                                         ; FFFFF(FFF)hex).
            DW       0000h               ; base 15..0   (base is
                                         ; 00000000h).
            DB       FFh                 ; base 23..16.
            DB       10011011b           ; access byte: 32-bit code segment,
                                         ; present, DPL=0, not conforming,
                                         ; readable, accessed.
            DB       10001111b           ; granularity: page,  limit 31..28.
            DB       FFh                 ; base 31..24.
```

Figure D.2   GDT and IDT Images for 32-bit Simple Protected System (*Continued***).**

```
GDT_2:                              ;Descriptor 2: 32-bit Supervi-
                                    ; sor Data Segment (starts at 0
                                    ; and extends for 4 gigabytes)
          DW      FFFFh             ; limit 15..0  (limit is
                                    ; FFFFF(FFF)hex).
          DW      0000h             ; base 15..0   (base is 00000000h).
          DB      FFh               ; base 23..16.
          DB      10010011b         ; access byte: 32-bit data segment,
                                    ; present, DPL=0, expand up,
                                    ; writeable, accessed.
          DB      10001111b         ; granularity: page,  limit 31..28.
          DB      FFh               ; base 31..24.

GDT_END:                            ;End of GDT table.

IDT:                                ;Beginning of the IDT table.
IDT_0:                              ;Gate 0: Trap Gate for Exception 0
          DW      XXXXh             ; offset 15..0 (points to en-
                                    ; try point of service routing).
          DW      0010h             ; selector 15..0 (refers to
                                    ; supervisor code segment).
          DB      00h               ; upper bits 000b, remainder unused.
          DB      11101111h         ; access byte: trap gate, present,
                                    ; DPL=3 (so user code can vector
                                    ; through the trap gate).
          DW      XXXXh             ; offset 31..16.

;

IDT Trap Gates 1 through 31 are the same as Trap Gate above, except
;  each gate may point to a unique entry point in the supervisor code
;  segment.
;
IDT_32:                             ;Gate 32: Interrupt Gate for
                                    ; Interrupt 32
          DW      XXXXh             ; offset 15..0 (points to en-
                                    ; try point of service routine).
          DW      0010h             ; selector 15..0 (refers to
                                    ; supervisor code segment).
          DB      00h               ; upper bits 000b, remainder unused.
          DB      11100101h         ; access byte: interrupt gate,
                                    ; present,
                                    ; DPL=3 (so user code can vector
                                    ; through the interrupt gate).
          DW      XXXXh             ; offset 31..16.

IDT_33:                             ;Gate 33: Interrupt Gate for
                                    ; Interrupt 33
          DW      XXXXh             ; offset 15..0 (points to entry pt).
          DW      0010h             ; selector 15..0 (refers to
                                    ; supervisor code segment).
          DB      00h               ; upper bits 000b, remainder unused.
          DB      11100101h         ; access byte: interrupt gate,
                                    ; present, DPL=3 (so user code can
                                    ; vector through the interrupt gate).
          DW      XXXXh             ; offset 31..16.
```

Figure D.2 *(Continued).*

```
;
;  IDT Interrupt Gates 34 through 255 are the same as Interrupt Gates
;  above, except each gate may point to a unique entry point in the
;  supervisor code segment.
;
IDT_END:                                ;End of the IDT Table.

INITIAL    ENDS
```

Figure D.2   (*Continued*).

Chapter 11 presents the code and data needed to establish a 32-bit PROTECTED-mode system with two privilege levels.

APPENDIX E

INITIALIZATION CODE FOR 32-BIT PROTECTED-MODE SYSTEM WITH TWO PRIVILEGE LEVELS

The 80386 begins operation in the 8086-compatible REAL mode and requires a small program to enter PROTECTED mode. Chapter 11 presents all code and data needed to establish a 32-bit PROTECTED-mode system with two privilege levels.

Nevertheless, this appendix builds upon the example of Chapter 11, to present an alternate and more powerful method for the supervisor to dispatch user programs within a two-level system. Chapter 11 explains that a two-level system requires a Task State Segment (TSS) in memory. The TSS stores the initial SS:ESP for the supervisor-level stack and is automatically referred to whenever the 80386 enters the supervisor level from the user level.

As this example shows, additional features of the TSS can be utilized. In particular, the TSS is extremely useful when the supervisor wishes to dispatch a user program. The TSS provides a simple, elegant method of dispatching the user program at its entry point, with all other registers at a known state.

The TSS method of dispatching the user program eliminates the need to create a stack frame for the RET instruction that actually performs the dispatch (See Chapter 11). The TSS method is more elegant and more powerful.

When utilizing the TSS dispatch method, the operating system loads the initial user state of all registers into the 32-bit TSS. Given the defined 32-bit TSS format, the operating system loads the CS and EIP images with the user-program entry point, loads the SS and ESP images with the initial-user stack pointer, and loads any other register images with desired initial values. Then, with a single JMP instruction that performs a task switch, the user program is dispatched. The jump instruction must be an intersegment JMP (opcode EAh), with the TSS selector as an operand. The full-offset operand required by such a JMP instruction is actually not used when a task switch is performed: The TSS defines the entry point.

In this example, where the TSS selector is 0008h, the JMP instruction object code bytes are as follows:

$$\underbrace{\text{EAh}}_{\text{opcode}} \quad \underbrace{\text{08h} \quad \text{00h}}_{\text{selector}} \quad \underbrace{\overbrace{\text{11h} \quad \text{11h} \quad \text{11h} \quad \text{11h.}}}_{\text{offset (value is } \textit{don't care}\text{)}}$$

When used in this way, the JMP instruction dispatches the user program, with known initial data in the other 80386 registers.

When using the TSS dispatch method, the GDT and TSS should be in RAM, so they can be modified. In the GDT, the TSS descriptor should be marked *not busy* (See Chapters 14 and 15) as required, prior to any JMP instruction that references the TSS. Also prior to the JMP instruction, the TSS image should be written with the appropriate register information for the dispatch.

Figure E.1 lists an assembly-language declaration of the TSS data structure, along with comments suitable for its use with the TSS dispatch method.

```
TABLEDATA  SEGMENT

TSS:                              ;Beginning of the Task State Segment.
                                  ;This TSS is designed for the 32-bit
                                  ; simple protected system.  Most of its
                                  ; fields are zero since the simple
                                  ; system does not perform hardware
                                  ; multitasking, the operation which
                                  ; fully utilizes the TSS.
           DD      00000000h      ; back link selector
           DD      00400000h      ; ESP for level 0 (same as ESP initial-
                                  ; ization used in code (Figure D.1).
           DW      0000h          ; unused.
           DW      0018h          ; selector for supervisor data segment
                                  ; that is used for supervisor stack seg.
           DD      00000000h      ; SS for level 1 (unused for this
                                  ; since privilege level 1 is unused.).
           DD      00000000h      ; ESP for level 1 (unused for this
                                  ; since privilege level 1 is unused.).
           DD      00000000h      ; SS for level 2 (unused for this
                                  ; since privilege level 2 is unused.).
           DD      00000000h      ; ESP for level 2 (unused for this
                                  ; since privilege level 2 is unused.).
           DD      00000000h      ; CR3 storage (unused for this since
                                  ; paging is not enabled).
           DD      00000000h      ; EIP storage (prior to dispatching,
                                  ; initialize with user program entry
                                  ; point).
           DD      00000000h      ; EFLAGS storage (prior to dispatch-
                                  ; ing, initialize for user program).
           DD      00000000h      ; EAX storage (prior to dispatching,
                                  ; initialize for user program).
           DD      00000000h      ; ECX storage (prior to dispatching,
                                  ; initialize for user program).
           DD      00000000h      ; EDX storage (prior to dispatching,
                                  ; initialize for user program).
```

Figure E.1   TSS Image for 32-bit Simple Protected System (*Continued*).

```
        DD      00000000h   ; EBX storage (prior to dispatching,
                            ; initialize for user program).
        DD      00000000h   ; ESP storage (prior to dispatching,
                            ; initialize for user program).
        DD      00000000h   ; EBP storage (prior to dispatching,
                            ; initialize for user program).
        DD      00000000h   ; ESI storage (prior to dispatching,
                            ; initialize for user program).
        DD      00000000h   ; EDI storage (prior to dispatching,
                            ; initialize for user program).
        DW      0000h       ; unused.
        DW      0000h       ; ES storage (prior to dispatching,
                            ; initialize for user program).
        DW      0000h       ; unused.
        DW      0000h       ; CS storage (prior to dispatching,
                            ; initialize for user program entry
                            ; point).
        DW      0000h       ; unused.
        DW      0000h       ; SS storage (prior to dispatching,
                            ; initialize for user program stack).
        DW      0000h       ; unused.
        DW      0000h       ; DS storage (prior to dispatching,
                            ; initialize for user program).
        DW      0000h       ; unused.
        DW      0000h       ; FS storage (prior to dispatching,
                            ; initialize for user program).
        DW      0000h       ; unused.
        DW      0000h       ; GS storage (prior to dispatching,
                            ; initialize for user program).
        DW      0000h       ; unused.
        DW      0000h       ; LDTR storage (unused for this).
        DW      FFFFh       ; I/O Permission Bitmap pointer
                            ; (unused for this).
        DW      0000h       ; upper 15 bits unused, lowest T bit
                            ; for trapping (unused for this).

TSS_END:                    ;End of the TSS.

TABLEDATA   ENDS
```

Figure E.1 (*Continued*).

APPENDIX F

RETURNING TO REAL MODE
FROM PROTECTED MODE

This appendix describes the procedure necessary to return from operation in PRO-TECTED mode to REAL mode. Even if this procedure is not immediately useful, it provides enlightening insights into the operation of the 80386 descriptor-cache registers and their use in address formation. Keep in mind that the descriptor-cache contents are used, although behind the scenes, for address formation and limit checking even in REAL mode.

There are several functions that the routine needs to perform, namely:

1. It must set up the 80386 internal descriptor-cache registers so that they look like they do in REAL mode (e.g., the 80386 sets them up following a processor reset)
2. Reenter REAL mode
3. Jump to the REAL-mode code to be executed

The first objective requires resetting the segment descriptor-cache registers to look like REAL mode. It is useful to understand why this is necessary. While in REAL mode, the 80386 uses exactly the same memory management functions as in PRO-TECTED mode. However, when the 80386 performs its reset activities, the values internally loaded into the descriptor cache registers make the segment *appear* as if they are 8086/8088 style segments. In REAL mode, when a segment is loaded under program control (e.g., MOV to segment register) only the *base* field of the descriptor cache is changed; in particular, the value placed into the base is *selector × 16*. Since only the base is changed in REAL mode, it is necessary to set the limit and access rights fields while still in PROTECTED mode. This is accomplished by loading a descriptor having the appropriate limit and attributes. The value loaded into each of DS, ES, FS, GS, and SS descriptor-cache registers is

Limit = 0000FFFFh   (64K)
Byte-granular (G = 0)
Expand Up (E = 0)
Writable (W = 1)

Present (P = 1)
Base = Don't Care

The base field is not critical, since it will be set again after reentering REAL mode. The attributes above make segments act exactly as in REAL mode.

Two additional segments must be reset—the Interrupt Descriptor Table (IDT) and the Code Segment (CS). Since the LIDT instruction works in REAL mode, it will be reset there. The CS is a special case: Since it is not possible to make the CS writable while in PROTECTED mode, a special architectural feature reloads REAL mode attributes into the CS descriptor cache during intersegment JMP instructions in REAL mode.

The second objective, reentering REAL mode, is easy to do since the Protection Enable (PE) bit in Control Register 0 (CR0), alias MSW, is not sticky, as it is in the MSW of the 80286. The PE bit of CR0 can be reset to 0. When resetting the PE bit to return to REAL mode, the same rules apply as when switching into PROTECTED mode: The internal-instruction queue must be cleared by performing a jump instruction. The transition becomes more difficult if paging has been enabled. That case will be discussed later.

Finally, once in REAL mode, the Interrupt Descriptor Table Regiser (IDTR) must be loaded with the LIDT instruction, and the CS access rights get set when an intersegment JMP is executed (the same JMP used to access the code to be executed). Also note that, for system integrity, the possibility of interrupts must be removed while changing modes. Normal INTR interrupts can be inhibited by a CLI instruction. Nonmaskable interrupts, however, cannot be disabled. To prevent these, either external circuitry can be used to mask out NMIs or, just before returning to REAL mode, the PROTECTED-mode IDT, which is used during the transition, must contain a REAL-mode interrupt vector for NMI at offset 8 in the IDT.

The following code example performs the functions described above. The fragment assumes that the code is in a 16-bit code segment at privilege level 0 and that the CS-limit is FFFFh (64K). The limit of 64K is necessary to reset the CS-limit value back to the REAL-mode value.

```
START_SEGMENT:
        MOV     AX, REAL_MODE_SEL
        MOV     DS, AX          ;load DS cache with REAL-mode-like
                                ;limit and access rights
        MOV     ES, AX          ;load ES cache with REAL-mode-like
                                ;limit and access rights
        MOV     SS, AX          ;load FS cache with REAL-mode-like
                                ;limit and access rights
        MOV     FS, AX          ;load GS cache with REAL-mode-like
                                ;limit and access rights
        MOV     GS, AX          ;load SS cache with REAL-mode-like
                                ;limit and access rights
        MOV     EAX, CR0
        AND     EAX, 07FFFFFFEh ;turn off paging and REAL mode
```

```
            CLI
            MOV     CR0, EAX            ;put value back into CR0
            JMP     FLUSH_Q_REAL
FLUSH_Q_REAL:                          ;now in REAL mode again
            MOV     AX, IDTLOADSEGMENT
            MOV     DS, AX
            LIDT    IDT_PTR            ;establish interrupt vector table at
                                       ;memory address 0
            STI
                                       ;load up segment base values as
                                       ;needed by target REAL mode code
            MOV     AX, 1000h          ;use 1000h as an example value
            MOV     DS, AX
            MOV     ES, AX
            MOV     SS, AX
            MOV     FS, AX
            MOV     GS, AX             ;all segments now REAL mode
            JMP     FAR_POINTER_REAL_DEST    ;back to target program
```

If paging was enabled in PROTECTED mode at the moment of returning to REAL mode, special care must be taken when reentering REAL mode. (Actually, this also applies any time paging is turned off or on.) Prior to turning off paging, ensure that the code is executing out of an *identity-mapped page* (i.e., make sure that the linear address equals the physical address). This is required so that, when paging is turned off, execution will continue at the same point. After paging is turned off, Control Register 3 (CR3), the page-directory base register, should be reloaded to clear out the paging TLB. The sequence below will turn off paging and clear out the TLB. This code should be executed prior to reentering REAL mode.

```
            MOV     EAX, CR0
            AND     EAX, 7FFFFFFFh     ;reset the Paging (PG) bit
            MOV     CR0, EAX           ;turn off paging
            XOR     EAX, EAX           ;clear EAX to 0
            MOV     CR3, EAX           ; reload CR3 to clear out the TLB
```

APPENDIX G

VIRTUAL 8086 MODE EXAMPLE FOR PC-DOS

This listing is a fully verified example for enabling the PROTECTED mode and for running PC-DOS in VIRTUAL 8086 mode. It illustrates how a programmer can establish VIRTUAL 8086 mode. This code can be assembled using an 8086-style assembler, since the PROTECTED-mode opcodes required in this example have been defined using Define Byte (DB) assembler statements.

The program runs as a command from the DOS prompt. When the command returns with the next DOS prompt, the 80386 is running DOS in VIRTUAL 8086 mode under control of a simple PROTECTED mode supervisor. The program establishes the PROTECTED mode supervisor, which remains resident in memory. IOPL equals 3 so that DOS running in VIRTUAL 8086 mode is freely allowed to perform I/O and enable/disable the Interrupt Enable Flag (IF). Since only one DOS environment is provided by this supervisor, DOS continues to have access to all the machine's memory and peripheral devices.

When an interrupt occurs while in VIRTUAL 8086 mode, this supervisor receives the interrupt but reflects it back to DOS, by constructing an interrupt stack frame on the DOS stack and beginning execution at the first instruction of the DOS service routine for the event. Whenever the supervisor dispatches DOS, it uses the IRET instruction from privilege level 0.

```
;*       *       *       *       *       *       *       *       *********
; NOTE:
;        the gs register is set and kept at the mon_data
;*       *       *       *       *       *       *       *       *********
;        WHEN     WHAT
;        6/22/86 after AT386 1st stage virtual DOS monitor.
;*       *       *       *       *       *       *       *       *********


;4/03/86  4:21 a.m.
;
;ONLY DESIGNED TO BE RUN FROM REAL MODE!  REAL MODE MUST BE
;RE-ESTABLISHED TO RUN AGAIN!  (either that or the program has
;to check for multiple invocations of vm86 so that the
;8086-type cs is loaded correctly each time).
;for SDM-286:
```

```
;using cicos4.a38 routines for protected mode code,
;and modified cicos4.a38 code (in this module) for the vm86
;code.
;verify proper operation and handling of ex. 13 in virtual 86
;mode.  Will force ex.13 by trying to access a word at 0ffffh.
;tests i/o module
;now for console i/o, too!
;getting closer
;Attempt to do a simple task switch into Virtual 86 Mode, write a small
;section of memory (using the DS reg loaded with an 8086-type
;segment base), then task switch back to 386 protected mode.
;next: workaround for pmon bug: "initial task reset to not busy by pmon".
;we will try jumping from a dummy task to our initial task in hopes that
;only the dummy task will be reset by pmon.  However, it is probable that
;the initial task will still be reset to "not busy" if any breakpoints are
;set or any single-stepping is done in the initial task.
;and now, jump to separate task to do console i/o.
;now in separate modules and segments.
;and now in asm386!
;mod: returns to pmon386 via int 1.
;VERSION: now echoes input character.
;Protected mode version of SRPTM.A86, constructed using XENIX utilities.
```

```
= 000D                      CR          EQU     0DH
= 000A                      LF          EQU     0AH
= 00FF                      EOS         EQU     0FFH

= 0021                      DOS         EQU     21h

= 0066                      OP_SIZE     EQU     66h
= 0067                      P_SIZE      EQU     67h

= 0089                      MOV_PBX_AX  EQU     89h              ; mov [bx+i8],ax


                            ; 80386 eflag bits
= 0002                      VMFL        EQU     2h
= 0001                      RFFL        EQU     1h
= 4000                      NTFL        EQU     04000h
= 3000                      IOPLFL      EQU     03000h


                            ;
                            ; 8086 flag bits
= 0800                      OFL         EQU     00800h
= 0400                      DFL         EQU     00400h
= 0200                      IFL         EQU     00200h
= 0100                      TFL         EQU     00100h

= 0080                      SFL         EQU     00080h
= 0040                      ZFL         EQU     00040h
= 0010                      AFL         EQU     00010h
= 0004                      PFL         EQU     00004h
= 0001                      CFL         EQU     00001h
```

```
              ;*     *     *     *     *     *     *     *     *********
                           ;
= 0004                     LDT_BIT        EQU    4

= 0000                     NULL_ALIAS     EQU    00h         ; or 04h for LDT null
= 0008                     GDT_ALIAS      EQU    08h
= 000C                     LDT_ALIAS      EQU    0Ch
= 0010                     IDT_ALIAS      EQU    10h

= 0018                     MON_TSS_SEL    EQU    18h
= 0020                     TMP_TSS_SEL    EQU    20h
= 0028                     MON_LDT_SEL    EQU    28h

= 0030                     FLAT_SEL       EQU    30h

                           ; ldts
= 0014                     MON_CODE_SEL   EQU    14h
= 001C                     MON_DATA_SEL   EQU    1Ch
= 0024                     MON_STACK_SEL  EQU    24h

                           ; VM_CODE_SEL  EQU    1Ch
                           ; VM_DATA_SEL  EQU    24h

                           ; typical
                           ;     access   DB     10010001b   ; access
                                                                 byte
                           ;     gran     DB     11001111b   ; granularity
                                                                 byte
                           ;
                           ; granularity
                           ;     g        limit granularity
                           ;     b        stack type
                           ;     o
                           ;     avl      availible
                           ;     limit    bits 19-16
                           ; access
                           ;     p        present
                           ;     dpl      priviledge level
                           ;     s        code/DATA seg
                           ;     e        executable
                           ;     d        expand down
                           ;     w        writable
                           ;     a        accessed
                           ;
                           ; granularity  access
                           ; GBOALLLL     pPPSEDWA
              ;*     *     *     *     *     *     *     *     *********
                           ; 386 Descriptor template
                           ;         DESCRIPTOR BIT MAPS
                           ; B_15-0<< <<<<<<<< L_15-0<< <<<<<<<<
                           ; B_31-24< GBOAL<<< pP<SEDWA B_23-16<
                           ;
                           DESC           STRUC
0000  0000                     lim_0_15   DW     0           ; limit bits (0..15)
0002  0000                     bas_0_15   DW     0           ; base bits (0..15)
0004  00                       bas_16_23  DB     0           ; base bits (16..23)
0005  00                       access     DB     0           ; access byte
```

```
0006    00                                      gran        DB      0       ; granularity byte
0007    00                                      bas_24_31   DB      0       ; base bits (24..31)
0008                            DESC            ENDS

                                ; 386 GATE template
                                ;
                                GDESC   STRUC
0000    0000                                    off_0_15    DW      0       ; offset (0..15)
0002    0000                                    sel         DW      0       ; selector
0004    00                                      dw_count    DB      0       ; 0-31 (upper 3
                                                                            ; bits 0)
0005    00                                      gaccess     DB      0       ; access byte
0006    0000                                    off_16_31   DW      0       ; offset (16..31)
0008                            GDESC   ENDS

                                TSS_STRUC       STRUC
0000    ????????                                tss_back    DD      ?
0004    ????????????????                        tss_stk0    DQ      ?
000C    ????????????????                        tss_stk1    DQ      ?
0014    ????????????????                        tss_stk2    DQ      ?
001C    ????????                                tss_cr3     DD      ?
0020    ????????                                tss_eip     DD      ?
0024    ????????                                tss_eflag   DD      ?
0028    ????????                                tss_eax     DD      ?
002C    ????????                                tss_ecx     DD      ?
0030    ????????                                tss_edx     DD      ?
0034    ????????                                tss_ebx     DD      ?
0038    ????????                                tss_esp     DD      ?
003C    ????????                                tss_ebp     DD      ?
0040    ????????                                tss_esi     DD      ?
0044    ????????                                tss_edi     DD      ?
0048    ????????                                tss_ES      DD      ?
004C    ????????                                tss_CS      DD      ?
0050    ????????                                tss_SS      DD      ?
0054    ????????                                tss_DS      DD      ?
0058    ????????                                tss_FS      DD      ?
005C    ????????                                tss_GS      DD      ?
0060    ????????                                tss_LDT     DD      ?
0064    ????                                    tss_dtb     DW      ?
0066    ????                                    tss_iobm_off DW     ?
0068       01 [FF]                              tss_iobitmap DB     1       DUP(0FFH)

0069                            TSS_STRUC       ENDS




0000                            AFIRST          SEGMENT PARA
0000                            AFIRST          ENDS
0000                            TDATA           SEGMENT
0000                            TDATA           ENDS
0000                            MON_DATA        SEGMENT
0000                            MON_DATA        ENDS
0000                            MON_STACK       SEGMENT
0000                            MON_STACK       ENDS
0000                            MON_CODE        SEGMENT
0000                            MON_CODE        ENDS
```

```
0000                          VM_DATA        SEGMENT
0000                          VM_DATA        ENDS
0000                          VM_CODE        SEGMENT
0000                          VM_CODE        ENDS
0000                          ZLAST          SEGMENT PARA
0000                          ZLAST          ENDS


0000                          AFIRST  SEGMENT PARA
                              ;
            ;*      *       *        *       *       *       *       *       *********
0000  ????                    first_data     DW      ?

0002                          AFIRST  ENDS


0000                          TDATA   SEGMENT
                              ;
            ;*      *       *        *       *       *       *       *       *********


0000                          GDT_pword      LABEL   BYTE
0000  0038                            DW      end_gdt-gdt
0002  000C R                  b0      DW      gdt
0004  0000                            DW      0


0006                          IDT_pword      LABEL   BYTE
0006  0808                            DW      end_idt-idt
0008  0044 R                  b1      DW      idt
000A  0000                            DW      0


            ;*      *       *        *       *       *       *       *       *********
                              ; null
                              ; gdt alias
                              ; idt alias
                              ; mon tss
                              ; tmp tss
                              ; mon lds
                              ; NOT mon tss alias
                              ;
000C                          gdt     LABEL   BYTE
                                      ; null
000C  00 00 00 00 00 00       DQ      0       ; null
      00 00
                                      ; gdt alias
0014  0038                            DW      end_gdt-gdt     ; limit bits (0..15)
0016  000C R                  b2      DW      gdt     ; bas (0..15)
0018  00                              DB      0       ; bas (16..23)
0019  92                              DB      092h    ; access
001A  00                              DB      0       ; granularity
001B  00                              DB      0       ; bas (24..31)
                                      ; idt alias
001C  0808                            DW      end_idt-idt     ; limit bits (0..15)
001E  0044 R                  b3      DW      idt     ; bas (0..15)
0020  00                              DB      0       ; bas (16..23)
0021  92                              DB      092h    ; access
0022  00                              DB      0       ; granularity
0023  00                              DB      0       ; bas (24..31)
```

```
                                         ; mon tss
0024   00E8                      DW       end_mon_tss-mon_tss    ; limit bits (0..15)
0026   0874 R            b4      DW       mon_tss ; bas (0..15)
0028   00                        DB       0       ; bas (16..23)
0029   89                        DB       089h    ; access
002A   00                        DB       0       ; granularity
002B   00                        DB       0       ; bas (24..31)
                                         ; tmp tss
002C   0069                      DW       end_tmp_tss-tmp_tss    ; limit bits (0..15)
002E   095D R            b5      DW       tmp_tss ; bas (0..15)
0030   00                        DB       0       ; bas (16..23)
0031   89                        DB       089h    ; access
0032   00                        DB       0       ; granularity
0033   00                        DB       0       ; bas (24..31)
                                         ; mon ldt
0034   0028                      DW       end_mon_ldt-mon_ldt    ; limit bits (0..15)
0036   084C R            b6      DW       mon_ldt ; bas (0..15)
0038   00                        DB       0       ; bas (16..23)
0039   82                        DB       082h    ; access
003A   00                        DB       0       ; granularity
003B   00                        DB       0       ; bas (24..31)
                                         ; flat_des    DESC <0FFFFH,0,0,92h,0CFh,0>
003C   FFFF                      DW       0FFFFh  ; limit bits (0..15)
003E   0000                      DW       0       ; bas (0..15)
0040   00                        DB       0       ; bas (16..23)
0041   92                        DB       092h    ; access
0042   CF                        DB       0CFh    ; granularity
0043   00                        DB       0       ; bas (24..31)
                          ;              ; mon tss alias
                          ;      DW       end_mon_tss-mon_tss    ; limit bits (0..15)
                          ;      DW       mon_tss ; bas (0..15)
                          ;      DB       0       ; bas (16..23)
                          ;      DB       089h    ; access
                          ;      DB       0       ; granularity
                          ;      DB       0       ; bas (24..31)
                          ;              ; vm tss
                          ;      DW       end_vm_tss-vm_tss      ; limit bits (0..15)
                          ;      DW       vm_tss  ; bas (0..15)
                          ;      DB       0       ; bas (16..23)
                          ;      DB       089h    ; access
                          ;      DB       0       ; granularity
                          ;      DB       0       ; bas (24..31)
0044                      end_gdt LABEL   BYTE

              ;*      *       *       *       *       *       *       *       *********
                          ; dos +13
                          ;
0044                      idt     LABEL   BYTE
0044   0D [????????????????]      DQ       12+1 DUP(?)

                                         ; ex13          our_ex13_iv    LABEL    BYTE
00AC   0719 R                    DW       ex13_int
00AE   0014                      DW       MON_CODE_SEL    ; sel mon code
00B0   00                        DB       0
00B1   EE                        DB       0EEh             ; - dpl=3 - 386 interrupt
                                                                                  gate
00B2   00                        DB       0
```

```
00B3  00                              DB      0

00B4  F3 [????????????????]          DQ      256-13 DUP(?)

084C                          end_idt LABEL   BYTE

              ;*     *     *      *      *      *      *      *    *********
                              ; null
                              ; alias
                              ; mon_code
                              ; mon_data
                              ; mon_stack
                              ; NOT vm_task_alias
                              ; NOT vm_ldt_alias
                              ;
084C                          mon_ldt LABEL   BYTE
                                      ; null
084C  00 00 00 00 00 00       DQ      0
      00 00
                                      ; mon_ldt alias
0854  0028                            DW      end_mon_ldt-mon_ldt  ; limit bits (0..15)
0856  084C R              b7          DW      mon_ldt ; bas (0..15)
0858  00                              DB      0       ; bas (16..23)
0859  92                              DB      092h    ; access
085A  00                              DB      0       ; granularity
085B  00                              DB      0       ; bas (24..31)
                                      ; mon code
085C  086C R                          DW      end_mon_code    ; limit bits (0..15)
085E  0000               bmc0         DW      0       ; bas (0..15)
0860  00                              DB      0       ; bas (16..23)
0861  9A                              DB      09Ah    ; access
0862  00                              DB      0       ; granularity
0863  00                              DB      0       ; bas (24..31)
                                      ; mon data
0864  0000 R                          DW      end_mon_data    ; limit bits (0..15)
0866  0000               bmd1         DW      0       ; bas (0..15)
0868  00                              DB      0       ; bas (16..23)
0869  92                              DB      092h    ; access
086A  00                              DB      0       ; granularity
086B  00                              DB      0       ; bas (24..31)
                                      ; mon stack
086C  0424 R                          DW      end_mon_stack   ; limit bits (0..15)
086E  0000               bms2         DW      0       ; bas (0..15)
0870  00                              DB      0       ; bas (16..23)
0871  92                              DB      092h    ; access
0872  00                              DB      0       ; granularity
0873  00                              DB      0       ; bas (24..31)
                                      ;
                                      ; idt selectors
                              ; idt_sels  DQ   256 DUP(?)

                              ;      ; vm tss alias
                              ;      DW      end_vm_tss-vm_tss   ; limit bits (0..15)
                              ;      DW      vm_tss ; bas (0..15)
                              ;      DB      0       ; bas (16..23)
                              ;      DB      092h    ; access
                              ;      DB      0       ; granularity
```

```
               ;        DB      0        ; bas (24..31)
               ;        ; vm ldt alias
               ;        DW      end_vm_ldt-vm_ldt    ; limit bits (0..15)
               ;        DW      vm_ldt  ; bas (0..15)
               ;        DB      0        ; bas (16..23)
               ;        DB      092h     ; access
               ;        DB      0        ; granularity
               ;        DB      0        ; bas (24..31)
0874           end_mon_ldt   LABEL   BYTE


               ;
        ;;*     *       *        *       *       *        *        *      *********
               ;; null
               ;; alias
               ;; vm86_code
               ;; vm86_data
               ;; vm86_stack
               ;;
               ;vm_ldt LABEL   BYTE
               ;        ; null
               ;        DQ      0        ; null
               ;        ; vm ldt alias
               ;        DW      end_vm_ldt-vm_ldt    ; limit bits (0..15)
               ;        DW      vm_ldt  ; bas (0..15)
               ;        DB      0        ; bas (16..23)
               ;        DB      092h     ; access
               ;        DB      0        ; granularity
               ;        DB      0        ; bas (24..31)
               ;        ; vm code
               ;        DW      end_vm_code-vm_code   ; limit bits (0..15)
               ;        DW      vm_code ; bas (0..15)
               ;        DB      0        ; bas (16..23)
               ;        DB      0FAh     ; access
               ;        DB      0        ; granularity
               ;        DB      0        ; bas (24..31)
               ;        ; vm data
               ;        DW      end_vm_data-vm_data   ; limit bits (0..15)
               ;        DW      vm_data ; bas (0..15)
               ;        DB      0        ; bas (16..23)
               ;        DB      0F2h     ; access
               ;        DB      0        ; granularity
               ;        DB      0        ; bas (24..31)
               ;        ; vm stack
               ;        DW      end_vm_stack-vm_stack ; limit bits (0..15)
               ;        DW      vm_stack        ; bas (0..15)
               ;        DB      0        ; bas (16..23)
               ;        DB      0F2h     ; access
               ;        DB      0        ; granularity
               ;        DB      0        ; bas (24..31)
               ;end_vm_ldt    LABEL   BYTE


        ;*      *       *        *       *       *        *        *      *********
               ;
0874           mon_tss LABEL   BYTE
0874   00 00 00 00             DD      0                               ; mon_back
0878   0400 R 0000 0024 0000   DW      mon_tos,0,MON_STACK_SEL,0       ; mon_stk0
0880   00 00 00 00 00 00       DQ      0                               ; mon_stk1
```

```
         00 00
0888  00 00 00 00 00 00          DQ      0                           ; mon_stk2
         00 00
0890  00 00 00 00                DD      0                           ; mon_cr3
0894  0000 R 0000               DW      begin_mon,0                 ; mon_eip
0898  0000 0000                 DW      0,0                         ; mon_eflag IFL,0
089C  00 00 00 00                DD      0                           ; mon_eax
08A0  00 00 00 00                DD      0                           ; mon_ecx
08A4  00 00 00 00                DD      0                           ; mon_edx
08A8  00 00 00 00                DD      0                           ; mon_ebx
08AC  0400 R 0000               DW      mon_tos,0                   ; mon_esp
08B0  00 00 00 00                DD      0                           ; mon_ebp
08B4  00 00 00 00                DD      0                           ; mon_esi
08B8  00 00 00 00                DD      0                           ; mon_edi
08BC  001C 0000                 DW      MON_DATA_SEL,0              ; mon_ES
08C0  0014 0000                 DW      MON_CODE_SEL,0              ; mon_CS
08C4  0024 0000                 DW      MON_STACK_SEL,0            ; mon_SS
08C8  001C 0000                 DW      MON_DATA_SEL,0              ; mon_DS
08CC  001C 0000                 DW      MON_DATA_SEL,0              ; mon_FS
08D0  001C 0000                 DW      MON_DATA_SEL,0              ; mon_GS
08D4  0028 0000                 DW      MON_LDT_SEL,0              ; mon_LDT
08D8  0000                      DW      0                           ; mon_dtb
08DA  0068                      DW      $ +2 -mon_tss              ; mon_bm_off
                                                                    ;i/o bitmap (bm)
08DC    80 [00]                  DB      401h /8 DUP(0)             ; the bm ;7/15 B0
                                                                              chip


095C                    end_mon_tss   LABEL   BYTE
095C  FF                         DB      0FFH                       ; end_bm


            ;*      *      *      *      *      *      *      *      *********
            ;
095D                    tmp_tss LABEL   BYTE
095D  00 00 00 00                DD      0                           ; _back
0961  0400 R 0000 0024 0000     DW      mon_tos,0,MON_STACK_SEL,0 ; _stk0
0969  00 00 00 00 00 00          DQ      0                           ; _stk1
         00 00
0971  00 00 00 00 00 00          DQ      0                           ; _stk2
         00 00
0979  00 00 00 00                DD      0                           ; _cr3
097D  0000 R 0000               DW      begin_mon,0                 ; _eip
0981  0200 0000                 DW      IFL,0                      ; _eflag
0985  00 00 00 00                DD      0                           ; _eax
0989  00 00 00 00                DD      0                           ; _ecx
098D  00 00 00 00                DD      0                           ; _edx
0991  00 00 00 00                DD      0                           ; _ebx
0995  0400 R 0000               DW      mon_tos,0                   ; _esp
0999  00 00 00 00                DD      0                           ; _ebp
099D  00 00 00 00                DD      0                           ; _esi
09A1  00 00 00 00                DD      0                           ; _edi
09A5  001C 0000                 DW      MON_DATA_SEL,0              ; _ES
09A9  0014 0000                 DW      MON_CODE_SEL,0              ; _CS
09AD  0024 0000                 DW      MON_STACK_SEL,0            ; _SS
09B1  001C 0000                 DW      MON_DATA_SEL,0              ; _DS
09B5  001C 0000                 DW      MON_DATA_SEL,0              ; _FS
09B9  001C 0000                 DW      MON_DATA_SEL,0              ; _GS
09BD  0028 0000                 DW      MON_LDT_SEL,0              ; _LDT
```

```
09C1  0000                              DW      0                              ; _dtb
09C3  095E R                            DW      end_mon_tss +2                 ; _bm_off
09C5  FF                                DB      0FFH                           ; end_bm
09C6                      end_tmp_tss    LABEL    BYTE

09C6   10 [??]                          DB      16 DUP(?)


              ;*      *      *      *      *      *      *      *      *********
                     ; baseinit
                     ;
09D6  000B                              DW      (end_base_table -base_table) /4
09D8                     base_table     LABEL    WORD
09D8  0002 R                            DW      b0
09DA  ---- R                            DW      TDATA
09DC  0008 R                            DW      b1
09DE  ---- R                            DW      TDATA
09E0  0016 R                            DW      b2
09E2  ---- R                            DW      TDATA
09E4  001E R                            DW      b3
09E6  ---- R                            DW      TDATA
09E8  0026 R                            DW      b4
09EA  ---- R                            DW      TDATA
09EC  002E R                            DW      b5
09EE  ---- R                            DW      TDATA
09F0  0036 R                            DW      b6
09F2  ---- R                            DW      TDATA
09F4  0856 R                            DW      b7
09F6  ---- R                            DW      TDATA
09F8  085E R                            DW      bmc0
09FA  ---- R                            DW      MON_CODE
09FC  0866 R                            DW      bmd1
09FE  ---- R                            DW      MON_DATA
0A00  086E R                            DW      bms2
0A02  ---- R                            DW      MON_STACK
0A04                     end_base_table  LABEL   WORD

0A04                     TDATA   ENDS


0000                     MON_DATA                    SEGMENT
                     ;
              ;*      *      *      *      *      *      *      *      *********

0000                     end_mon_data   LABEL    BYTE
0000                     MON_DATA       ENDS


0000                     MON_STACK      SEGMENT
                     ;
              ;*      *      *      *      *      *      *      *      *********

0000  0200 [????]                       DW      512 DUP(?)

                     ; mon_tos       LABEL    DWORD
0400  0040 R 0000      mon_tos DW       dos_ret,0
0404  ---- R 0000               DW      VM_CODE,0
```

```
0408  3200 0002                          DW      IFL OR IOPLFL, VMFL
040C  0400 R 0000  ---- R               DW      vm_tos,0,VM_DATA,0
      0000
0414  ---- R 0000  ---- R               DW      VM_DATA,0,VM_DATA,0,VM_DATA,0,VM_DATA,0
      0000  ---- R 0000  ----
      R 0000


0424                      end_mon_stack  LABEL    BYTE
0424                      MON_STACK      ENDS


                         BEEP    MACRO
                         LOCAL   self
                                 in      al,61h
                                 mov     ah,al
                                 or      al,3
                                 nop
                                 nop
                                 nop
                                 nop
                                 nop
                                 nop
                                 out     61h,al                  ; beeper
                                 mov     cx,1000h
                         self:   loop    self
                                 mov     al,ah
                                 out     61h,al
                         ENDM


                         PUTCH_VL        MACRO
                         LOCAL   wait1
                                 push    ES
                                 mov     cx,0b000h
                                 mov     ES,cx
                                 mov     BYTE PTR ES:[0],al
                                 mov     BYTE PTR ES:[2],' '
                                 mov     BYTE PTR ES:[4],' '

                                 mov     cx,0
                         wait1:
                                 loop    wait1
                                 mov     BYTE PTR ES:[0],' '
                                 pop     ES
                         ENDM


                         PUTCH_PL        MACRO
                         LOCAL   wait1
                                 push    ES

                                 mov     cx,FLAT_SEL
                                 mov     ES,cx
                                 cld

                                 DB      OP_SIZE
                                 mov     di,0
                                 DW      00Bh
```

```
                                    DB      P_SIZE
                                    stosb
                                    inc     di
                                    mov     al,' '
                                    DB      P_SIZE
                                    stosb
                                    inc     di
                                    DB      P_SIZE
                                    stosb

                                    mov     cx,0
                            wait1:
                                    loop    wait1

                                    DB      OP_SIZE
                                    mov     di,0
                                    DW      00Bh

                                    DB      P_SIZE
                                    stosb
                                    inc     di
                                    DB      P_SIZE
                                    stosb
                                    inc     di
                                    DB      P_SIZE
                                    stosb

                                    pop     ES
                            ENDM


0000                        MON_CODE                SEGMENT
                            ;
           ;*      *       *       *       *       *       *       *       ********

                            ASSUME  CS:MON_CODE, DS:nothing, ES:nothing


           ;*      *       *       *       *       *       *       *       ********
                            ;       mv86 entry and monitor
                            ;
           ;*      *       *       *       *       *       *       *       ********
                            ;       main entry
                            ; CS            code segment
                            ; DS,ES,SS      ps
                            ;
0000                        begin_mon:
                                    BEEP
0000  E4 61         +               in      al,61h
0002  8A E0         +               mov     ah,al
0004  0C 03         +               or      al,3
0006  90            +               nop
0007  90            +               nop
0008  90            +               nop
0009  90            +               nop
000A  90            +               nop
```

```
000B  90              +           nop
000C  E6 61           +           out     61h,al              ; beeper
000E  B9 1000         +           mov     cx,1000h
0011  E2 FE           + ??0000:   loop    ??0000
0013  8A C4           +           mov     al,ah
0015  E6 61           +           out     61h,al

0017                  end_entry:
0017  66                          DB      OP_SIZE
0018  CF                          iret


              ;*       *       *       *       *       *       *       *       *********
              ;
0019                  rf0:
0019  55                          push    bp
001A  BD 0000                     mov     bp,0
001D  E9 07AE R       jmp         reflect
= 0007                SIZE_RF EQU     $ -rf0


0020                  rf1:
0020  55                          push    bp
0021  BD 0001                     mov     bp,1
0024  E9 080F R       jmp         exs_int
0027                  rf2:
0027  55                          push    bp
0028  BD 0002                     mov     bp,2
002B  E9 07AE R       jmp         reflect
002E                  rf3:
002E  55                          push    bp
002F  BD 0003                     mov     bp,3
0032  E9 07AE R       jmp         reflect
0035                  rf4:
0035  55                          push    bp
0036  BD 0004                     mov     bp,4
0039  E9 07AE R       jmp         reflect
003C                  rf5:
003C  55                          push    bp
003D  BD 0005                     mov     bp,5
0040  E9 07AE R       jmp         reflect
0043                  rf6:
0043  55                          push    bp
0044  BD 0006                     mov     bp,6
0047  E9 080F R       jmp         exs_int
004A                  rf7:
004A  55                          push    bp
004B  BD 0007                     mov     bp,7
004E  E9 080F R       jmp         exs_int
0051                  rf8:
0051  55                          push    bp
0052  BD 0008                     mov     bp,8
0055  E9 07AE R       jmp         reflect
0058                  rf9:
0058  55                          push    bp
0059  BD 0009                     mov     bp,9
005C  E9 07AE R       jmp         reflect
005F                  rf10:
005F  55                          push    bp
```

```
0060  BD 000A                         mov     bp,10
0063  E9 080F R          jmp         exs_int
0066                     rf11:
0066  55                             push    bp
0067  BD 000B                         mov     bp,11
006A  E9 080F R          jmp         exs_int
006D                     rf12:
006D  55                             push    bp
006E  BD 000C                         mov     bp,12
0071  E9 080F R          jmp         exs_int
0074                     rf13:
0074  55                             push    bp
0075  BD 000D                         mov     bp,13
0078  E9 07AE R          jmp         reflect
007B                     rf14:
007B  55                             push    bp
007C  BD 000E                         mov     bp,14
007F  E9 07AE R          jmp         reflect
```

(Note that rf15: through rf248: have been omitted for brevity)

```
06E8                     rf249:
06E8  55                             push    bp
06E9  BD 00F9                         mov     bp,249
06EC  E9 07AE R          jmp         reflect
06EF                     rf250:
06EF  55                             push    bp
06F0  BD 00FA                         mov     bp,250
06F3  E9 07AE R          jmp         reflect
06F6                     rf251:
06F6  55                             push    bp
06F7  BD 00FB                         mov     bp,251
06FA  E9 07AE R          jmp         reflect
06FD                     rf252:
06FD  55                             push    bp
06FE  BD 00FC                         mov     bp,252
0701  E9 07AE R          jmp         reflect
0704                     rf253:
0704  55                             push    bp
0705  BD 00FD                         mov     bp,253
0708  E9 07AE R          jmp         reflect
070B                     rf254:
070B  55                             push    bp
070C  BD 00FE                         mov     bp,254
070F  E9 07AE R          jmp         reflect
0712                     rf255:
0712  55                             push    bp
0713  BD 00FF                         mov     bp,255
0716  E9 07AE R          jmp         reflect


  =                      TRgs    EQU     WORD PTR [bp] +36
  =                      TRfs    EQU     WORD PTR [bp] +32
  =                      TRds    EQU     WORD PTR [bp] +28
```

```
=                              TRes    EQU     WORD PTR [bp] +24
=                              TRss    EQU     WORD PTR [bp] +20
=                              TRsp    EQU     WORD PTR [bp] +16
=                              TRflag  EQU     WORD PTR [bp] +12
=                              TRcs    EQU     WORD PTR [bp] +8
=                              TRip    EQU     WORD PTR [bp] +4
=                              TRerr   EQU     WORD PTR [bp] +0


           ;*      *      *      *      *      *      *      *      *********
                               ; all we have to do here is modify
                               ; EIP to skip the faulting instruction,
                               ; then get back to the
                               ; faulting instruction.
                               ;
                               ;      ex sequence
                               ; switch stack to level in cs selector of gate.
                               ; push 86 style: gs,gs,ds,es (as 32 bit)
                               ; load segs with 0
                               ; push 86: ss, esp, eflag, cs, eip
                               ; load cs:eip from gate, and go.
                               ;
                               ; all as 32 bit:
                               ;      gs     40
                               ;      fs     36
                               ;      ds     32
                               ;      es     28
                               ;      ss     24
                               ;      sp     20
                               ;      flag   16
                               ;      cs     12
                               ;      ip     8
                               ;      errcode 4
                               ;
                               ;      bp
                               ;      bp     <SP
                               ;
0719                           ex13_int:
                               ;start ;7/15/86
                               ;      mov     bp,0dh
                               ;      jmp     exs_int
                               ;end
0719  83 C4 04                        add     sp,4            ; skip past the error code!
071C  55                             push    bp
071D  55                             push    bp
071E  8B EC                          mov     bp,sp
0720  50                             push    ax
0721  53                             push    bx
0722  51                             push    cx
0723  52                             push    dx
0724  57                             push    di
0725  56                             push    si
0726  81 4E 0C 3000                  or      TRflag,IOPLFL

072B  BB 0030                        mov     bx,FLAT_SEL
072E  8E DB                          mov     DS,bx
```

```
0730  66                              DB      OP_SIZE
0731  33 DB                           xor     bx,bx
0733  8B 5E 08                        mov     bx,TRCS

0736  66                              DB      OP_SIZE
0737  D1 E3                           shl     bx,1
0739  66                              DB      OP_SIZE
073A  D1 E3                           shl     bx,1
073C  66                              DB      OP_SIZE
073D  D1 E3                           shl     bx,1
073F  66                              DB      OP_SIZE
0740  D1 E3                           shl     bx,1

0742  66                              DB      OP_SIZE
0743  03 5E 04                        add     bx,TRIP

0746  B0 5E                           mov     al,'^'
                                   PUTCH_PL
0748  06                  +           push    ES
0749  B9 0030             +           mov     cx,FLAT_SEL
074C  8E C1               +           mov     ES,cx
074E  FC                  +           cld
074F  66                  +           DB      OP_SIZE
0750  BF 0000             +           mov     di,0
0753  000B                +           DW      00Bh
0755  67                  +           DB      P_SIZE
0756  AA                  +           stosb
0757  47                  +           inc     di
0758  B0 20               +           mov     al,' '
075A  67                  +           DB      P_SIZE
075B  AA                  +           stosb
075C  47                  +           inc     di
075D  67                  +           DB      P_SIZE
075E  AA                  +           stosb
075F  B9 0000             +           mov     cx,0
0762                      +   ??0001:
0762  E2 FE               +           loop    ??0001
0764  66                  +           DB      OP_SIZE
0765  BF 0000             +           mov     di,0
0768  000B                +           DW      00Bh
076A  67                  +           DB      P_SIZE
076B  AA                  +           stosb
076C  47                  +           inc     di
076D  67                  +           DB      P_SIZE
076E  AA                  +           stosb
076F  47                  +           inc     di
0770  67                  +           DB      P_SIZE
0771  AA                  +           stosb
0772  07                  +           pop     ES
                                   BEEP
0773  E4 61               +           in      al,61h
0775  8A E0               +           mov     ah,al
0777  0C 03               +           or      al,3
0779  90                  +           nop
077A  90                  +           nop
077B  90                  +           nop
077C  90                  +           nop
```

```
077D  90              +           nop
077E  90              +           nop
077F  E6 61           +           out     61h,al            ; beeper
0781  B9 1000         +           mov     cx,1000h
0784  E2 FE           + ??0002:   loop    ??0002
0786  8A C4           +           mov     al,ah
0788  E6 61           +           out     61h,al

078A  B9 3000                     mov     cx,3000h
078D                  wait999:
078D  E2 FE                       loop    wait999

078F  80 3F F4                    cmp     BYTE PTR [bx],0F4h            ; hlt
0792  75 0C                       jne     not_hlt
                                  ;
0794  FB                          sti
0795  F4                          hlt

0796  5E                          pop     si
0797  5F                          pop     di
0798  5A                          pop     dx
0799  59                          pop     cx
079A  5B                          pop     bx
079B  58                          pop     ax

079C  5D                          pop     bp
079D  5D                          pop     bp

079E  66                          db      OP_SIZE
079F  CF                          iret

07A0                  not_hlt:
07A0  5E                          pop     si
07A1  5F                          pop     di
07A2  5A                          pop     dx
07A3  59                          pop     cx
07A4  5B                          pop     bx
07A5  58                          pop     ax

07A6  5D                          pop     bp
07A7  5D                          pop     bp

07A8  B8 4C01                     mov     ax,4C01h
07AB  E9 0100 R          jmp      rf33


        ;*    *     *     *     *     *     *     *     *********
        ;          interrupt/exception reflectors
        ;*    *     *     *     *     *     *     *     *********

        ;*    *     *     *     *     *     *     *     *********
                      ; build 86 handler frame
                      ; change trap frame to 86 int frame
                      ; ARGS  ax    int type
                      ;
07AE                  reflect:
07AE  50                          push    ax
```

```
07AF  8B C5              mov   ax,bp
07B1  8B EC              mov   bp,sp
07B3  53                 push  bx

07B4  50                 push  ax                    ; save int type

07B5  B8 0030            mov   ax,FLAT_SEL
07B8  8E D8              mov   DS,ax

07BA  66                 DB    OP_SIZE
07BB  33 C0              xor   ax,ax
07BD  8B 46 10           mov   ax,TRSP               ; change tos
07C0  2D 0006            sub   ax,3*2
07C3  89 46 10           mov   TRSP,ax

07C6  66                 DB    OP_SIZE
07C7  33 DB              xor   bx,bx
07C9  8B 5E 14           mov   bx,TRSS
                       ; shl   bx,4
07CC  66                 DB    OP_SIZE
07CD  D1 E3              shl   bx,1
07CF  66                 DB    OP_SIZE
07D0  D1 E3              shl   bx,1
07D2  66                 DB    OP_SIZE
07D3  D1 E3              shl   bx,1
07D5  66                 DB    OP_SIZE
07D6  D1 E3              shl   bx,1
07D8  66                 DB    OP_SIZE
07D9  03 D8              add   bx,ax

07DB  8B 46 04           mov   ax,TRIP               ;7/13/86
                       ; mov   [bx] +0,ax
07DE  67 89 43 00        DB    P_SIZE, MOV_PBX_AX, 43h, 0

07E2  8B 46 08           mov   ax,TRCS
                       ; mov   [bx] +2,ax
07E5  67 89 43 02        DB    P_SIZE, MOV_PBX_AX, 43h, 2

07E9  8B 46 0C           mov   ax,TRFLAG
                       ; mov   [bx] +4,ax
07EC  67 89 43 04        DB    P_SIZE, MOV_PBX_AX, 43h, 4

07F0  5B                 pop   bx

07F1  D1 E3              shl   bx,1
07F3  D1 E3              shl   bx,1
07F5  8B 07              mov   ax,[bx] +0
07F7  89 46 04           mov   TRIP,ax
07FA  8B 47 02           mov   ax,[bx] +2
07FD  89 46 08           mov   TRCS,ax
0800  81 4E 0E 0002      or    TRFLAG +2,VMFL
0805  81 66 0C FDFF      and   TRFLAG +0,NOT IFL     ;7/14/86

080A  5B                 pop   bx
080B  58                 pop   ax
080C  5D                 pop   bp
```

```
080D  66                        DB        OP_SIZE
080E  CF                        iret

             ;*    *    *    *    *    *    *    *********
                                ; 1,6,7,8,a,b,c
                                ;
080F                            exs_int:                            ;7/15/86
080F  8B C5                     mov       ax,bp

0811  04 30                     add       al,30h
0813  3C 3A                     cmp       al,3ah
0815  72 02                     jb        end_al
                                ;
0817  04 07                     add       al,7
0819                  end_al:
                                PUTCH_PL
0819  06             +          push      ES
081A  B9 0030        +          mov       cx,FLAT_SEL
081D  8E C1          +          mov       ES,cx
081F  FC             +          cld
0820  66             +          DB        OP_SIZE
0821  BF 0000        +          mov       di,0
0824  000B           +          DW        00Bh
0826  67             +          DB        P_SIZE
0827  AA             +          stosb
0828  47             +          inc       di
0829  B0 20          +          mov       al,' '
082B  67             +          DB        P_SIZE
082C  AA             +          stosb
082D  47             +          inc       di
082E  67             +          DB        P_SIZE
082F  AA             +          stosb
0830  B9 0000        +          mov       cx,0
0833                 + ??0003:
0833  E2 FE          +          loop      ??0003
0835  66             +          DB        OP_SIZE
0836  BF 0000        +          mov       di,0
0839  000B           +          DW        00Bh
083B  67             +          DB        P_SIZE
083C  AA             +          stosb
083D  47             +          inc       di
083E  67             +          DB        P_SIZE
083F  AA             +          stosb
0840  47             +          inc       di
0841  67             +          DB        P_SIZE
0842  AA             +          stosb
0843  07             +          pop       ES

                                BEEP
0844  E4 61          +          in        al,61h
0846  8A E0          +          mov       ah,al
0848  0C 03          +          or        al,3
084A  90             +          nop
084B  90             +          nop
084C  90             +          nop
084D  90             +          nop
084E  90             +          nop
```

```
064F  90                    +          nop
0650  E6 61                 +          out     61h,al              ; beeper
0652  B9 1000               +          mov     cx,1000h
0655  E2 FE                 + ??0004:  loop    ??0004
0657  8A C4                 +          mov     al,ah
0659  E6 61                 +          out     61h,al

065B  66                               DB      OP_SIZE
065C  33 C0                            xor     ax,ax
                                       ; mov CR0,ax
065E  0F 22 C0                         DB      00Fh,022h,0C0h

0661  EB 01 90                         jmp     flush0
0664                        flush0:
0664  EA 0669 ---- R                   jmp     FAR PTR fflush
0669                        fflush LABEL    FAR
0669  CD 19                            int     19h
066B  F4                               hlt


            ;*      *       *       *       *       *       *       *       *********
                                    ; emulate to faulting opcode
                                    ; ARGS   ds:si   opcode p
                                    ; RET    ax      opcode size
                                    ;
                                    ; emulate        PROC    NEAR
                                    ; emulate        ENDP

066C                        end_mon_code    LABEL   BYTE
066C                        MON_CODE                ENDS


0000                        VM_DATA SEGMENT
                                    ;
            ;*      *       *       *       *       *       *       *       *********
0000  0200 [????]                   DW      512 DUP(?)

0400                        vm_tos LABEL    WORD

0400                        VM_DATA ENDS


0000                        VM_CODE SEGMENT
                                    ;
            ;*      *       *       *       *       *       *       *       *********

                            ASSUME  CS:VM_CODE, DS: TDATA, ES: nothing

            ;*      *       *       *       *       *       *       *       *********
                                    ;       main vm code
                                    ; from dos
                                    ;
0000                        begin_vm:
0000  90                            NOP
0001  90                            NOP
0002  90                            NOP
0003  90                            NOP
```

```
0004  90                          NOP
0005  90                          NOP
0006  90                          NOP
0007  90                          NOP

0008  B8 ---- R                   mov     ax,TDATA
000B  8E D8                       mov     DS,ax
000D  8E C0                       mov     ES,ax

000F  B8 ---- R                   mov     ax,VM_DATA
0012  8E D0                       mov     SS,ax
0014  BC 0400 R         mov       sp,OFFSET vm_tos


            ;*      *     *       *      *      *      *       *********
                              ; setup tables
                              ;
0017  FC                          cld
0018  E8 00B2 R         call      init_bases
001B  E8 00DF R         call      init_idt


                              ; lidt  idt_pword
001E  0F 01 1E                    DB      00Fh,001h,01Eh
0021  0006 R                      DW      idt_pword


                              ; lgdt  gdt_pword
0023  0F 01 16                    DB      00Fh,001h,016h
0026  0000 R                      DW      gdt_pword


0028  BB 0020                     mov     bx,TMP_TSS_SEL


002B  FA                          cli
                              ; mov     ax,cr0
                              ; DB      0F20C0
002C  B8 0001                     mov     ax,1
                              ; mov     cr0,ax
002F  0F 22 C0                    DB      00Fh,022h,0C0h


0032  EB 00                       jmp     SHORT flush
0034                    flush:                          ; in protected mode level 0


                              ; ltr  bx
0034  0F 00 DB                    DB      00Fh,000h,0DBh
                         ;      sti                     ; in task switch


            ;*      *     *       *      *      *      *       *********
                              ; go virtual
                              ;
0037  2E: FF 2E 003C R            jmp     CS:DWORD PTR vm_entry
003C                    vm_entry          LABEL     DWORD
003C  0000 0018         DW        0, MON_TSS_SEL


                              ; back to dos
0040                    dos_ret:
0040  90                          NOP
                         ;start ;7/15/86
0041  B0 21                       mov     al,'!'
                                  PUTCH_VL
```

```
0043  06                          +           push    ES
0044  B9 B000                     +           mov     cx,0b000h
0047  8E C1                       +           mov     ES,cx
0049  26: A2 0000                 +           mov     BYTE PTR ES:[0],al
004D  26: C6 06 0002 20           +           mov     BYTE PTR ES:[2],' '
0053  26: C6 06 0004 20           +           mov     BYTE PTR ES:[4],' '
0059  B9 0000                     +           mov     cx,0
005C                              +   ??0005:
005C  E2 FE                       +           loop    ??0005
005E  26: C6 06 0000 20           +           mov     BYTE PTR ES:[0],' '
0064  07                          +           pop     ES


0065  FA                                      cli
                                              BEEP
0066  E4 61                       +           in      al,61h
0068  8A E0                       +           mov     ah,al
006A  0C 03                       +           or      al,3
006C  90                          +           nop
006D  90                          +           nop
006E  90                          +           nop
006F  90                          +           nop
0070  90                          +           nop
0071  90                          +           nop
0072  E6 61                       +           out     61h,al          ; beeper
0074  B9 1000                     +           mov     cx,1000h
0077  E2 FE                       +   ??0006: loop    ??0006
0079  8A C4                       +           mov     al,ah
007B  E6 61                       +           out     61h,al
007D  FB                                      sti


007E  B0 40                                   mov     al,'
                                              PUTCH_VL
0080  06                          +           push    ES
0081  B9 B000                     +           mov     cx,0b000h
0084  8E C1                       +           mov     ES,cx
0086  26: A2 0000                 +           mov     BYTE PTR ES:[0],al
008A  26: C6 06 0002 20           +           mov     BYTE PTR ES:[2],' '
0090  26: C6 06 0004 20           +           mov     BYTE PTR ES:[4],' '
0096  B9 0000                     +           mov     cx,0
0099                              +   ??0007:
0099  E2 FE                       +           loop    ??0007
009B  26: C6 06 0000 20           +           mov     BYTE PTR ES:[0],' '
00A1  07                          +           pop     ES


00A2  BA ---- R                               mov     dx,ZLAST        ; dx    keep paragraph size
00A5  81 EA ---- R                            sub     dx,AFIRST
00A9  42                                      inc     dx
00AA  B8 3100                                 mov     ax,3100h        ; al    return code
00AD  CD 21                                   int     DOS
00AF  CD 19                                   int     19h
00B1  F4                                      hlt


              ;*      *       *       *       *       *       *       *       *********
                                    ; turn all 16 bit offsets into 20 bit linear addresses
                                    ;
00B2                                init_bases      PROC    NEAR
00B2  1E                                      push    DS
```

```
00B3  B8  ---- R              mov     ax,TDATA
00B6  8E D8                   mov     DS,ax
00B8  BE 09D8 R        mov    si,OFFSET base_table
00BB  8B 0E 09D6 R            mov     cx,base_table -2
00BF  FC                      cld
00C0                   base_fill:
00C0  AD                      lodsw
00C1  8B D8                   mov     bx,ax
00C3  AD                      lodsw
00C4  33 D2                   xor     dx,dx
00C6  D1 E0                   shl     ax,1
00C8  D1 D2                   rcl     dx,1
00CA  D1 E0                   shl     ax,1
00CC  D1 D2                   rcl     dx,1
00CE  D1 E0                   shl     ax,1
00D0  D1 D2                   rcl     dx,1
00D2  D1 E0                   shl     ax,1
00D4  D1 D2                   rcl     dx,1
00D6  01 07                   add     [bx],ax
00D8  10 57 02                adc     [bx] +2,dl      ;6/27/86
00DB  E2 E3                   loop    base_fill

00DD  1F                      pop     DS
00DE  C3                      ret
00DF                   init_bases      ENDP
           ;*      *      *      *      *      *      *      *      ********
                      ;      DW      ex13_int
                      ;      DW      MON_CODE_SEL    ; sel mon code
                      ;      DB      0
                      ;      DB      0EEh            ; - dpl=3 - 386 interrupt
                                                                 gate
                      ;      DB      0
                      ;      DB      0
                      ;
00DF                   init_idt        PROC    NEAR
00DF  1E                      push    DS
00E0  06                      push    ES

00E1  B8  ---- R              mov     ax,TDATA
00E4  8E D8                   mov     DS,ax                   ; ds    tdata
00E6  8E C0                   mov     ES,ax                   ; es    ints

00E8  BA 0019 R        mov    dx,OFFSET rf0
00EB  BF 0044 R        mov    di,OFFSET idt
00EE  B9 0100                 mov     cx,256
00F1                   idt_fill:
00F1  8B C2                   mov     ax,dx
00F3  83 C2 07                add     dx,SIZE_RF

00F6  83 C7 08                add     di,8
00F9  81 F9 00F3              cmp     cx,256-13
00FD  74 0F                   je      over_fill
                              ;
00FF  83 EF 08                sub     di,8

0102  AB                      stosw
0103  B8 0014                 mov     ax,MON_CODE_SEL
```

```
0106  AB                               stosw
0107  B8 EE00                          mov    ax,0EE00h
010A  AB                               stosw
010B  33 C0                            xor    ax,ax
010D  AB                               stosw
010E                          over_fill:
010E  E2 E1                            loop   idt_fill

0110  07                               pop    ES
0111  1F                               pop    DS
0112  C3                               ret
0113                          init_idt        ENDP



                ;*      *       *       *       *       *       *       *       *********
                        ;          UTILITIES
                ;*      *       *       *       *       *       *       *       *********

                ;*      *       *       *       *       *       *       *       *********
                        ; ARGS   ax         selector value
                        ; RET    ax         segment value
                        ;
0113                    sel2seg            PROC    NEAR
0113  1E                         push   DS
0114  53                         push   bx

0115  BB 0008                    mov    bx,GDT_ALIAS
0118  A9 0004                    test   ax,4
011B  74 03                      jz     have_table
                                 ;
011D  BB 000C                    mov    bx,LDT_ALIAS
0120                    have_table:
0120  8E DB                      mov    DS,bx

0122  8B D8                      mov    bx,ax
0124  81 E3 FFF8                 and    bx,NOT 7
0128  8B 47 02                   mov    ax,[bx] +2                      ; get 16
bit base
012B  A9 0003                    test   ax,3
012E  74 01                      jz     ok_selector
                                 ;
0130  CC                         int    3
0131                    ok_selector:
0131  D1 E8                      shr    ax,1
0133  D1 E8                      shr    ax,1

0135  5B                         pop    bx
0136  1F                         pop    DS
0137  C3                         ret
0138                    sel2seg            ENDP


0138                    VM_CODE ENDS
```

```
0000                        ZLAST    SEGMENT PARA
0000   ????                 last_data          DW      ?
0002                        ZLAST    ENDS

DS:TDATA, SS:vm_tos
                                     END     begin_vm
```

APPENDIX H

BIT-STRING MANIPULATION
USING NEW DOUBLE SHIFTS

These code sequences are efficient methods of performing extremely fast manipulation of general unaligned bit strings up to thirty-two bits long. The bit-manipulation operations coded below are

1. Bit BLock Transfer (Bit BLT)
2. Bit String Insertion when string is up to thirty-two bits long and therefore, with misalignment, can span up to five memory bytes
3. Bit String Extract when string is up to thirty-two bits long and therefore, with misalignment, can span up to five memory bytes

These bit-string manipulations are coded assuming that the string length is known at compile time (static) and that the string bit offset is held in a register (dynamic). When the bit offset is also known at compile time (static), the code is even simpler than shown here, since the compiler can create any needed masks as immediate operands for AND and OR instructions.

Fast Bit-BLock Transfer (Bit BLT)

One purpose of the new double-shift instructions SHLD and SHRD is to allow fast bit-string moves, even with arbitrary misalignment of the strings. An example of this is moving a bit string from an arbitrary offset into a BYTE-aligned destination bit string. A string is moved thirty-two bits at a time if a double-shift instruction is used within the inner loop.

```
MOV     ESI, SrcDwordAddr
MOV     EDI, DestDwordAddr
MOV     EBX, WordCnt
MOV     CL,  RelOffset        ;relative bit offset Src - Dest
MOV     EDX, [ESI]            ;load first DWORD of source
ADD     ESI, 4               ;increment source address
CLD                          ;cause string instructions within
                             ; loop (LODSD and STSOD) to increment
                             ; index register.
```

```
BLTloop:                            ;Bit Block Transfer loop
   LODSD                            ;load new low-order DWORD of source
   SHLD   EDX, EAX, CL              ;EDX := EDX:EAX<off+31,off>
   XCHG   EDX, EAX                  ;Swap high and low order parts
                                    ; so high-order part this iteration
                                    ; becomes low-order part next iteration.
   STOSD                            ;write out aligned string
   DEC    EBX                       ;decrement count register
   JA     BLTloop                   ;short jump until count expires
```

This loop allows the bit string to be processed thirty-two bits at a time, for highest performance. Without using the double-shift instructions on a sixty-four-bit operand, the best that could be achieved is a sixteen-bit-per-loop iteration, by using an ordinary shift instruction on a thirty-two-bit operand. The XCHG would be replaced with a ROR 16 to swap the high and low halves of a thirty-two-bit register.

A more general loop than that shown (if the destination were not BYTE-aligned) would require some extra masking on the first destination DWORD moved (before the main loop) and on the last destination DWORD moved (after the main loop), but it would have the same basic thirty-two-bit-per-iteration loop as shown above.

Insertion of Bit String to Memory (Full 5-byte Span)

A right-justified bit string in a register is to be inserted to memory. The string length in the register is up to thirty-two bits and static, but the bit offset is dynamic (held in a register at run time). Because the bit string is up to thirty-two bits long, it is possible for the string to span five bytes in memory when placed in memory with an arbitrary bit offset.

Note the important use of the double shift instructions to manipulate the five bytes spanned by the string. It is most efficient in this case to use the double-shift instructions once the five bytes are brought into the register set.

```
;ESI holds the right-justified bit string to be inserted.
;EDI holds the bit offset of the start of the destination substring
   (bit offset is relative from string base STRINGBASE).
;Registers EAX, EBX and ECX are also used by this insert operation.
;
      MOV    ECX, EDI              ;temp storage for offset
      SAR    EDI, 3                ;signed divide offset by 3 to get byte offset
      AND    CL, 7H                ;isolate bit offset (0..7) in register CL
      MOV    EAX, [EDI]STRINGBASE  ;load 1st DWORD containing destination
      SHRD   EBX, EAX, CL          ;bits that are right of offset saved in EBX
      MOV    DL, [EDI+4]STRINGBASE ;load fifth BYTE to allow 5 byte span
      SHRD   EAX, EDX              ;field now entirely in EAX, right-justified
      SHR    EDX, CL               ;make EDX ready to receive EAX at first SHLD below
      AND    EAX, LENGTHMASKᵥ      ;clobber old field with lengthmaskᵥ
      AND    ESI, LENGTHMASK       ;purify register containing new field with lengthmask
      OR     EAX, ESI              ;perform the insertion
```

```
        SHLD    EDX, EAX            ;create the new fifth BYTE in DL,
                                       shifting bits left from EAX
        SHLD    EAX, EBX            ;create new DWORD in EAX,
                                       retrieving bits in left shift from EBX
        MOV     [EDI]STRINGBASE, EAX  ;store new DWORD at destination
        MOV     [EDI+4]STRINGBASE,DL  ;store new fifth BYTE at destination

        ;this 5-byte span case requires just 40 clock cycles; 2usec at 20MHz.
        ;algorithm conceived by james burke.
```

Extraction of Bit String from Memory (Full 5-byte Span)

A bit string containing up to thirty-two bits of arbitrary bit offset is to be extracted from memory and placed into a register, right-justified. The string length in the register is known at compile time (static), but the bit offset is dynamic (held in a register at run time). Because the bit string is up to thirty-two bits long, it is possible for the string to span five bytes in memory. Note the convenient use of SHRD.

```
;EDI holds the bit offset of the start of the source substring
   (bit offset is relative from string base STRINGBASE).
;EAX holds the right-justified bit string extracted from memory.
;Registers EAX, EBX and ECX are also used by this insert operation.
;
        MOV     ECX,  EDI           ;temp storage for offset
        SAR     EDI, 3              ;signed divide offset by 3 to get byte offset
        AND     CL, 7H              ;isolate bit offset (0..7) in register CL
        MOV     EAX, [EDI]STRINGBASE  ;load 1st DWORD containing destination
        MOV     DL, [EDI+4]STRINGBASE ;load fifth BYTE to allow 5 byte span
        SHRD    EAX, EDX, CL        ;entire field to be extracted is now in EAX,
                                       right-justified
        AND     EAX, LENGTHMASK     ;bits not belonging to the extracted string are zeroed

        ;this 5-byte span case requires just 20 clock cycles; 1usec at 20MHz.
        ;algorithm conceived by james burke.
```

INDEX

About the Author

Ed Strauss enjoyed writing this book, covering the 32-bit 80386 microprocessor comprehensively. He draws on his experience of six years' employment with Intel Corporation, manufacturer of the 80386 and the world-standard 80286 and 8086 microprocessors. At Intel, he has designed 80386 software and hardware for such applications as single- and multiuser personal computers, multiuser office systems, machine vision, and artificial-intelligence processors. This is his second book published by Brady Books.

Mr. Strauss brings to Intel a background including an MSEE from Stanford University, where his thesis included design of an integrated circuit (containing, however, just one-hundredth the transistors of an 80386!), employment at Hewlett-Packard, Data Terminals Division in Cupertino, and a BSEE from Purdue University.

Mr. Strauss has established a corporation in Reno, Nevada, concentrating on upgrade products for personal computers. He finds this a rewarding, stable market, where customers are grateful for products that breathe new life into their mature machines. The company promotes ongoing ties with the nearby University of Nevada, Intel Corporation, the technical press, several distributors, and user networks. Mr. Strauss can be reached at the company, ES Quality Products, for your comments about the 80386 and about this book.